PRINCIPLES and TECHNIQUES in COMBINATORICS

PRINCIPLES and TECHNIQUES in COMBINATORICS

CHEN Chuan-Chong & KOH Khee-Meng

Department of Mathematics
National University of Singapore

World Scientific

NEW JERSEY · LONDON · SINGAPORE · BEIJING · SHANGHAI · HONG KONG · TAIPEI · CHENNAI

Published by

World Scientific Publishing Co. Pte. Ltd.
5 Toh Tuck Link, Singapore 596224
USA office: 27 Warren Street, Suite 401-402, Hackensack, NJ 07601
UK office: 57 Shelton Street, Covent Garden, London WC2H 9HE

British Library Cataloguing-in-Publication Data
A catalogue record for this book is available from the British Library.

PRINCIPLES AND TECHNIQUES IN COMBINATORICS

ISBN-13 978-981-02-1114-1
ISBN-10 981-02-1114-7
ISBN-13 978-981-02-1139-4 (pbk)
ISBN-10 981-02-1139-2 (pbk)

Preface

Over the years, Combinatorial Analysis has always been a popular course among our undergraduate students. The basic principles and techniques taught in the course have found more and more applications in other fields, especially in computer science and operational research. Problems in Combinatorics are not only challenging for researchers, but also appear very frequently in various mathematical competitions, particularly the International Mathematical Olympiad (IMO). Both the authors have been involved in the teaching of the subject as well as in the training of the Singapore International Mathematical Olympiad Teams for many years. All along, we have been longing for a book that is suitable for our purposes. Hence, in writing this book, we have two main objectives in mind: (1) it could be used as a text-book for undergraduate courses, and (2) it could be used for the training of our International Mathematical Olympiad Teams. To achieve these objectives, we have tried to present the material very explicitly so that students with some mathematical maturity will find it very easy to read. We also find that students often neglect some of the basic principles in combinatorics, such as the Addition Principle, the Multiplication Principle, the Principle of Complementation, the Injection Principle, and the Bijection Principle, perhaps due to their rather unsophisticated appearances. In this book, we shall lay special emphasis on the importance of these principles, together with others, such as the Principle of Inclusion and Exclusion and the Pigeonhole Principle. By providing a plethora of carefully chosen examples, we hope that the applications of these principles as well as the techniques of generating functions and recurrence relations would be much more appreciated by the reader. We have also included a wide range of examples and exercises with various degrees of difficulty at the end of each chapter. All in all, we have about 490 problems, which include combinatorial problems taken from mathematical competitions such as the IMO, the William Lowell Putnam Mathematical Competition, the American Invitational Mathematics Examination, the Singapore Mathematical

Olympiad, the Asian Pacific Mathematics Olympiad, the USA Mathematical Olympiad and other Mathematical Olympiads from various nations. Some of the problems are specially drawn from sources, such as the American Mathematical Monthly, Crux Mathematicorum, the College Mathematics Journal and the Mathematical Magazine. We shall like to express here our gratitude to all the above publications and organizations associated with the various mathematical competitions for kindly allowing us to include these problems as exercises. The sources of these problems are clearly indicated at the end of each respective problem, so that the interested reader may consult the relevant literature for further readings. We also made an effort to be sure that the results included in here are up-to-date and to provide the reader with a good list of references at the end of each chapter and also at the end of the book so that the reader may pursue a topic further to get to the frontier of the subject.

To make reading a little easier and pleasant, a mark ∎ is placed at the end of a proof, or an example, or a solution to indicate completion. The numberings of the sections, identities, problems, figures, and tables are split into parts separated by decimal points. For instance, Problem 3.5 means the Problem 5 in Exercise 3, Section 4.2 means the second section of Chapter 4, Figure 2.3.1 means the first figure in the third section of Chapter 2, etc.. There are two kinds of references in the book. References indicated by letters in square-brackets, such as [K] or [Ro], are articles that can be found at the end of the corresponding chapter, whereas, references indicated by numbers in square-brackets, such as [3], are books that can be found in the Bibliography at the end of the book.

We wish to express our special thanks to Chan Onn for very patiently and carefully reading through the first draft of the book and for his many invaluable suggestions which certainly enhanced the contents as well as the presentation of the book. We wish to thank also our students Chan Hock Peng, Goh Beng Huay, Ng Wee Leng, Ngan Ngiap Teng, Tan Ban Pin and Teo Chung Piaw for reading through the many problems in the exercises. Last but not least, we are grateful to the National University of Singapore for granting us local leave during which this book was written.

Chen, Chuan-Chong and *Koh, Khee-Meng*

Notation and Abbreviation

N	$=$	$\{1, 2, 3, \ldots\}$, (p.5)
N$^\bullet$	$=$	$\{0, 1, 2, 3, \ldots\}$, (p.104)
N$_k$	$=$	$\{1, 2, 3, \ldots, k\}$, (p.62)
N$_k^\bullet$	$=$	$\{0, 1, 2, 3, \ldots, k\}$, (p.91)
Z	$=$	$\{\ldots, -2, -1, 0, 1, 2, 3, \ldots\}$, (p.3)
R	$=$	the set of real numbers, (p.187)
(AP)	:	Addition Principle, (p.1)
(BP)	:	Bijection Principle, (p.27)
(CP)	:	Complementation Principle, (p.16)
(IP)	:	Injection Principle, (p.27)
(MP)	:	Multiplication Principle, (p.4)
(PP)	:	Pigeonhole Principle, (p.120)
(GPP)	:	Generalized Pigeonhole Principle, (p.133)
(PIE)	:	Principle of Inclusion and Exclusion, (p.146)
(GPIE)	:	Generalized Principle of Inclusion and Exclusion, (p.150)
(RP)	:	Reflection Principle, (p.91)
LHS	:	Left hand side, (p.192)
RHS	:	Right hand side, (p.151)
$\Leftrightarrow$	:	if and only if, (p.79)
iff	:	if and only if, (p.95)

$a|b$: a divides b, (p.94)

$a \nmid b$: a does not divide b, (p.94)

$\lfloor x \rfloor$ =   the largest integer less than or equal to x (p.94)

$\lceil x \rceil$ =   the smallest integer greater than or equal to x (p.124)

$a \equiv b \pmod{m}$: a is congruent to b modulo m, i.e. $m|(a-b)$ (p.94)

HCF   :   highest common factor, (p.113)

LCM   :   Lowest common multiple, (p.147)

$|S|$ =   the number of elements in the finite set S, (p.2)

$s(r,n)$ =   Stirling number of the first kind

         =   the number of ways to arrange r distinct objects around n identical circles such that each circle has at least one object, (p.25)

$S(r,n)$ =   Stirling number of the second kind

         =   the number of ways of distributing r distinct objects into n identical boxes such that no box is empty, (p.47)

B_r =   the rth Bell number $= \displaystyle\sum_{n=1}^{r} S(r,n)$, (p.50)

$C_r^n = \dbinom{n}{r}$ =   the number of r-element subsets of an n-element set

         = $\dfrac{n!}{r!(n-r)!}$, (p.17)

P_r^n =   the number of r-permutations of n distinct objects

         = $\dfrac{n!}{(n-r)!}$, (p.7)

H_r^n = $\dbinom{r+n-1}{r}$, (p.37)

$P(r; r_1, \ldots, r_n)$ = $\dfrac{r!}{r_1! r_2! \cdots r_n!}$, (p.34)

Q_r^n = the number of r-circular permutations of n distinct objects

         = $\dfrac{P_r^n}{r}$, (p.13)

D_n = the number of derangements of N_n, (p.160)

$D(n, r, k)$ = the number of r-permutations of N_n that have exactly k fixed points, (p.160)

$\mathcal{P}(X)$ = the power set of X, (p.28)

$\varphi(n)$ = the Euler φ-function, (p.160)

$R(p, q)$ = the smallest natural number "n" such that for any colouring of the edges of an n-clique by 2 colours: blue or red (one colour for each edge), there exists either a "blue p-clique" or a "red q-clique", (p.132)

$R(p_1, \ldots, p_n)$ = the smallest natural number "n" such that for any colouring of the edges of an n-clique by k colours: colour 1, colour 2, ..., colour k, there exist a colour i ($i = 1, 2, ..., k$) and a p_i-clique in the resulting configuration such that all edges in the p_i-clique are coloured by colour i, (p.136)

$\dbinom{n}{n_1, n_2, \ldots, n_m}$ = $\dfrac{n!}{n_1! n_2! \cdots n_m!}$, (p.96)

$p(n)$ = the number of different partitions of n, (p.196)

MO   : Mathematical Olympiad

IMO   : International Mathematical Olympiad

APMO   : Asian Pacific Mathematics Olympiad

AIME   : American Invitational Mathematics Examination

Contents

Chapter 1

Permutations and Combinations

1.1. Two Basic Counting Principles

In our everyday lives, we often need to enumerate "events" such as, the arrangement of objects in a certain way, the partition of things under a certain condition, the distribution of items according to a certain specification, and so on. For instance, we may come across counting problems of the following types:

"How many ways are there to arrange 5 boys and 3 girls in a row so that no two girls are adjacent?"

"How many ways are there to divide a group of 10 people into three groups consisting of 4, 3 and 2 people respectively, with 1 person rejected?"

These are two very simple examples of counting problems related to what we call "permutations" and "combinations". Before we introduce in the next three sections what permutations and combinations are, we state in this section two principles that are fundamental in all kinds of counting problems.

The Addition Principle (AP) Assume that there are

n_1 ways for the event E_1 to occur,
n_2 ways for the event E_2 to occur,
$\vdots$
n_k ways for the event E_k to occur,

where $k \geq 1$. If these ways for the different events to occur are pairwise disjoint, then the number of ways for at least one of the events $E_1, E_2, \ldots,$ or E_k to occur is $n_1 + n_2 + \cdots + n_k = \sum_{i=1}^{k} n_i$.

Example 1.1.1.   One can reach city Q from city P by sea, air and road. Suppose that there are 2 ways by sea, 3 ways by air and 2 ways by road (see Figure 1.1.1). Then by (AP), the total number of ways from P to Q by sea, air or road is $2 + 3 + 2 = 7$. ∎

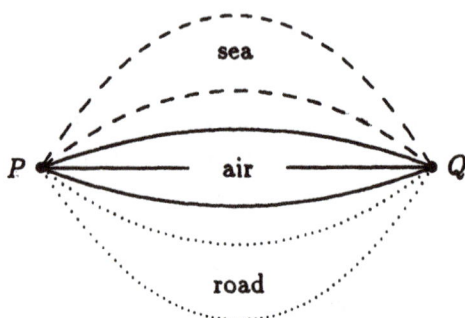

Figure 1.1.1.

An equivalent form of (AP), using set-theoretic terminology, is given below.

Let $A_1, A_2, \ldots, A_k$ be any k finite sets, where $k \geq 1$. If the given sets are pairwise disjoint, i.e., $A_i \cap A_j = \emptyset$ for $i, j = 1, 2, \ldots, k$, $i \neq j$, then

$$\left| \bigcup_{i=1}^{k} A_i \right| = |A_1 \cup A_2 \cup \cdots \cup A_k| = \sum_{i=1}^{k} |A_i|.$$

Example 1.1.2.   Find the number of ordered pairs (x, y) of integers such that $x^2 + y^2 \leq 5$.

Solution.   We may divide the problem into 6 disjoint cases: $x^2 + y^2 = 0, 1, \ldots, 5$. Thus for $i = 0, 1, \ldots, 5$, let

$$S_i = \{(x, y) \mid x, y \in \mathbf{Z}, \quad x^2 + y^2 = i\}.$$

It can be checked that

$S_0 = \{(0, 0)\}$,

$S_1 = \{(1, 0), (-1, 0), (0, 1), (0, -1)\}$,

$S_2 = \{(1, 1), (1, -1), (-1, 1), (-1, -1)\}$,

$S_3 = \emptyset$,

$S_4 = \{(0, 2), (0, -2), (2, 0), (-2, 0)\}$,   and

$S_5 = \{(1, 2), (1, -2), (2, 1), (2, -1), (-1, 2), (-1, -2), (-2, 1), (-2, -1)\}$.

Thus by (AP), the desired number of ordered pairs is

$$\sum_{i=0}^{5} |S_i| = 1 + 4 + 4 + 0 + 4 + 8 = 21. \quad \blacksquare$$

Remarks.   1) In the above example, one can find out the answer "21" simply by listing all the required ordered pairs (x, y). The above method, however, provides us with a systematical way to obtain the answer.

2) One may also divide the above problem into disjoint cases: $x^2 = 0, 1, \ldots, 5$, find out the number of required ordered pairs in each case, and obtain the desired answer by applying (AP).

The Multiplication Principle (MP) Assume that an event E can be decomposed into r ordered events $E_1, E_2, \ldots, E_r$, and that there are

$\quad n_1$ ways for the event E_1 to occur,

$\quad n_2$ ways for the event E_2 to occur,

$\quad \vdots$

$\quad n_r$ ways for the event E_r to occur.

Then the total number of ways for the event E to occur is given by:

$$n_1 \times n_2 \times \cdots \times n_r = \prod_{i=1}^{r} n_i.$$

Example 1.1.3.   To reach city D from city A, one has to pass through city B and then city C as shown in Figure 1.1.2.

Figure 1.1.2.

If there are 2 ways to travel from A to B, 5 ways from B to C, and 3 ways from C to D, then by (MP), the number of ways from A to D via B and C is given by $2 \times 5 \times 3 = 30$. ∎

An equivalent form of (MP) using set-theoretic terminology, is stated below.

Let

$$\prod_{i=1}^{r} A_i = A_1 \times A_2 \times \cdots \times A_r = \{(a_1, a_2, ..., a_r) \mid a_i \in A_i, i = 1, 2, ..., r\}$$

denote the cartesian product of the finite sets $A_1, A_2, ..., A_r$. Then

$$\left| \prod_{i=1}^{r} A_i \right| = |A_1| \times |A_2| \times \cdots \times |A_r| = \prod_{i=1}^{r} |A_i|.$$

A sequence of numbers $a_1 a_2 \ldots a_n$ is called a *k-ary sequence*, where $n, k \in \mathbf{N}$, if $a_i \in \{0, 1, ..., k-1\}$ for each $i = 1, 2, ..., n$. The *length* of the sequence $a_1 a_2 \ldots a_n$ is defined to be n, which is the number of terms contained in the sequence. At times, such a sequence may be denoted by $(a_1, a_2, ..., a_n)$. A k-ary sequence is also called a *binary, ternary,* or *quaternary* sequence when $k = 2, 3$ or 4, respectively. Thus, $\{000, 001, 010, 100, 011, 101, 110, 111\}$ is the set of all $8 (= 2^3)$ binary sequences of length 3. For given $k, n \in \mathbf{N}$, how many different k-ary sequences of length n can we form? This will be discussed in the following example. You will find the result useful later on.

Example 1.1.4. To form a k-ary sequence $a_1a_2...a_n$ of length n, we first select an a_1 from the set $B = \{0, 1, ..., k-1\}$; then an a_2 from the same set B; and so on until finally an a_n again from B. Since there are k choices in each step, the number of distinct k-ary sequences of length n is, by (MP), $\underbrace{k \times k \times \cdots \times k}_{n} = k^n$. ∎

Example 1.1.5. Find the number of positive divisors of 600, inclusive of 1 and 600 itself.

Solution. We first note that the number '600' has a unique prime factorization, namely, $600 = 2^3 \times 3^1 \times 5^2$. It thus follows that a positive integer m is a divisor of 600 if and only if m is of the form $m = 2^a \times 3^b \times 5^c$, where $a, b, c \in \mathbf{Z}$ such that $0 \le a \le 3, 0 \le b \le 1$ and $0 \le c \le 2$. Accordingly, the number of positive divisors of '600' is the number of ways to form the triples (a, b, c) where $a \in \{0, 1, 2, 3\}, b \in \{0, 1\}$ and $c \in \{0, 1, 2\}$, which by (MP), is equal to $4 \times 2 \times 3 = 24$. ∎

Remark. By applying (MP) in a similar way, one obtains the following general result.

If a natural number n has as its prime factorization,

$$n = p_1^{k_1} p_2^{k_2} \cdots p_r^{k_r}$$

where the p_i's are distinct primes and the k_i's are positive integers, then the number of positive divisors of n is given by $\prod_{i=1}^{r}(k_i + 1)$.

In the above examples, we have seen how (AP) and (MP) were separately used to solve some counting problems. Very often, solving a more complicated problem may require a 'joint' application of both (AP) and (MP). To illustrate this, we give the following example.

Example 1.1.6. Let $X = \{1, 2, ..., 100\}$ and let

$$S = \{(a, b, c) \mid a, b, c \in X, a < b \text{ and } a < c\}.$$

Find $|S|$.

Solution. The problem may be divided into disjoint cases by considering $a = 1, 2, ..., 99$.

For $a = k \in \{1, 2, ..., 99\}$, the number of choices for b is $100 - k$ and that for c is also $100 - k$. Thus the number of required ordered triples (k, b, c) is $(100 - k)^2$, by (MP). Since k takes on the values $1, 2, ..., 99$, by applying (AP), we have

$$|S| = 99^2 + 98^2 + \cdots + 1^2.$$

Using the formula $\sum_{k=1}^{n} k^2 = \frac{1}{6}n(n + 1)(2n + 1)$, we finally obtain

$$|S| = \frac{1}{6} \times 99 \times 100 \times 199 = 328350. \quad \blacksquare$$

As mathematical statements, both (AP) and (MP) are really 'trivial'. This could be a reason why they are very often neglected by students. Actually, they are very fundamental in solving counting problems. As we shall witness in this book, a given counting problem, no matter how complicated it is, can always be 'decomposed' into some simpler 'sub-problems' that in turn can be counted by using (AP) and/or (MP).

1.2. Permutations

At the beginning of Section 1.1, we mentioned the following problem: "How many ways are there to arrange 5 boys and 3 girls in a row so that no two girls are adjacent?" This is a typical example of a more general problem of arranging some distinct objects subject to certain additional conditions.

Let $A = \{a_1, a_2, ..., a_n\}$ be a given set of n distinct objects. For $0 \le r \le n$, an *r-permutation* of A is a way of arranging any r of the objects of A in a row. When $r = n$, an n-permutation of A is simply called a *permutation* of A.

Example 1.2.1. Let $A = \{a, b, c, d\}$. All the 3-permutations of A are shown below:

$$
\begin{array}{cccccc}
abc, & acb, & bac, & bca, & cab, & cba, \\
abd, & adb, & bad, & bda, & dab, & dba, \\
acd, & adc, & cad, & cda, & dac, & dca, \\
bcd, & bdc, & cbd, & cdb, & dbc, & dcb.
\end{array}
$$

There are altogether 24 in number. $\quad \blacksquare$

Let P_r^n denote the number of r-permutations of A. Thus $P_3^4 = 24$ as shown in Example 1.2.1. In what follows, we shall derive a formula for P_r^n by applying (MP).

An r-permutation of A can be formed in r steps, as described below: First, we choose an object from A and put it in the first position (see Figure 1.2.1). Next we choose an object from the remaining ones in A and put it in the second position. We proceed on until the rth-step in which we choose an object from the remaining $(n - r + 1)$ elements in A and put it in the rth-position.

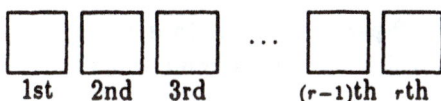

Figure 1.2.1

There are n choices in step 1, $(n - 1)$ choices in step 2, ..., $n - (r - 1)$ choices in step r. Thus by (MP),

$$P_r^n = n(n - 1)(n - 2) \cdots (n - r + 1). \qquad (1.2.1)$$

If we use the factorial notation: $n! = n(n - 1) \cdots 2 \cdot 1$, then

$$P_r^n = \frac{n!}{(n - r)!}. \qquad (1.2.2)$$

Remark. By convention, $0! = 1$. Note that $P_0^n = 1$ and $P_n^n = n!$.

Example 1.2.2. Let $E = \{a, b, c, ..., x, y, z\}$ be the set of the 26 English alphabets. Find the number of 5-letter words that can be formed from E such that the first and last letters are distinct vowels and the remaining three are distinct consonants.

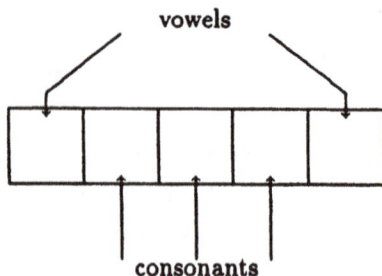

Figure 1.2.2.

Solution. There are 5 vowels and 21 consonants in E. A required 5-letter word can be formed in the following way.

Step 1. Choose a 2-permutation of $\{a, e, i, o, u\}$ and then put the first vowel in the 1st position and the second vowel in the 5th position (see Figure 1.2.2).

Step 2. Choose a 3-permutation of $E\backslash\{a, e, i, o, u\}$ and put the 1st, 2nd and 3rd consonants of the permutation in the 2nd, 3rd and 4th positions respectively (see Figure 1.2.2).

There are P_2^5 choices in Step 1 and P_3^{21} choices in Step 2. Thus by (MP), the number of such 5-letter words is given by

$$P_2^5 \times P_3^{21} = (5 \times 4) \times (21 \times 20 \times 19) = 159600. \quad \blacksquare$$

Example 1.2.3. There are 7 boys and 3 girls in a gathering. In how many ways can they be arranged in a row so that

(i) the 3 girls form a single block (i.e. there is no boy between any two of the girls)?

(ii) the two end-positions are occupied by boys and no girls are adjacent?

Solution. (i) Since the 3 girls must be together, we can treat them as a single entity. The number of ways to arrange 7 boys together with this entity is $(7 + 1)!$. As the girls can permute among themselves within the entity in 3! ways, the desired number of ways is, by (MP),

$$8! \times 3!.$$

(ii) We first consider the arrangements of boys and then those of girls. There are 7! ways to arrange the boys. Fix an arbitrary one of the arrangements. Since the end-positions are occupied by boys, there are only 6 spaces available for the 3 girls G_1, G_2 and G_3.

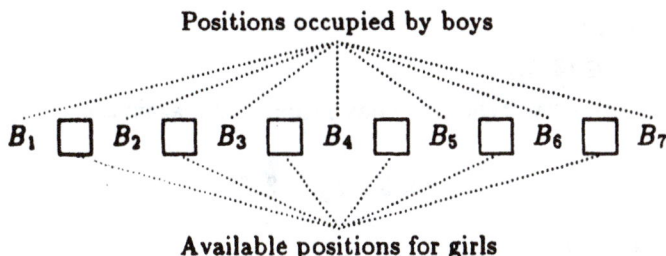

Positions occupied by boys

B_1 ☐ B_2 ☐ B_3 ☐ B_4 ☐ B_5 ☐ B_6 ☐ B_7

Available positions for girls

G_1 has 6 choices. Since no two girls are adjacent, G_2 has 5 choices and G_3 has 4. Thus by (MP), the number of such arrangements is

$$7! \times 6 \times 5 \times 4. \quad \blacksquare$$

Remark. Example 1.2.3 can also be solved by considering the arrangements for the girls first. This will be discussed in Example 1.7.2.

Example 1.2.4. Between 20000 and 70000, find the number of even integers in which no digit is repeated.

Solution. Let *abcde* be a required even integer. As shown in the following diagram, the 1st digit a can be chosen from $\{2,3,4,5,6\}$ and the 5th digit e can be chosen from $\{0,2,4,6,8\}$.

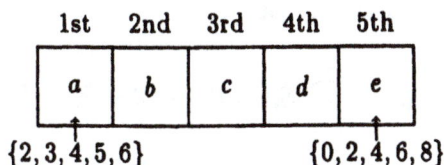

1st	2nd	3rd	4th	5th
a	b	c	d	e

$\{2,3,4,5,6\}$ $\{0,2,4,6,8\}$

Since $\{2,3,4,5,6\} \cap \{0,2,4,6,8\} = \{2,4,6\}$, we divide the problem into 2 disjoint cases:

Case 1. $a \in \{2, 4, 6\}$.

In this case, a has 3 choices, e then has $4 (= 5 - 1)$ choices, and bcd has $P_3^{(10-2)} = P_3^8$ choices. By (MP), there are

$$3 \times 4 \times P_3^8 = 4032$$

such even numbers.

Case 2. $a \in \{3, 5\}$.

In this case, a has 2 choices, e has 5 choices and again bcd has P_3^8 choices. By (MP), there are

$$2 \times 5 \times P_3^8 = 3360$$

such even numbers.

Now, by (AP), the total number of required even numbers is $4032 + 3360 = 7392$. ∎

Example 1.2.5. Let S be the set of natural numbers whose digits are chosen from $\{1, 3, 5, 7\}$ such that no digits are repeated. Find

(i) $|S|$;

(ii) $\sum\limits_{n \in S} n$.

Solution (i) We divide S into 4 disjoint subsets consisting of:

(1) 1-digit numbers: $1, 3, 5, 7$;

(2) 2-digit numbers: $13, 15, \ldots$;

(3) 3-digit numbers: $135, 137, \ldots$;

(4) 4-digit numbers: $1357, 1375, \ldots$;

and find $|S|$ by applying (AP). Thus for $i = 1, 2, 3, 4$, let S_i denote the set of i-digit natural numbers formed by 1,3,5,7 with no repetition. Then $S = S_1 \cup S_2 \cup S_3 \cup S_4$ and by (AP),

$$|S| = \sum_{i=1}^4 |S_i| = P_1^4 + P_2^4 + P_3^4 + P_4^4$$
$$= 4 + 12 + 24 + 24 = 64.$$

(ii) Let $\alpha = \sum\limits_{n \in S} n$. It is tedious to determine α by summing up all the 64 numbers in S. Instead, we use the following method.

Let α_1 denote the sum of unit-digits of the numbers in S; α_2 that of ten-digits of the numbers in S; α_3 that of hundred-digits of the numbers in S; and α_4 that of thousand-digits of the numbers in S. Then

$$\alpha = \alpha_1 + 10\alpha_2 + 100\alpha_3 + 1000\alpha_4.$$

We first count α_1. Clearly, the sum of unit-digits of the numbers in S_1 is

$$1 + 3 + 5 + 7 = 16.$$

In S_2, there are P_1^3 numbers whose unit-digits are, respectively, 1, 3, 5 and 7. Thus the sum of the unit-digits of the number is S_2 is

$$P_1^3 \times (1 + 3 + 5 + 7) = 3 \times 16 = 48.$$

In S_3, there are P_2^3 numbers whose unit-digits are, respectively, 1, 3, 5 and 7. Thus the sum of unit-digits of the numbers in S_3 is

$$P_2^3 \times (1 + 3 + 5 + 7) = 6 \times 16 = 96.$$

In S_4, there are P_3^3 numbers whose unit-digits are, respectively, 1, 3, 5 and 7. Thus the sum of unit-digits of the numbers in S_4 is

$$P_3^3 \times (1 + 3 + 5 + 7) = 6 \times 16 = 96.$$

Hence by (AP),

$$\alpha_1 = 16 + 48 + 96 + 96 = 256.$$

Similarly, we have:

$$\begin{aligned}
\alpha_2 &= P_1^3 \times (1 + 3 + 5 + 7) + P_2^3 \times (1 + 3 + 5 + 7) \\
&\quad + P_3^3 \times (1 + 3 + 5 + 7) = 240; \\
\alpha_3 &= (P_2^3 + P_3^3) \times (1 + 3 + 5 + 7) = 192;
\end{aligned}$$

$$\text{and} \quad \alpha_4 = P_3^3 \times (1 + 3 + 5 + 7) = 96.$$

Thus,

$$\begin{aligned}
\alpha &= \alpha_1 + 10\alpha_2 + 100\alpha_3 + 1000\alpha_4 \\
&= 256 + 2400 + 19200 + 96000 \\
&= 117856. \quad \blacksquare
\end{aligned}$$

Remark. There is a shortcut to compute the sum $\alpha = \sum(n \mid n \in S)$ in part (ii). Observe that the 4 numbers in S_1 can be paired off as $\{1,7\}$ and $\{3,5\}$ so that the sum of the two numbers in each pair is equal to 8 and the 12 numbers in S_2 can be paired off as $\{13,75\}$, $\{15,73\}$, $\{17,71\}$, $\{35,53\}$, ... so that the sum of the two numbers in each pair is 88. Likewise, the 24 numbers in S_3 and the 24 numbers in S_4 can be paired off so that the sum of the two numbers in each pair is equal to 888 and 8888 respectively. Thus

$$\alpha = 8 \times \frac{4}{2} + 88 \times \frac{12}{2} + 888 \times \frac{24}{2} + 8888 \times \frac{24}{2}$$
$$= 117856.$$

1.3. Circular Permutations

The permutations discussed in Section 1.2 involved arrangements of objects *in a row*. There are permutations which require arranging objects in a circular closed curve. These are called circular permutations.

Consider the problem of arranging 3 distinct objects a, b, c in 3 positions around a circle. Suppose the 3 positions are *numbered* (1), (2) and (3) as shown in Figure 1.3.1. Then the three arrangements of a, b, c shown in the figure can be viewed as the permutations:

$$abc, \quad cab, \quad bca$$

respectively.

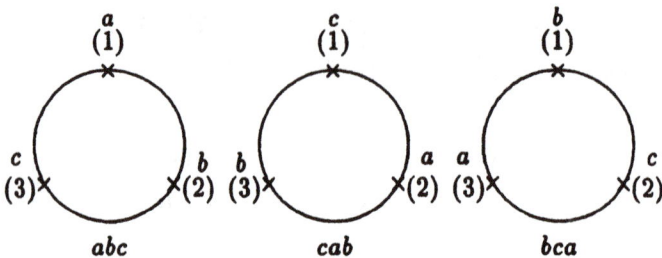

Figure 1.3.1.

In this case, such "circular permutations" are identical with the usual permutations, and thus there is nothing new worth discussing. To get something interesting, let us now neglect the numbering of the positions (and thus only "relative positions" of objects are concerned). As shown in Figure 1.3.2, any of the 3 arrangements is a rotation of every other; i.e., the relative positions of the objects are invariant under rotation. In this case, we shall agree to say that the 3 arrangements of Figure 1.3.2 are identical. In general, two circular permutations of the same objects are *identical* if any one of them can be obtained by a rotation of the other.

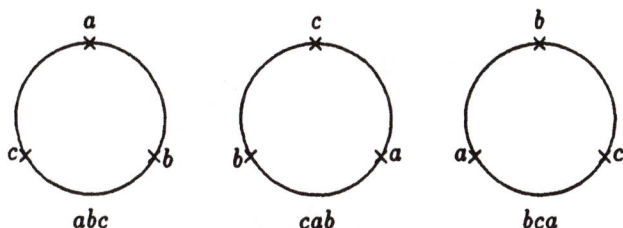

Figure 1.3.2.

Let A be a set of n distinct objects. For $0 \leq r \leq n$, an *r-circular permutation* of A is a circular permutation of any r distinct objects taken from A. Let Q_r^n denote the number of r-circular permutations of A. We shall derive a formula for Q_r^n.

Example 1.3.1. Let $A = \{a, b, c, d\}$. There are altogether $P_3^4(= 24)$ 3-permutations of A and they are shown in Example 1.2.1. These 24 3-permutations are re-grouped into 8 subsets as shown below:

abc	cab	bca	acb	bac	cba
abd	dab	bda	adb	bad	dba
acd	dac	cda	adc	cad	dca
bcd	dbc	cdb	bdc	cbd	dcb

It is noted that every 3-circular permutation of A gives rise to a unique

such subset. For instance,

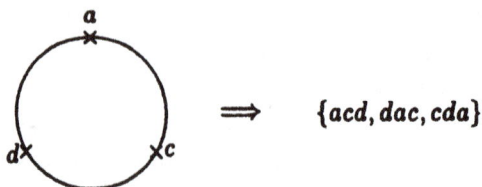

$$\Longrightarrow \qquad \{acd, dac, cda\}$$

Conversely, every such subset corresponds to a unique 3-circular permutation of A. For instance,

$$\{adb, bad, dba\} \qquad \Longrightarrow$$

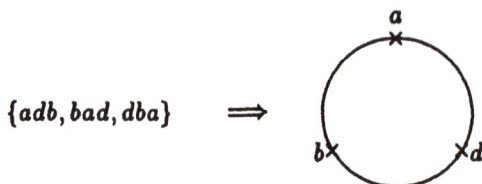

Thus we see that

$$Q_3^4 = \frac{24}{3} = 8. \quad \blacksquare$$

Example 1.3.1 tells us that $Q_3^4 = \frac{1}{3}P_3^4$. What is the relation between Q_r^n and P_r^n in general?

A circular permutation of r distinct objects $x_1, x_2, ..., x_r$ shown below:

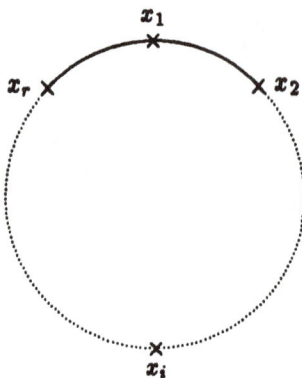

gives rise to a unique subset of r r-permutations:

$$x_1 x_2 \cdots x_r, \; x_r x_1 x_2 \cdots x_{r-1}, \; \cdots, \; x_2 x_3 \cdots x_r x_1$$

obtained through a rotation of the circular permutation. Conversely, every such subset of r r-permutations of A corresponds to a unique r-circular permutation of A. Since all the r-permutations of A can be equally divided into such subsets, we have

$$Q_r^n = \frac{P_r^n}{r} . \tag{1.3.1}$$

In particular,

$$Q_n^n = \frac{P_n^n}{n} = (n-1)! . \tag{1.3.2}$$

Example 1.3.2.   In how many ways can 5 boys and 3 girls be seated around a table if

(i) there is no restriction?

(ii) boy B_1 and girl G_1 are not adjacent?

(iii) no girls are adjacent?

Solution (i)   The number of ways is $Q_8^8 = 7!$.

(ii) The 5 boys and 2 girls not including G_1 can be seated in $(7-1)!$ ways. Given such an arrangement as shown in Figure 1.3.3, G_1 has $5(= 7-2)$ choices for a seat not adjacent to B_1. Thus the desired number of ways is

$$6! \times 5 = 3600.$$

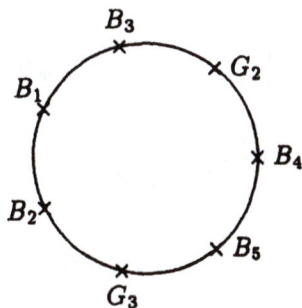

Figure 1.3.3.

We may obtain another solution by using what we call the Principle of Complementation as given below:

> **Principle of Complementation (CP)** If A is a subset of a finite universal set $\mathcal{U}$, then
>
> $$|\mathcal{U} \setminus A| = |\mathcal{U}| - |A|.$$

Now, the number of ways to arrange the 5 boys and 3 girls around a table so that boy B_1 and girl G_1 are adjacent (treating $\{B_1, G_1\}$ as an entity) is

$$(7-1)! \times 2 = 1440.$$

Thus the desired number of ways is by (CP),

$$7! - 1440 = 3600.$$

(iii) We first seat the 5 boys around the table in $(5-1)! = 4!$ ways. Given such an arrangement as shown in Figure 1.3.4, there are 5 ways to seat girl G_1. As no girls are adjacent, G_2 and G_3 have 4 and 3 choices respectively. Thus the desired number of ways is

$$4! \times 5 \times 4 \times 3 = 1440. \quad \blacksquare$$

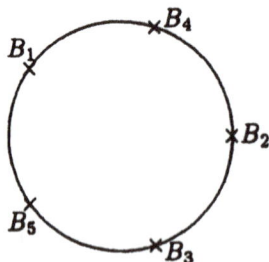

Figure 1.3.4.

Example 1.3.3. Find the number of ways to seat n married couples around a table in each of the following cases:

(i) Men and women alternate;

(ii) Every woman is next to her husband.

Solution. (i) The n men can first be seated in $(n-1)!$ ways. The n women can then be seated in the n spaces between two men in $n!$ ways. Thus the number of such arrangements is $(n-1)! \times n!$.

(ii) Each couple is first treated as an entity. The number of ways to arrange the n entities around the table is $(n-1)!$. Since the two people in each entity can be permuted in $2!$ ways, the desired number of ways is

$$(n-1)! \times 2^n.$$

Remark. A famous and much more difficult problem related to the above problem is the following: How many ways are there to seat n married couples ($n \geq 3$) around a table such that men and women alternate and each woman is not adjacent to her husband? This problem, known as the problem of *ménages*, was first introduced by the French mathematician Francis Edward Anatole Lucas (1842 – 1891). A solution to this problem will be given in Chapter 4.

1.4. Combinations

Let A be a set of n distinct objects. A *combination* of A is simply a subset of A. More precisely, for $0 \leq r \leq n$, an *r-combination* of A is an r-element subset of A. Thus, for instance, if $A = \{a, b, c, d\}$, then the following consists of all the 3-combinations of A:

$$\{a, b, c\}, \ \{a, b, d\}, \ \{a, c, d\}, \ \{b, c, d\}.$$

There are 4 in number. Let C_r^n or $\binom{n}{r}$ (which is read 'n choose r') denote the number of r-combinations of an n-element set A. Then the above example says that $C_3^4 = \binom{4}{3} = 4$. We shall soon derive a formula for C_r^n.

What is the difference between a permutation and a combination of a set of objects? A permutation is an *arrangement* of certain objects and thus the ordering of objects is important, whereas a combination is just a *set* of objects and thus the ordering of objects is immaterial. As a matter of fact, every r-permutation of A can be obtained in the following way:

Step 1. Form an r-combination B of A.

Step 2. Arrange the r objects of B in a row.

This provides us with a means to relate the numbers P_r^n and C_r^n. Indeed, we have by (MP):

$$P_r^n = C_r^n \times r!$$

and thus

$$C_r^n = \binom{n}{r} = \frac{P_r^n}{r!} = \frac{n!}{r!(n-r)!} \ . \tag{1.4.1}$$

In particular,

$$C_0^n = \binom{n}{0} = 1 \quad \text{and} \quad C_n^n = \binom{n}{n} = 1.$$

Note that

$$C_r^n = \frac{n!}{r!(n-r)!} = \frac{n!}{(n-r)!(n-(n-r))!} = C_{n-r}^n,$$

i.e.

$$\binom{n}{r} = \binom{n}{n-r} . \tag{1.4.2}$$

For convenience, we show in Table 1.4.1 the values of $\binom{n}{r}$, where $0 \le r \le n \le 9$. For instance, we have $\binom{6}{3} = 20$ and $\binom{9}{4} = 126$.

n \ r	0	1	2	3	4	5	6	7	8	9
0	1									
1	1	1								
2	1	2	1							
3	1	3	3	1						
4	1	4	6	4	1					
5	1	5	10	10	5	1				
6	1	6	15	20	15	6	1			
7	1	7	21	35	35	21	7	1		
8	1	8	28	56	70	56	28	8	1	
9	1	9	36	84	126	126	84	36	9	1

Table 1.4.1. The values of $\binom{n}{r}$, $0 \le r \le n \le 9$

One can see from Table 1.4.1 that

$$\binom{8}{3} + \binom{8}{4} = 56 + 70 = 126 = \binom{9}{4} .$$

In general, we have:

Example 1.4.1. Prove that

$$\binom{n}{r} = \binom{n-1}{r-1} + \binom{n-1}{r}, \tag{1.4.3}$$

where $n, r \in \mathbb{N}$ with $r \leq n$.

Proof. *Algebraic Proof.* By (1.4.1),

$$\begin{aligned}
\binom{n-1}{r-1} + \binom{n-1}{r} &= \frac{(n-1)!}{(r-1)!(n-r)!} + \frac{(n-1)!}{r!(n-1-r)!} \\
&= \frac{(n-1)!r + (n-1)!(n-r)}{r!(n-r)!} \\
&= \frac{(n-1)!(r+n-r)}{r!(n-r)!} \\
&= \frac{n!}{r!(n-r)!} = \binom{n}{r}. \quad\blacksquare
\end{aligned}$$

Combinatorial Proof. Let $A = \{1, 2, ..., n\}$. By definition, there are $\binom{n}{r}$ ways to form r-combinations S of A. We shall count the number of such S in a different way.

Every r-combination S of A either contains "1" or not. If $1 \in S$, the number of ways to form S is $\binom{n-1}{r-1}$. If $1 \notin S$, the number of ways to form S is $\binom{n-1}{r}$. Thus by (AP), we have

$$\binom{n}{r} = \binom{n-1}{r-1} + \binom{n-1}{r}. \quad\blacksquare$$

Remark. In the second proof, we fix an enumeration problem and count it in two different ways, giving rise to an equality relating two different expressions. This is a useful way to derive combinatorial identities.

Example 1.4.2. By Example 1.1.4, there are 2^7 binary sequences of length 7. How many such sequences are there which contain 3 0's and 4 1's?

Solution. To form such a sequence of length 7:

$$\square \quad \square \quad \square \quad \square \quad \square \quad \square \quad \square$$
$$(1) \quad (2) \quad (3) \quad (4) \quad (5) \quad (6) \quad (7)$$

we first select 3 of the 7 spaces for '0' and then leave the remaining spaces for '1'. There are $\binom{7}{3}$ ways in the first step and $\binom{4}{4} = 1$ way in the next. Thus the number of such binary sequences is given by $\binom{7}{3}$. $\quad\blacksquare$

Remarks. (1) In the above example, you may first select 4 of the 7 spaces for '1' and obtain the answer $\binom{7}{4}$, which is equal to $\binom{7}{3}$ by identity (1.4.2).

(2) In general, the number of binary sequences of length n with m 0's and $(n-m)$ 1's, where $0 \le m \le n$, is given by $\binom{n}{m}$.

Example 1.4.3. In how many ways can a committee of 5 be formed from a group of 11 people consisting of 4 teachers and 7 students if

(i) there is no restriction in the selection?

(ii) the committee must include exactly 2 teachers?

(iii) the committee must include at least 3 teachers?

(iv) a particular teacher and a particular student cannot be both in the committee?

Solution. (i) The number of ways is $\binom{11}{5} = 11!/(5!6!) = 462$.

(ii) We first select 2 teachers from 4 and then $(5-2)$ students from 7. The number of ways is

$$\binom{4}{2}\binom{7}{3} = 6 \times 35 = 210.$$

(iii) There are two cases: either 3 teachers or 4 teachers are in the committee. In the former case, the number of ways is

$$\binom{4}{3}\binom{7}{2} = 4 \times 21 = 84,$$

while in the latter, the number of ways is

$$\binom{4}{4}\binom{7}{1} = 7.$$

Thus by (AP), the desired number of ways is $84 + 7 = 91$.

(iv) Let T be the particular teacher and S the particular student. We first find the number of ways to form a committee of 5 which includes both T and S. Evidently, such a committee of 5 can be formed by taking the union of $\{T, S\}$ and a subset of 3 from the remaining 9 people. Thus the number of ways to form a committee of 5 including T and S is $\binom{9}{3} = 84$.

Hence the number of ways to form a committee of 5 which does not include both T and S is by (CP):

$$\binom{11}{5} - \binom{9}{3} = 462 - 84 = 378, \quad \text{by (i).} \quad \blacksquare$$

Suppose that there are 8 players a, b, c, d, e, f, g, h taking part in the singles event of a tennis championship. In the first round of the competition, they are divided into 4 pairs so that the two players in each pair play against each other. There are several ways to do so. For instance,

or
$$\begin{array}{llll}
(1) & a \text{ vs } b, & c \text{ vs } f, & d \text{ vs } h, & e \text{ vs } g, \\
(2) & a \text{ vs } h, & b \text{ vs } g, & c \text{ vs } f, & d \text{ vs } e.
\end{array}$$

What is the number of ways that this arrangement can be made?

To phrase this sort of questions mathematically, let A be a set of $2n$ distinct objects. A *pairing* of A is a partition of A into 2-element subsets; i.e., a collection of pairwise disjoint 2-element subsets whose union is A. For instance, if A is the set of 8 players $\{a, b, c, d, e, f, g, h\}$ as given above, then

$$\{\{a, b\}, \{c, f\}, \{d, h\}, \{e, g\}\}$$
$$\text{and} \quad \{\{a, h\}, \{b, g\}, \{c, f\}, \{d, e\}\}$$

are different pairings of A. We note that the order of the subsets and the order of the 2 elements in each subset are immaterial.

Example 1.4.4.   Let A be a $2n$-element set where $n \geq 1$. Find the number of different pairings of A.

Solution.   We shall give 3 different methods for solving the problem.

Method 1. Pick an arbitrary element, say x, of A. The number of ways to select x's partner, say y, is $2n - 1$ (and $\{x, y\}$ forms a 2-element subset). Pick an arbitrary element, say z, from the $2n - 2$ elements of $A \backslash \{x, y\}$. The number of ways to select z's partner is $2n - 3$. Continuing in this manner and applying (MP), the desired number of ways is given by

$$(2n - 1)(2n - 3) \cdots 5 \cdot 3 \cdot 1.$$

Method 2. First, form a 2-element subset of A and put it in position (1) as shown below. There are $\binom{2n}{2}$ ways to do so.

$$\underline{\{\ ,\ \}} \quad \underline{\{\ ,\ \}} \quad \underline{\{\ ,\ \}} \quad \underline{\{\ ,\ \}} \quad \cdots \quad \underline{\{\ ,\ \}}$$
$$\ \ (1) \qquad (2) \qquad (3) \qquad \qquad \qquad \quad (n)$$

Next, form a 2-element subset from the remainder of A and put it in the position (2). There are $\binom{2n-2}{2}$ ways to do so. Continuing in this manner and applying (MP), we see that the number of ways of arranging the n 2-element subsets *in a row* is:

$$\binom{2n}{2}\binom{2n-2}{2}\cdots\binom{4}{2}\binom{2}{2}.$$

Since the order of the n subsets is immaterial, the desired number of ways is:

$$\frac{\binom{2n}{2}\binom{2n-2}{2}\cdots\binom{4}{2}\binom{2}{2}}{n!}.$$

Method 3. We first arrange the $2n$ elements of A in a row by putting them in the $2n$ spaces as shown below:

$$\{\ \underset{(1)}{\ } \quad , \quad \underset{(2)}{\ } \ \}, \ \{\ \underset{(3)}{\ } \quad , \quad \underset{(4)}{\ } \ \}, \ \cdots, \ \{\ \underset{(2n-1)}{\ } \quad , \quad \underset{(2n)}{\ } \ \}$$

There are $(2n)!$ ways to do so. Since the order of the elements in each 2-element subset and the order of the n subsets are immaterial, the desired number of ways is given by

$$\frac{(2n)!}{\underbrace{2!\times 2!\times\cdots\times 2!}_{n}\times n!} = \frac{(2n)!}{n!\times 2^n}. \quad \blacksquare$$

It can be checked that the above 3 answers are all the same.

The above problem can be generalized in the following way. Let A be a set of kn distinct elements, where $k, n \in \mathbf{N}$. A *k-grouping* of A is a partition of A into k-element subsets; i.e., a collection of pairwise disjoint k-element subsets whose union is A. Thus if $A = \{a_1, a_2, \ldots, a_{12}\}$, then

$$\{\{a_1, a_4, a_9, a_{12}\}, \{a_2, a_5, a_8, a_{10}\}, \{a_3, a_6, a_7, a_{11}\}\}$$

is a 4-grouping of A. Clearly, a pairing of a $2n$-element set A is a 2-grouping of A. What is the number of different k-groupings of a set with kn elements? (See Problem 1.43.)

Example 1.4.5. (IMO, 1989/3) Let n and k be positive integers and let S be a set of n points in the plane such that

(i) no three points of S are collinear, and

(ii) for any point P of S, there are at least k points of S equidistant from P.

Prove that $k < \frac{1}{2} + \sqrt{2n}$.

Proof. For convenience, we call a line segment in the plane an *edge* if it joins up any two points in S. Let ℓ be the number of edges in the plane. We shall consider the quantity ℓ.

First, since there are n distinct points in S and any two of them determine an edge, we have,

$$\ell = \binom{n}{2}. \tag{1}$$

Next, for each point P of S, by condition (ii), one can draw a circle with centre P whose circumference $C(P)$ contains at least k points of S. Clearly, the points of S on $C(P)$ determine at least $\binom{k}{2}$ edges. As there are n points P in S, the total number of these edges, counted with repetition, is at least $n\binom{k}{2}$.

Now, let us look at those edges which are counted more than once. An edge is counted more than once when and only when it is a common chord of at least 2 circles. Since two circles can have at most one common chord and there are n such circles, the number of common chords, counted with repetition, is at most $\binom{n}{2}$. Thus

$$\ell \geq n\binom{k}{2} - \binom{n}{2}. \tag{2}$$

Combining (1) with (2), we have

$$n\binom{k}{2} - \binom{n}{2} \leq \binom{n}{2}$$

or

$$n\binom{k}{2} \leq 2\binom{n}{2},$$

which implies that

$$k^2 - k - 2(n-1) \leq 0.$$

Hence

$$k \leq \frac{1 + \sqrt{1 + 8(n-1)}}{2}$$
$$< \frac{1}{2} + \frac{1}{2}\sqrt{8n} = \frac{1}{2} + \sqrt{2n},$$

as required. ∎

Comments. (1) In the above proof, the quantity "ℓ" is first introduced, and it is then counted as well as estimated from two different perpectives, thereby leading to the inequality: $n\binom{k}{2} - \binom{n}{2} \leq \ell = \binom{n}{2}$. This is a common and useful technique, in combinatorics, in establishing inequalities linking up some parameters.

(2) From the proof above, we see that condition (i) is not necessary since, even if A, B, C are three collinear points, AB, BC, CA are regarded as three distinct edges in the above argument.

In Section 1.3, we studied circular permutations, which are arrangements of objects around a circle. We shall extend such arrangements to more than one circle.

Example 1.4.6. If there must be at least one person in each table, in how many ways can 6 people be seated
  (i) around two tables?
  (ii) around three tables?
(We assume that the tables are indistinguishable.)

Solution. (i) For 2 tables, there are 3 cases to consider according to the numbers of people to be seated around the 2 respective tables, namely,

$$(1) \quad 5 + 1 \qquad (2) \quad 4 + 2 \qquad (3) \quad 3 + 3.$$

Case (1). There are $\binom{6}{5}$ ways to divide the 6 people into 2 groups of sizes 5 and 1 each. By formula (1.3.2), the 5 people chosen can be seated around a table in $(5-1)!$ ways and the 1 chosen in $0!$ way around the other. Thus by (MP), the number of ways in this case is

$$\binom{6}{5} \times 4! \times 0! = 144.$$

Case (2). There are $\binom{6}{4}$ ways to divide the 6 people into 2 groups of size 4 and 2 each. Thus, again, the number of ways in this case is

$$\binom{6}{4} \times 3! \times 1! = 90.$$

Case (3). We have to be careful in this case. The number of ways to divide the 6 people into 2 groups of size 3 each is $\frac{1}{2}\binom{6}{3}$ (why?). Thus the number of arrangements is

$$\frac{1}{2}\binom{6}{3} \times 2! \times 2! = 40.$$

Hence by (AP), the desired number of arrangements is $144 + 90 + 40 = 274$.

(ii) For 3 tables, there are also 3 cases to consider depending on the number of people distributed to the 3 respective tables, namely,

$$(1) \quad 4 + 1 + 1 \qquad (2) \quad 3 + 2 + 1 \qquad (3) \quad 2 + 2 + 2.$$

The number of arrangements in these cases are given below:

$$(1) \quad \frac{1}{2}\binom{6}{4}\binom{2}{1} \times 3! \times 0! \times 0! = 90;$$

$$(2) \quad \binom{6}{3}\binom{3}{2} \times 2! \times 1! = 120;$$

$$(3) \quad \frac{1}{3!}\binom{6}{2}\binom{4}{2} \times 1! \times 1! \times 1! = 15.$$

Hence by (AP), the desired number of arrangements is $90 + 120 + 15 = 225$. ∎

Given $r, n \in \mathbf{Z}$ with $0 \le n \le r$, let $s(r,n)$ denote the number of ways to arrange r distinct objects around n (indistinguishable) circles such that each circle has at least one object. These numbers $s(r,n)$ are called the *Stirling numbers of the first kind*, named after James Stirling (1692–1770). From Example 1.4.6, we see that $s(6,2) = 274$ and $s(6,3) = 225$. Other obvious results are:

$$
\begin{aligned}
s(r,0) &= 0 & &\text{if } r \ge 1, \\
s(r,r) &= 1 & &\text{if } r \ge 0, \\
s(r,1) &= (r-1)! & &\text{for } r \ge 2, \\
s(r,r-1) &= \binom{r}{2} & &\text{for } r \ge 2.
\end{aligned}
$$

The following result, which resembles (1.4.3) in Example 1.4.1, tells us how to compute $s(r,n)$ for larger r and n from smaller r and n.

Example 1.4.7. Show that

$$s(r,n) = s(r-1, n-1) + (r-1)s(r-1, n) \tag{1.4.4}$$

where $r, n \in \mathbf{N}$ with $n \le r$.

Proof. For simplicity, we denote the r distinct objects by $1, 2, ..., r$. Consider the object "1". In any arrangement of the objects, either (i) "1" is the only object in a circle or (ii) "1" is mixed with others in a circle. In case (i), there are $s(r-1, n-1)$ ways to form such arrangements. In case (ii), first of all, the $r-1$ objects $2, 3, ..., r$ are put in n circles in $s(r-1, n)$ ways; then "1" can be placed in one of the $r-1$ distinct spaces to the "immediate right" of the corresponding $r-1$ distinct objects. By (MP), there are $(r-1)s(r-1, n)$ ways to form such arrangements in case (ii). The identity now follows from the definition of $s(r, n)$ and (AP). ∎

Using the initial values $s(0,0) = 1, s(r, 0) = 0$ for $r \ge 1$ and $s(r, 1) = (r-1)!$ for $r \ge 1$, and applying the identity (1.4.4), one can easily find out the values of $s(r, n)$ for small r and n. For r, n with $0 \le n \le r \le 9$, the values of $s(r, n)$ are recorded in Table 1.4.2.

r \ n	0	1	2	3	4	5	6	7	8	9
0	1									
1	0	1								
2	0	1	1							
3	0	2	3	1						
4	0	6	11	6	1					
5	0	24	50	35	10	1				
6	0	120	274	225	85	15	1			
7	0	720	1764	1624	735	175	21	1		
8	0	5040	13068	13132	6769	1960	322	28	1	
9	0	40320	109584	118124	67284	22449	4536	546	36	1

Table 1.4.2. The values of $s(r, n)$, $0 \le n \le r \le 9$

1.5. The Injection and Bijection Principles

Suppose that a group of n students attend a lecture in a lecture theatre with 200 seats. Assume that no student occupies more than one seat and no two students share a seat. If it is known that every student has a seat, then we must have $n \leq 200$. If it is known, furthermore, that no seat is vacant, then we are sure that $n = 200$ without actually counting the number of students. This is an example which illustrates two simple principles that we are going to state. Before doing so, we first give some definitions. Let A, B be finite sets. A mapping $f : A \to B$ from A to B is *injective* (or *one-one*) if $f(a_1) \neq f(a_2)$ in B whenever $a_1 \neq a_2$ in A. f is *surjective* (or *onto*) if for any $b \in B$, there exists $a \in A$ such that $f(a) = b$. f is *bijective* if f is both injective and surjective. Every injective (resp., surjective and bijective) mapping is also called an *injection* (resp., a *surjection* and a *bijection*).

The Injection Principle (IP) Let A and B be two finite sets. If there is an injection from A to B, then $|A| \leq |B|$.

The Bijection Principle (BP) Let A and B be two finite sets. If there is an bijection from A to B, then $|A| = |B|$.

Just like (AP), (MP) and (CP), the two principles (IP) and (BP) as given above are also trivially true. However, as we will see below, they are also useful and powerful as tools for solving counting problems.

Example 1.5.1. A student wishes to walk from the corner X to the corner Y through streets as given in the street map shown in Figure 1.5.1. How many shortest routes are there from X to Y available to the student?

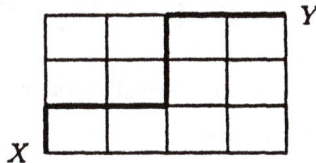

Figure 1.5.1.

Solution.   Let A be the set of all shortest routes from X to Y. We shall find $|A|$.

We first note that every route in A consists of 7 continuous segments (a segment is part of a street connecting two adjacent junctions) of which 4 are horizontal and 3 vertical. Thus if we use a '0' to denote a horizontal segment and a '1' to denote a vertical segment, then every route in A can be uniquely represented by a binary sequence of length 7 with 4 0's and 3 1's (for instance, the shortest route shown by bold line segments in Figure 1.5.1 is represented by 1001100). This way of representing a route clearly defines a mapping f from A to the set B of all binary sequences of length 7 with 4 0's and 3 1's. It is easy to see that f is both one-one and onto, and hence it is a bijection from A to B. Thus by (BP) and Example 1.4.2, we have $|A| = |B| = \binom{7}{3}$.   ∎

Remark.   The street map of Figure 1.5.1 is a 5×4 rectangular grid. In general, if it is an $(m + 1) \times (n + 1)$ rectangular grid consisting of $m + 1$ vertical streets and $n + 1$ horizontal streets, then the number of shortest routes form the southwest corner X to the northeast corner Y is equal to the number of binary sequences of length $m + n$ with m 0's and n 1's, which by Remark (2) of Example 1.4.2, is given by

$$\binom{m + n}{m} \quad \text{or} \quad \binom{m + n}{n}.$$

Given a set X, the *power set* of X, denoted by $\mathcal{P}(X)$, is the set of all subsets of X, inclusive of X and the empty set $\emptyset$. Thus, for instance, if $X = \{1, 2, 3\}$, then

$$\mathcal{P}(X) = \{\emptyset, \{1\}, \{2\}, \{3\}, \{1, 2\}, \{1, 3\}, \{2, 3\}, X\}.$$

We observe that $|\mathcal{P}(X)| = 8$. In general, what can be said about $|\mathcal{P}(X)|$ if X consists of n distinct elements?

Example 1.5.2.   Show that if $|X| = n$, then $|\mathcal{P}(X)| = 2^n$ for all $n \in \mathbb{N}$.

Proof. We may assume that $X = \{1, 2, ..., n\}$. Now, let

$$B = \{a_1 a_2 \ldots a_n \mid a_i = 0 \text{ or } 1, \ i = 1, 2, ..., n\}$$

be the set of all binary sequences of length n.

Define a mapping $f : \mathcal{P}(X) \to B$ as follows: For each $S \in \mathcal{P}(X)$ (i.e., $S \subseteq X$), we put

$$f(S) = b_1 b_2 \ldots b_n$$

where

$$b_i = \begin{cases} 1 & \text{if } i \in S, \\ 0 & \text{if } i \notin S. \end{cases}$$

(For instance, if $X = \{1, 2, 3, 4, 5\}$, $S_1 = \{4\}$ and $S_2 = \{2, 3, 5\}$, then $f(S_1) = 00010$ and $f(S_2) = 01101$.) It is easy to see that f is a bijection from $\mathcal{P}(X)$ to B. Thus by (BP), $|\mathcal{P}(X)| = |B|$. Since $|B| = 2^n$ by Example 1.1.4, we have $|\mathcal{P}(X)| = 2^n$, as required. ∎

Example 1.5.3. Let $X = \{1, 2, ..., n\}$, where $n \in \mathbb{N}$. Show that the number of r-combinations of X which contain no consecutive integers is given by

$$\binom{n - r + 1}{r},$$

where $0 \leq r \leq n - r + 1$.

As an illustration, consider $X = \{1, 2, ..., 7\}$. All the 3-combinations of X containing no consecutive integers are listed below:

$$\{1, 3, 5\}, \quad \{1, 3, 6\}, \quad \{1, 3, 7\}, \quad \{1, 4, 6\}, \quad \{1, 4, 7\},$$
$$\{1, 5, 7\}, \quad \{2, 4, 6\}, \quad \{2, 4, 7\}, \quad \{2, 5, 7\}, \quad \{3, 5, 7\}.$$

There are 10 in number and $\binom{7-3+1}{3} = 10$.

Proof. Let A be the set of r-combinations of X containing no consecutive integers, and B be the set of r-combinations of Y, where

$$Y = \{1, 2, ..., n - (r - 1)\}.$$

We shall establish a bijection from A to B.

Let $S = \{s_1, s_2, s_3, ..., s_r\}$ be a member in A. We may assume that $s_1 < s_2 < s_3 < \cdots < s_r$. Define

$$f(S) = \{s_1, s_2 - 1, s_3 - 2, ..., s_r - (r - 1)\}.$$

Observe that as s_i and s_{i+1} are non-consecutive, all the numbers in $f(S)$ are distinct. Thus $f(S) \in B$, and so f is a mapping from A to B. It is easy to see that f is injective. To see that f is surjective, let $T = \{t_1, t_2, t_3, ..., t_r\}$ be a member in B. Consider

$$S = \{t_1, t_2 + 1, t_3 + 2, ..., t_r + (r - 1)\}.$$

It can be checked that S is a member in A. Also $f(S) = T$ by definition.

This shows that $f : A \longrightarrow B$ is a bijection. Hence by (BP), we have

$$|A| = |B| = \binom{n - r + 1}{r}. \quad \blacksquare$$

Remark.   The above problem can be extended in the following way. Given $m \in \mathbf{N}$, a set $S = \{a_1, a_2, ..., a_r\}$ of positive integers, where $a_1 < a_2 < ... < a_r$, is said to be *m-separated* if $a_i - a_{i-1} \geq m$ for each $i = 2, 3, ..., r$. Thus S is 2-separated if and only if S contains no consecutive integers. Let $X = \{1, 2, ..., n\}$, where $n \in \mathbf{N}$. Using (BP), we can also find a formula for the number of r-element subsets of X which are m-separated. Readers who are interested may see Problem 1.91.

In the above three examples, three sets A (namely, the set of shortest routes, the power set $\mathcal{P}(X)$ and the set of r-combinations containing no consecutive integers) and their counterparts B (namely, the set of binary sequences of length 7 with 4 0's, the set of binary sequences of length n and the set of r-combinations, respectively) are considered. By establishing a bijection from A to B, we have by (BP), $|A| = |B|$. Note that in each case, the enumeration of $|A|$ by itself is not straightforward, while that of $|B|$ is fairly standard and so much easier. Thus with (BP), we can sometimes transform a hard problem into an easier one. This is always a crucial step in the process of solving a problem.

The above three examples involve only the applications of (BP). In what follows, we shall give an interesting example which makes use of both (BP) and (IP).

Example 1.5.4. (IMO, 1989/6) A permutation $x_1 x_2 ... x_{2n}$ of the set $\{1, 2, ..., 2n\}$, where $n \in \mathbb{N}$, is said to have property P if $|x_i - x_{i+1}| = n$ for at least one i in $\{1, 2, ..., 2n-1\}$. Show that, for each n, there are more permutations with property P than without.

This problem, proposed by Poland, was placed last in the set of the six problems for the 1989 IMO, and was considered a more difficult problem among the six. The original proof given by the proposer makes use of recurrence relations which is rather long and looks hard. However, it was a pleasant surprise that a contestant from the China team was able to produce a shorter and more elegant proof of the result. Before we see this proof, let us first try to understand the problem better.

Let $S = \{1, 2, ..., 2n\}$. Clearly, a permutation of S does not have property P if and only if for each $k = 1, 2, ..., n$, the pair of numbers k and $n+k$ are not adjacent in the permutation. For $n = 2$, the set A of permutations without P and the set B of permutations with P are given below:

$$A = \{1234, \ 1432, \ 2143, \ 2341, \ 3214, \ 3412, \ 4123, \ 4321\},$$

$$B = \{12\underline{43}, \ \underline{13}\,24, \ \underline{13}\,42, \ 14\underline{23}, \ 21\underline{34}, \ 23\underline{14}, \ \underline{24}\,13, \ \underline{24}\,31,$$
$$31\,24, \ \underline{31}\,42, \ 3\underline{24}1, \ 3\underline{42}1, \ 4\underline{13}2, \ \underline{42}\,13, \ \underline{42}\,31, \ 4\underline{31}2\}.$$

Clearly, $|B| = 16 > 8 = |A|$.

Proof. The case when $n = 1$ is trivial. Assume that $n \geq 2$. Let A (resp., B) be the set of permutations of $S = \{1, 2, ..., 2n\}$ without property P (resp., with P). To show that $|B| > |A|$, by (IP) and (BP), it suffices to establish a mapping $f : A \to B$ which is injective but not surjective.

For convenience, any number in the pair $\{k, n+k\}$ ($k = 1, 2, ..., n$) is called the *partner* of the other. If k and $n+k$ are adjacent in a permutation, the pair $\{k, n+k\}$ is called an *adjacent pair of partners*.

Let $\alpha = x_1 x_2 ... x_{2n}$ be an element in A. Since α does not have property P, the partner of x_1 is x_r where $3 \leq r \leq 2n$. Now we put

$$f(\alpha) = x_2 x_3 ... x_{r-1} \underline{x_1 x_r} x_{r+1} ... x_{2n}$$

by taking x_1 away and placing it just in front of its partner x_r. In $f(\alpha)$, it is clear that $\{x_1, x_r\}$ is the only adjacent pair of partners. (Thus, for instance, $f(\underline{12}34) = 2\underline{13}4$ and $f(2\underline{14}3) = 1\underline{24}3$.) Obviously, $f(\alpha) \in B$ and f defines a mapping from A to B.

We now claim that f is injective. Let

$$\alpha = x_1 x_2 ... x_{2n}$$

$$\beta = y_1 y_2 ... y_{2n}$$

be elements of A in which x_1's partner is x_r and y_1's partner is y_s, where $3 \leq r, s \leq 2n$. Suppose $f(\alpha) = f(\beta)$; i.e.,

$$x_2 x_3 ... x_{r-1} \underline{x_1 x_r} ... x_{2n} = y_2 y_3 ... y_{s-1} \underline{y_1 y_s} ... y_{2n}.$$

Since $\{x_1, x_r\}$ (resp., $\{y_1, y_s\}$) is the only adjacent pair of partners in $f(\alpha)$ (resp., $f(\beta)$), we must have $r = s$, $x_1 = y_1$ and $x_r = y_s$. These, in turn, imply that $x_i = y_i$ for all $i = 1, 2, ..., 2n$ and so $\alpha = \beta$, showing that f is injective.

Finally, we note that $f(A)$ consists of all permutations of S having exactly one adjacent pair of partners while there are permutations of S in B which contain more than one adjacent pair of partners. Thus we have $f(A) \subset B$, showing that f is not surjective. The proof is thus complete. ∎

1.6. Arrangements and Selections with Repetitions

In the previous sections we studied arrangements and selections of elements from a set in which no repetitions are allowed. In this section we shall consider arrangements and selections in which elements are allowed to be repeated.

Example 1.6.1. Let $A = \{a, b, c\}$. All the 2-permutations of A with repetitions allowed are given below:

$$aa, \ ab, \ ac, \ ba, \ bb, \ bc, \ ca, \ cb, \ cc.$$

There are 9 in number. ∎

In general, we have:

(I)   The number of r-permutations of the set

$$A = \{a_1, a_2, ..., a_n\},$$

where $r, n \in \mathbf{N}$, with repetitions allowed, is given by n^r.

Proof of (I). There are n choices for the first object of an r-permutation. Since repetitions are allowed, there are again n choices for each of the remaining $r-1$ objects of an r-permutation. Thus the number of such permutations is, by (MP), $\underbrace{n \cdot n \cdots n}_{r} = n^r$. ∎

Example 1.6.2. A 4-storey house is to be painted by some 6 different colours such that each storey is painted in one colour. How many ways are there to paint the house?

Solution. This is the number of 4-permutations of the set $\{1, 2, ..., 6\}$ of 6 colours with repetitions allowed. By (I), the desired number is 6^4. ∎

For those permutations considered in (I), an element of the set A can be repeated any number of times. We now consider another type of permutations in which the number of times an element can be repeated is limited.

Example 1.6.3. Find the number of permutations of the 5 letters: a, a, a, b, c.

Solution. Let α be the desired number of such permutations. Fix one of them, say $abaac$. Imagine now that the 3 a's are distinct, say a_1, a_2, a_3. We then observe from the following exhibition

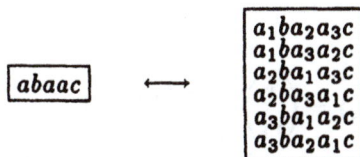

$$\boxed{abaac} \quad \longleftrightarrow \quad \boxed{\begin{matrix} a_1 b a_2 a_3 c \\ a_1 b a_3 a_2 c \\ a_2 b a_1 a_3 c \\ a_2 b a_3 a_1 c \\ a_3 b a_1 a_2 c \\ a_3 b a_2 a_1 c \end{matrix}}$$

that "$abaac$" corresponds to a set of $3! = 6$ permutations of the set $\{a_1, a_2, a_3, b, c\}$ keeping the pattern of $abaac$, and vice versa.

Since there are $5!$ permutations of $\{a_1, a_2, a_3, b, c\}$, we have

$$\alpha \cdot 3! = 5!,$$

$$\text{i.e.,} \quad \alpha = \frac{5!}{3!} = 20. \quad ∎$$

In general, we have:

(II)   Consider a collection of r objects, in which r_1 are of type 1, r_2 are of type 2, ..., and r_n are of type n, where $r_1 + r_2 + \cdots + r_n = r$. The number of different permutations of the collection of objects, denoted by $P(r; r_1, r_2, ..., r_n)$, is given by

$$P(r; r_1, r_2, ..., r_n) = \frac{r!}{r_1! r_2! \cdots r_n!}.$$

One may extend the idea shown in Example 1.6.3 to prove (II). We give a different approach here.

Proof of (II). In any permutation of the collection of r objects, there are r_i positions to place the r_i objects of type i, for each $i = 1, 2, ..., n$. Different choices of positions give rise to different permutations.

We first choose r_1 positions from the r distinct positions and place the r_1 identical objects of type 1 at the r_1 positions chosen. There are $\binom{r}{r_1}$ ways to do so. Next, we choose r_2 positions from the remaining $r - r_1$ positions and place the r_2 identical objects of type 2 at the r_2 positions chosen. There are $\binom{r-r_1}{r_2}$ ways to do so. We proceed in this manner till the final step when we choose r_n positions from the remaining $r - (r_1 + r_2 + \cdots + r_{n-1})(= r_n)$ positions and place the r_n identical objects of type n at the r_n positions left. There are $\binom{r-(r_1+r_2+\cdots+r_{n-1})}{r_n}$ ways to do so. By (MP) and formula (1.4.1), we then have

$$P(r; r_1, r_2, ..., r_n) = \binom{r}{r_1}\binom{r-r_1}{r_2}\cdots\binom{r-(r_1+r_2+\cdots+r_{n-1})}{r_n}$$

$$= \frac{r!}{r_1!(r-r_1)!} \cdot \frac{(r-r_1)!}{r_2!(r-r_1-r_2)!} \cdots \frac{(r-r_1-r_2-\cdots-r_{n-1})!}{r_n!(r-r_1-r_2-\cdots-r_n)!}$$

$$= \frac{r!}{r_1! r_2! \cdots r_n!}. \quad \blacksquare$$

The results (I) and (II) may be rephrased in a more convenient way by using a notion, called a multi-set. Just like a set, a *multi-set* is a collection of objects, but its members need not be distinct. Thus, for instance, $M = \{a, b, a, c, b, a\}$ is a multi-set consisting of 3 a's, 2 b's and 1 c. This multi-set can be written in a neater way as $M = \{3 \cdot a, 2 \cdot b, c\}$. In general, the multi-set

$$M = \{r_1 \cdot a_1, r_2 \cdot a_2, ..., r_n \cdot a_n\},$$

where $n, r_1, r_2, ..., r_n$ are nonnegative integers and $a_1, a_2, ..., a_n$ are distinct objects, consists of r_1 a_1's, r_2 a_2's, ... and r_n a_n's. For each $i = 1, 2, ..., n$, the number r_i is called the *repetition number* of the object a_i. For convenience, given an object a, we may write $\infty \cdot a$ to indicate that a can be repeated an infinite number of times. Thus a multi-set in which b and e occur an infinite number of times, and a, c, d have, respectively, the repetition numbers 2, 7, 4, is denoted by $\{2 \cdot a, \infty \cdot b, 7 \cdot c, 4 \cdot d, \infty \cdot e\}$.

An *r-permutation* of $M = \{r_1 \cdot a_1, r_2 \cdot a_2, \ldots, r_n \cdot a_n\}$ is an arrangement of r objects taken from M with at most r_i of a_i ($i = 1, 2, ..., n$) in a row. A *permutation* of M is an arrangement of all the objects of M in a row. An *r-permutation* of the multi-set $\{\infty \cdot a_1, \infty \cdot a_2, \ldots, \infty \cdot a_n\}$ is similarly defined, except that the number of a_i's chosen is not limited for all i.

Using the above terminology, we may re-state the results (I) and (II) as follows:

(I)   The number of r-permutations of the multi-set

$$\{\infty \cdot a_1, \infty \cdot a_2, \ldots, \infty \cdot a_n\}$$

is given by n^r.

(II)   Let $M = \{r_1 \cdot a_1, r_2 \cdot a_2, ..., r_n \cdot a_n\}$ and $r = r_1 + r_2 + \cdots + r_n$. Then the number $P(r; r_1, r_2, ..., r_n)$ of permutations of M is given by

$$P(r; r_1, r_2, ..., r_n) = \frac{r!}{r_1! r_2! \cdots r_n!}.$$

Example 1.6.4.   Find the number of ternary sequences of length 10 having two 0's, three 1's and five 2's.

Solution. The number of such ternary sequences is the number of permutations of the multi-set $\{2 \cdot 0, 3 \cdot 1, 5 \cdot 2\}$, which is equal to

$$\frac{10!}{2!3!5!} = 2520$$

by (II). ∎

Example 1.6.5. Find the number of ways to pave a 1×7 rectangle by 1×1, 1×2 and 1×3 blocks, assuming that blocks of the same size are indistinguishable.

As an illustration, two ways of paving are shown below:

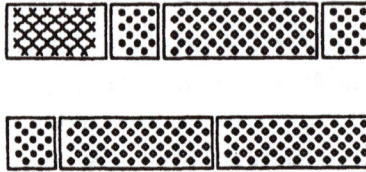

For $i = 1, 2, 3$, we let b_i denote an $1 \times i$ block. Thus the first way shown above may be represented by $b_2 b_1 b_3 b_1$, which is a permutation of $\{2 \cdot b_1, b_2, b_3\}$, while the second way by $b_1 b_3 b_3$, which is a permutation of $\{b_1, 2 \cdot b_3\}$. Note that in each case, the sum of the sub-indices of b_i's is "7".

Solution. From the above illustration, we see that the desired number of ways is equal to the number of permutations of some b_i's such that the sum of the sub-indices of such b_i's is 7. The following 8 cases cover all the possibilities:

(i)	$\{7 \cdot b_1\}$	(ii)	$\{5 \cdot b_1, b_2\}$
(iii)	$\{4 \cdot b_1, b_3\}$	(iv)	$\{3 \cdot b_1, 2 \cdot b_2\}$
(v)	$\{2 \cdot b_1, b_2, b_3\}$	(vi)	$\{b_1, 3 \cdot b_2\}$
(vii)	$\{b_1, 2 \cdot b_3\}$	(viii)	$\{2 \cdot b_2, b_3\}$.

For each case, the number of permutations of the multi-set is shown below:

(i)	1	(ii)	$\frac{6!}{5!} = 6$
(iii)	$\frac{5!}{4!} = 5$	(iv)	$\frac{5!}{3!2!} = 10$
(v)	$\frac{4!}{2!} = 12$	(vi)	$\frac{4!}{3!} = 4$
(vii)	$\frac{3!}{2!} = 3$	(viii)	$\frac{3!}{2!} = 3$.

Thus the desired number of ways is

$$1 + 6 + 5 + 10 + 12 + 4 + 3 + 3 = 44. \quad \blacksquare$$

Example 1.6.6. Show that $(4n)!$ is a multiple of $2^{3n} \cdot 3^n$, for each natural number n.

Proof. Consider the multi-set

$$M = \{4 \cdot a_1, 4 \cdot a_2, ..., 4 \cdot a_n\}.$$

By (II),

$$P(4n; \underbrace{4, 4, ..., 4}_{n}) = \frac{(4n)!}{(4!)^n} = \frac{(4n)!}{(2^3 \cdot 3)^n} = \frac{(4n)!}{2^{3n} \cdot 3^n}.$$

The result now follows as $P(4n; 4, 4, ..., 4)$ is a whole number. $\quad \blacksquare$

We now turn our attention to the problem of counting the number of combinations with repetitions.

Let $A = \{1, 2, 3, 4\}$. Then there are $\binom{4}{3} = 4$ ways to form 3-combinations of A in which no elements are repeated. Suppose now *elements are allowed to be repeated*. How many 3-combinations can be formed? One can find out the answer simply by listing all such 3-combinations as shown below. There are altogether 20 in number.

$$\{1,1,1\}, \quad \{1,2,2\}, \quad \{1,3,4\}, \quad \{2,2,4\}, \quad \{3,3,3\},$$
$$\{1,1,2\}, \quad \{1,2,3\}, \quad \{1,4,4\}, \quad \{2,3,3\}, \quad \{3,3,4\},$$
$$\{1,1,3\}, \quad \{1,2,4\}, \quad \{2,2,2\}, \quad \{2,3,4\}, \quad \{3,4,4\},$$
$$\{1,1,4\}, \quad \{1,3,3\}, \quad \{2,2,3\}, \quad \{2,4,4\}, \quad \{4,4,4\}.$$

Let

$$M = \{\infty \cdot a_1, \infty \cdot a_2, ..., \infty \cdot a_n\}$$

be a given multi-set where $n \in \mathbf{N}$. A multi-set of the form

$$\{m_1 \cdot a_1, m_2 \cdot a_2, ..., m_n \cdot a_n\},$$

where m_i's are nonnegative integers, is called a $(m_1 + m_2 + \cdots + m_n)$-element *multi-subset* of M. Thus, as shown above, there are 20 3-element multi-subsets of the multi-set $\{\infty \cdot 1, \infty \cdot 2, \infty \cdot 3, \infty \cdot 4\}$. For a nonnegative integer r, let H_r^n denote the number of r-element multi-subsets of M. The above example shows that $H_3^4 = 20$. We shall find a formula for H_r^n. To get to this, let us consider the following example.

Example 1.6.7. There are 3 types of sandwiches, namely chicken (C), fish (F) and ham (H), available in a restaurant. A boy wishes to place an order of 6 sandwiches. Assuming that there is no limit in the supply of sandwiches of each type, how many such orders can the boy place?

Solution. This problem amounts to computing H_6^3. It is tedious to find H_6^3 by listing all 6-element multi-subsets of $\{\infty \cdot C, \infty \cdot F, \infty \cdot H\}$ as how we did before. We introduce an indirect way here.

The table below shows 4 different orders:

	C	F	H
(1)	o o	o	o o o
(2)	o	o o o o	o
(3)		o o	o o o o
(4)	o o o		o o o

(1)	2 chicken,	1 fish and	3 ham sandwiches,
(2)	1 chicken,	4 fish and	1 ham sandwiches,
(3)		2 fish and	4 ham sandwiches,
(4)	3 chicken	and	3 ham sandwiches.

It is now interesting to note from the table that if we treat a "vertical stroke" as a '1', then order (1) can be uniquely represented by the binary sequence

$$00101000,$$

while (2), (3) and (4) respectively by

$$01000010,$$
$$10010000,$$

and
$$00011000.$$

In this way, we find that every order of 6 sandwiches corresponds to a binary sequence of length 8 with 6 0's and 2 1's, and different orders correspond to different binary sequences. On the other hand, every such binary sequence represents an order of 6 sandwiches. For instance, 01001000 represents the order of 1 chicken, 2 fish and 3 ham sandwiches. Thus, we see that there is a bijection between the set of such orders and the set of binary sequences with 6 0's and 2 1's. Hence by (BP) and Remark (2) of Example 1.4.2, the desired number of ways is $H_6^3 = \binom{8}{2}$. ∎

So, can you now generalize the above idea to obtain a formula for H_r^n?

Look at the following table. The first row of the table shows the n types of objects of the multi-set $M = \{\infty \cdot a_1, \infty \cdot a_2, ..., \infty \cdot a_n\}$ which are separated by $n - 1$ vertical strokes.

Using this framework, every multi-subset $S = \{r_1 \cdot a_1, r_2 \cdot a_2, ..., r_n \cdot a_n\}$ of M, where $r_i \geq 0$ for all i, can be represented by a row having r_i 0's within the interval under a_i. If we treat each vertical stroke as an '1', then every r-element multi- ubset of M corresponds to a unique binary sequence of length $r + n - 1$ with r 0's and $(n - 1)$ 1's. This correspondence is indeed a bijection between the family of all r-element multi-subsets of M and the family of all such binary sequences. Thus by (BP) and Remark (2) of Example 1.4.2, we obtain the following result.

(III)   Let $M = \{\infty \cdot a_1, \infty \cdot a_2, ..., \infty \cdot a_n\}$. The number H_r^n of r-element multi-subsets of M is given by

$$H_r^n = \binom{r + n - 1}{r}.$$

Result (III) can be proved in various ways. We give another proof below.

Another Proof of (III). For convenience, we represent a_i by i, $i = 1, 2, ..., n$, and so $M = \{\infty \cdot 1, \infty \cdot 2, ..., \infty \cdot n\}$. Let A be the family of all r-element multi-subsets of M and B be the family of all r-combinations of the set $\{1, 2, ..., r + n - 1\}$. Define a mapping $f : A \to B$ as follows: For each r-element multi-subset $S = \{b_1, b_2, ..., b_r\}$ of M, where $1 \leq b_1 \leq b_2 \leq ... \leq b_r \leq n$, let

$$f(S) = \{b_1, b_2 + 1, b_3 + 2, ..., b_r + (r - 1)\}.$$

It should be noted that members in $f(S)$ are distinct and so $f(S) \in B$. It is easy to see that f is injective. To show that f is surjective, let $T = \{c_1, c_2, ..., c_r\}$ be an r-combination of $\{1, 2, ..., r + n - 1\}$ with $c_1 < c_2 < \cdots < c_r$. Consider

$$S = \{c_1, c_2 - 1, c_3 - 2, ..., c_r - (r - 1)\}.$$

Observe that S is an r-element multi-subset of M and by definition, $f(S) = T$. This shows that f is surjective.

We thus conclude that f is a bijection from A to B. Hence by (BP),

$$H_r^n = |A| = |B| = \binom{r + n - 1}{r}. \quad \blacksquare$$

Remarks. (1) Let $M' = \{p_1 \cdot a_1, p_2 \cdot a_2, ..., p_n \cdot a_n\}$ be a multi-set. From the above discussion, we see that the number of r-element multi-subsets

$$\{r_1 \cdot a_1, r_2 \cdot a_2, ..., r_n \cdot a_n\},$$

$(0 \le r_i \le p_i$, for all i) of M' is also given by $\binom{r+n-1}{r}$ if $r \le p_i$ for all i.

On the other hand, if $r > p_i$ for some i, then the above statement is invalid. This case will be studied in Chapter 5.

(2) The reader might have noticed that there is some similarity between the above proof and that given in Example 1.5.3. Indeed, the rule defining f here is the same as that defining f^{-1} there.

1.7. Distribution Problems

We consider in this section the following problem: Count the number of ways of distributing r objects into n *distinct* boxes satisfying certain conditions. We split our consideration into two cases: (1) objects are distinct, (2) objects are identical (or indistinguishable).

Case (1) Distributing r *distinct objects into n distinct boxes.*

(i) If each box can hold *at most one* object, then the number of ways to distribute the objects is given by

$$n(n - 1)(n - 2) \cdots (n - r + 1) = P_r^n,$$

since object 1 can be put into any of the n boxes, object 2 into any of the $n-1$ boxes left, and so on.

(ii) If each box can hold any number of objects, then the number of ways to distribute the objects is given by

$$\underbrace{n \cdot n \cdots n}_{r} = n^r,$$

as each object can be put into any of the n boxes.

(iii) Assume that each box can hold any number of objects and the orderings of objects in each box count.

In this case, the 1st object, say a_1, can be put in any of the n places (namely, the n boxes); and the 2nd object, say a_2, can be put in any of the $n+1$ places (the $n-1$ boxes not containing a_1 plus the left and right positions of a_1 in the box containing a_1). Similarly, the 3rd object can be put in any of the $n+2$ places due to the presents of a_1 and a_2, and so on. Thus the number of ways that an arrangement can be made in this case is given by

$$n(n+1)(n+2)\cdots(n+(r-1)).$$

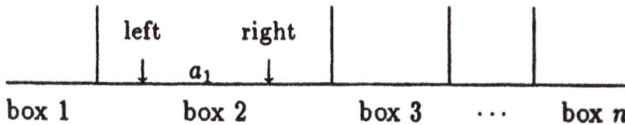

There is another way to solve the problem. As shown below,

one can establish a bijection between the set of such distributions of r distinct objects $a_1, a_2, ..., a_r$ into n distinct boxes and the set of arrangements of the multi-set $\{a_1, a_2, ..., a_r, (n-1)\cdot 1\}$ (we treat each vertical stroke separating adjacent boxes as a '1'). Thus by (BP) and result (II) in Section 1.6, the desired number of ways is given by

$$\frac{(n-1+r)!}{(n-1)!},$$

which agrees with the above result.

Case (2) <u>Distributing *r identical* objects into *n distinct* boxes.</u>

(i) Assume that each box can hold at most one object (and thus $r \leq n$).

In this case, there is a 1–1 correspondence between the ways of distribution and the ways of selecting r boxes from the given n distinct boxes. Thus the number of ways this can be done is given by $\binom{n}{r}$.

(ii) Assume that each box can hold any number of objects.

In this case, a way of distribution can be represented by

$$\{r_1 \cdot a_1, r_2 \cdot a_2, ..., r_n \cdot a_n\},$$

where r_i's are nonnegative integers with $r_1 + r_2 + \cdots + r_n = r$, which means that r_i objects are put in box i, $i = 1, 2, ..., n$. Thus a way of distribution can be considered as an r-element multi-subset of $M = \{\infty \cdot a_1, \infty \cdot a_2, ..., \infty \cdot a_n\}$, and conversely, every r-element multi-subset of M represents a way of distribution. Hence, the number of ways this can be done is given by

$$H_r^n = \binom{r+n-1}{r},$$

by result (III) in Section 1.6.

(iii) Assume that each box holds at least one object (and thus $r \geq n$); i.e., no box is empty.

In this case, we first put one object in each box to fulfill the requirement (this can be done in one way), and then distribute the remaining $r - n$ objects in the boxes in an arbitrary way. By (MP) and the result in (ii), the desired number of ways is given by

$$\binom{(r-n)+n-1}{r-n} = \binom{r-1}{r-n}.$$

By identity (1.4.2), this can also be written as

$$\binom{r-1}{n-1}.$$

Example 1.7.1. How many ways are there to arrange the letters of the word 'VISITING' if no two I's are adjacent?

Solution. *Method 1.* The letters used are V, S, T, N, G and 3 I's. We first arrange V, S, T, N, G in a row. There are 5! ways. Take one of these arrangements as shown below.

$$\underline{\quad} \; V \; \underline{\quad} \; S \; \underline{\quad} \; T \; \underline{\quad} \; N \; \underline{\quad} \; G \; \underline{\quad}$$
$$\text{1st} \qquad \text{2nd} \qquad \text{3rd} \qquad \text{4th} \qquad \text{5th} \qquad \text{6th}$$

There are 6 spaces separated by the 5 letters. The problem is now reduced to that of distributing the 3 identical I's in the 6 places such that each place can hold at most one I (no 2 I's are adjacent). By Case (2)(i), the number of ways to do so is given by $\binom{6}{3}$. Thus by (MP), the desired number of ways is

$$5!\binom{6}{3}. \quad \blacksquare$$

In the above method, we first consider "V, S, T, N, G" and then 3 I's. In the next method, we reverse the order.

Method 2. We first arrange the 3 I's in a row in one way:

$$\underline{\quad} \; I \; \underline{\quad} \; I \; \underline{\quad} \; I \; \underline{\quad}$$
$$\text{1st} \qquad \text{2nd} \qquad \text{3rd} \qquad \text{4th}$$

Then treat the 5 letters "V, S, T, N, G" as 5 identical "x". Since no 2 I's are adjacent, one 'x' must be put in the 2nd and 3rd places (this can be done in one way):

$$\underline{\quad} \; I \; \underline{x} \; I \; \underline{x} \; I \; \underline{\quad}$$
$$\text{1st} \qquad \text{2nd} \qquad \text{3rd} \qquad \text{4th}$$

Now, the remaining 3 x's can be put in the 4 places arbitrarily in $\binom{3+4-1}{3} = \binom{6}{3}$ ways by Case (2)(ii). Finally, by restoring the original letters that each "x" represents (so 5! ways to arrange them) and by applying (MP), the desired number of ways is given by

$$\binom{6}{3} \cdot 5!. \quad \blacksquare$$

Example 1.7.2. (Example 1.2.3(ii) revisited) In how many ways can 7 boys and 3 girls be arranged in a row so that the 2 end-positions are occupied by boys and no girls are adjacent?

In Example 1.2.3, this problem was solved by considering the arrangement of boys followed by that of girls. In the following solution, we reverse the order.

Solution. The 3 girls can be arranged in 3! ways. Fix one of them:

$$\underline{\quad}\ \ G_1\ \ \underline{\quad}\ \ G_2\ \ \underline{\quad}\ \ G_3\ \ \underline{\quad}$$

$$\text{1st}\qquad\text{2nd}\qquad\text{3rd}\qquad\text{4th}$$

Then treat the 7 boys as 7 identical "x". To meet the requirements, one "x" must be placed in each of the 4 places separated by the 3 girls as shown below:

$$x\ \ G_1\ \ x\ \ G_2\ \ x\ \ G_3\ \ x$$

Now the remaining 3 x's can be put in the 4 places arbitrarily in $\binom{3+4-1}{3} = \binom{6}{3}$ ways by Case (2)(ii). Finally, by restoring the meaning of 'x' and applying (MP), we obtain the desired number of ways:

$$3! \cdot \binom{6}{3} \cdot 7! = 7! \cdot 6 \cdot 5 \cdot 4. \quad \blacksquare$$

Example 1.7.3. (Example 1.5.3 revisited) Let $X = \{1, 2, ..., n\}$, where $n \in N$. Show that the number of r-combinations of X which contain no consecutive integers is given by $\binom{n-r+1}{r}$, where $0 \le r \le n - r + 1$.

Proof. We first establish a bijection between the set A of all such r-combinations of X and the set B of all binary sequences of length n with r 1's such that there is at least a '0' between any two 1's.

Define a mapping $f : A \to B$ as follows: given such an r-combination $S = \{k_1, k_2, ..., k_r\}$ of X, where $1 \le k_1 < k_2 < ... < k_r \le n$, let $f(S) = b_1 b_2 \cdots b_n$, where

$$b_i = \begin{cases} 1 & \text{if } i = k_1, k_2, ..., k_r, \\ 0 & \text{otherwise.} \end{cases}$$

For instance, if $n = 8$ and $r = 3$, then

$$f(\{2, 4, 7\}) = 01010010$$

$$\text{and} \qquad f(\{1, 5, 8\}) = 10001001.$$

It is easy to check that f is a bijection between A and B. Thus $|A| = |B|$.

Our next task is to count $|B|$. Observe that a binary sequence in B can be regarded as a way of distributing $n - r$ identical objects into $r + 1$ distinct boxes such that the 2nd, 3rd, ... and rth boxes are all nonempty as shown below:

01010010 $\longmapsto$	0	0	00	0
	1st	2nd	3rd	4th
10001001 $\longmapsto$		000	00	
	1st	2nd	3rd	4th

To get one such distribution, we first put one object each in the 2nd, 3rd, ... and rth boxes. We then distribute the remaining $(n-r)-(r-1) = n-2r+1$ objects in an arbitrary way to the $r + 1$ boxes including the 1st and last boxes. The first step can be done in one way while the second step, by the result of Case (2)(ii), in

$$\binom{(n - 2r + 1) + (r + 1) - 1}{n - 2r + 1}$$

ways. Thus we have

$$|A| = |B| = \binom{n - r + 1}{n - 2r + 1} = \binom{n - r + 1}{r},$$

by identity (1.4.2). ∎

We now turn our attention to consider the following important and typical problem in combinatorics, namely, finding the number of integer solutions to the linear equation:

$$x_1 + x_2 + \cdots + x_n = r \tag{1.7.1}$$

in n unknowns $x_1, x_2, ..., x_n$, where r and n are integers with $r \geq 0$ and $n \geq 1$.

An *integer solution* to the equation (1.7.1) is an n-tuple $(e_1, e_2, ..., e_n)$ of integers satisfying (1.7.1) when x_i is substituted by e_i, for each $i = 1, 2, ..., n$. Thus, for instance, $(-1, -4, 7), (2, 0, 0), (0, 1, 1), (0, 2, 0)$ and $(0, 0, 2)$ are some integer solutions to the equation

$$x_1 + x_2 + x_3 = 2.$$

There are infinitely many integer solutions to (1.7.1). In this section, we shall confine ourselves to "nonnegative" integer solutions (i.e., $e_i \geq 0$, for all i).

Example 1.7.4. Show that the number of nonnegative integer solutions to equation (1.7.1) is given by

$$\binom{r+n-1}{r}.$$

Proof. Every nonnegative integer solution $(e_1, e_2, ..., e_n)$ to (1.7.1) corresponds to a way of distributing r identical objects to n distinct boxes as shown below:

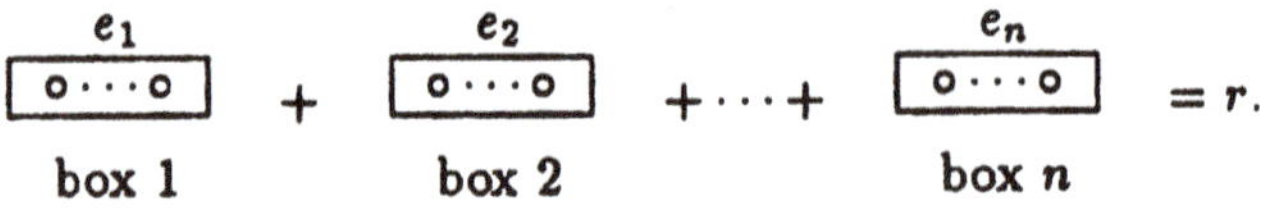

Clearly, different solutions to (1.7.1) correspond to different ways of distribution. On the other hand, every such way of distribution corresponds to a nonnegative integer solution to (1.7.1). Thus by (BP) and the result in Case (2)(ii), the desired number is given by

$$\binom{r+n-1}{r}. \quad \blacksquare$$

We now review all the problems in this chapter which give rise to the important number $\binom{r+n-1}{r}$.

The number of ways of selecting r objects from n different types of objects with repetitions allowed

$=$ the number of r-element multi-subsets of the multi-set

$$\{\infty \cdot a_1, \infty \cdot a_2, \ldots, \infty \cdot a_n\}$$

$=$ the number of ways of distributing r identical objects into n distinct boxes

$=$ the number of nonnegative integer solutions to the equation

$$x_1 + x_2 + \cdots + x_n = r$$

$= \binom{r + n - 1}{r}$

$= H_r^n.$

Some problems of distributing objects (identical or distinct) into distinct boxes have just been studied. In what follows, we shall study a problem of distributing distinct objects into identical boxes. Problems of distributing identical objects into identical boxes will be discussed in Chapter 5.

Given nonnegative integers r and n, the *Stirling number of the second kind*, denoted by $S(r,n)$, is defined as the number of ways of distributing r distinct objects into n identical boxes such that no box is empty.

The following results are obvious.

(i) $S(0,0) = 1$,
(ii) $S(r,0) = S(0,n) = 0$ for all $r, n \in \mathbb{N}$,
(iii) $S(r,n) > 0$ if $r \geq n \geq 1$,
(iv) $S(r,n) = 0$ if $n > r \geq 1$,
(v) $S(r,1) = 1$ for $r \geq 1$,
(vi) $S(r,r) = 1$ for $r \geq 1$.

We also have (see Problem 1.84):

$$
\begin{aligned}
\text{(vii)} \quad & S(r, 2) = 2^{r-1} - 1, \\
\text{(viii)} \quad & S(r, 3) = \tfrac{1}{2}(3^{r-1} + 1) - 2^{r-1}, \\
\text{(ix)} \quad & S(r, r - 1) = \binom{r}{2}, \\
\text{(x)} \quad & S(r, r - 2) = \binom{r}{3} + 3\binom{r}{4}.
\end{aligned}
$$

The following result bears some analogy to those given in Example 1.4.1 and Example 1.4.7.

Example 1.7.5.   Show that

$$
S(r, n) = S(r - 1, n - 1) + nS(r - 1, n) \tag{1.7.2}
$$

where $r, n \in \mathbb{N}$ with $r \geq n$.

Proof.   Let a_1 be a particular object of the r distinct objects. In any way of distributing the r objects into n identical boxes such that no box is empty, either (i) a_1 is the only object in a box or (ii) a_1 is mixed with others in a box. In case (i), the number of ways to do so is $S(r - 1, n - 1)$. In case (ii), the $r - 1$ objects (excluding a_1) are first put in the n boxes in $S(r - 1, n)$ ways; then a_1 can be put in any of the boxes in n ways (why?). Thus the number of ways this can be done in case (ii) is $nS(r - 1, n)$. The result now follows by (AP). ∎

Using some initial values of $S(r, n)$ and applying the identity (1.7.2), one can easily construct the following table:

Let $A = \{1, 2, ..., r\}$. For $n \in \mathbb{N}$, an *n-partition* of A is a collection $\{S_1, S_2, \ldots, S_n\}$ of n nonempty subsets of A such that

$$
\begin{aligned}
&\text{(i)} \quad S_i \cap S_j = \emptyset \text{ for } i \neq j \\
\text{and} \quad &\text{(ii)} \quad \bigcup_{i=1}^{n} S_i = A.
\end{aligned}
$$

A *partition* of A is an n-partition of A for some $n = 1, 2, ..., r$.

A binary relation R on A is an *equivalence relation* on A if

(i) R is reflexive; i.e., aRa for all $a \in A$,

(ii) R is symmetric; i.e., if $a, b \in A$ and aRb, then bRa, and

(iii) R is transitive; i.e., if $a, b, c \in A$, aRb and bRc, then aRc.

r \ n	0	1	2	3	4	5	6	7	8	9
0	1									
1	0	1								
2	0	1	1							
3	0	1	3	1						
4	0	1	7	6	1					
5	0	1	15	25	10	1				
6	0	1	31	90	65	15	1			
7	0	1	63	301	350	140	21	1		
8	0	1	127	966	1701	1050	266	28	1	
9	0	1	255	3025	7770	6951	2646	462	36	1

Table 1.7.1. The values of $S(r, n)$, $0 \leq n \leq r \leq 9$

Let $S = \{S_1, S_2, ..., S_n\}$ be a partition of A. Define a binary relation R on A by putting

$$x R y \iff x, y \in S_i \quad \text{for some } i = 1, 2, ..., n.$$

It can be checked that R is an equivalence relation on A called the *equivalence relation induced by S*; and in this way, different partitions of A induce different equivalence relations on A.

Conversely, given an equivalence relation R on A and $a \in A$, let

$$[a] = \{x \in A \mid x R a\}$$

be the *equivalence class determined by a*. Then it can be checked that the set

$$S = \{[a] \mid a \in A\}$$

of subsets of A is a partition of A such that the equivalence relation induced by S is R.

The above discussion shows that there is a bijection between the family of partitions of A and the family of equivalence relations on A.

It is obvious that a way of distributing r distinct objects $1, 2, ..., r$ to n identical boxes such that no box is empty can be regarded as an n-partition of the set $A = \{1, 2, ..., r\}$. Thus, by definition, $S(r, n)$ counts the number of n-partitions of A, and therefore

$$\sum_{n=1}^{r} S(r, n) = \text{ the number of partitions of } \{1, 2, ..., r\}$$

$$= \text{ the number of equivalence relations on } \{1, 2, ..., r\}.$$

The sum $\sum_{n=1}^{r} S(r, n)$, usually denoted by B_r, is called a *Bell number* after E.T. Bell (1883 – 1960). The first few Bell numbers are:

$$B_1 = 1, \ B_2 = 2, \ B_3 = 5, \ B_4 = 15, \ B_5 = 52, \ B_6 = 203, \ldots.$$

Exercise 1

1. Find the number of ways to choose a pair $\{a, b\}$ of distinct numbers from the set $\{1, 2, ..., 50\}$ such that

   (i) $|a - b| = 5$; (ii) $|a - b| \leq 5$.

2. There are 12 students in a party. Five of them are girls. In how many ways can these 12 students be arranged in a row if

   (i) there are no restrictions?

   (ii) the 5 girls must be together (forming a block)?

   (iii) no 2 girls are adjacent?

   (iv) between two particular boys A and B, there are no boys but exactly 3 girls?

3. m boys and n girls are to be arranged in a row, where $m, n \in \mathbf{N}$. Find the number of ways this can be done in each of the following cases:

   (i) There are no restrictions;

   (ii) No boys are adjacent $(m \leq n + 1)$;

   (iii) The n girls form a single block;

   (iv) A particular boy and a particular girl must be adjacent.

4. How many 5-letter words can be formed using $A, B, C, D, E, F, G, H, I, J,$

   (i) if the letters in each word must be distinct?

   (ii) if, in addition, A, B, C, D, E, F can only occur as the first, third or fifth letters while the rest as the second or fourth letters?

5. Find the number of ways of arranging the 26 letters in the English alphabet in a row such that there are exactly 5 letters between x and y.

6. Find the number of *odd* integers between 3000 and 8000 in which no digit is repeated.

7. Evaluate
$$1 \cdot 1! + 2 \cdot 2! + 3 \cdot 3! + \cdots + n \cdot n!,$$
where $n \in \mathbf{N}$.

8. Evaluate
$$\frac{1}{(1+1)!} + \frac{2}{(2+1)!} + \cdots + \frac{n}{(n+1)!},$$
where $n \in \mathbf{N}$.

9. Prove that for each $n \in \mathbf{N}$,
$$(n+1)(n+2)\cdots(2n)$$
is divisible by 2^n. (Spanish Olympiad, 1985)

10. Find the number of common positive divisors of 10^{40} and 20^{30}.

11. In each of the following, find the number of positive divisors of n (inclusive of n) which are multiples of 3:
    (i) $n = 210$;   (ii) $n = 630$;   (iii) $n = 151200$.

12. Show that for any $n \in \mathbf{N}$, the number of positive divisors of n^2 is always odd.

13. Show that the number of positive divisors of "$\underbrace{111\ldots1}_{1992}$" is even.

14. Let $n, r \in \mathbf{N}$ with $r \leq n$. Prove each of the following identities:
    (i) $P_r^n = nP_{r-1}^{n-1}$,
    (ii) $P_r^n = (n - r + 1)P_{r-1}^n$,
    (iii) $P_r^n = \frac{n}{n-r}P_r^{n-1}$, where $r < n$,
    (iv) $P_r^{n+1} = P_r^n + rP_{r-1}^n$,
    (v) $P_r^{n+1} = r! + r(P_{r-1}^n + P_{r-1}^{n-1} + \cdots + P_{r-1}^r)$.

15. In a group of 15 students, 5 of them are female. If exactly 3 female students are to be selected, in how many ways can 9 students be chosen from the group
    (i) to form a committee?
    (ii) to take up 9 different posts in a committee?

16. Ten chairs have been arranged in a row. Seven students are to be seated in seven of them so that no two students share a common chair. Find the number of ways this can be done if no two empty chairs are adjacent.

17. Eight boxes are arranged in a row. In how many ways can five distinct balls be put into the boxes if each box can hold at most one ball and no two boxes without balls are adjacent?

18. A group of 20 students, including 3 particular girls and 4 particular boys, are to be lined up in two rows with 10 students each. In how many ways can this be done if the 3 particular girls must be in the front row while the 4 particular boys be in the back?

19. In how many ways can 7 boys and 2 girls be lined up in a row such that the girls must be separated by exactly 3 boys?

20. In a group of 15 students, 3 of them are female. If at least one female student is to be selected, in how many ways can 7 students be chosen from the group

    (i) to form a committee?

    (ii) to take up 7 different posts in a committee?

21. Find the number of $(m + n)$-digit binary sequences with m 0's and n 1's such that no two 1's are adjacent, where $n \leq m + 1$.

22. Two sets of parallel lines with p and q lines each are shown in the following diagram:

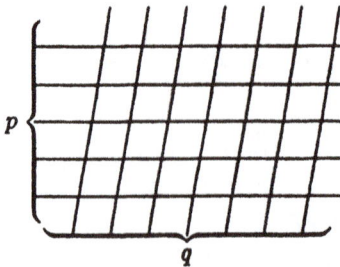

Find the number of parallelograms formed by the lines?

23. There are 10 girls and 15 boys in a junior class, and 4 girls and 10 boys in a senior class. A committee of 7 members is to be formed from these 2 classes. Find the number of ways this can be done if the committee must have exactly 4 senior students and exactly 5 boys.

24. A box contains 7 identical white balls and 5 identical black balls. They are to be drawn randomly, one at a time without replacement, until the box is empty. Find the probability that the 6th ball drawn is white, while before that exactly 3 black balls are drawn.

25. In each of the following cases, find the number of shortest routes from O to P in the street network shown below:

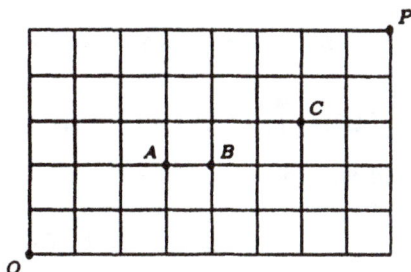

    (i) The routes must pass through the junction A;
   (ii) The routes must pass through the street AB;
  (iii) The routes must pass through junctions A and C;
   (iv) The street AB is closed.

26. Find the number of ways of forming a group of $2k$ people from n couples, where $k, n \in \mathbf{N}$ with $2k \leq n$, in each of the following cases:

    (i) There are k couples in such a group;
   (ii) No couples are included in such a group;
  (iii) At least one couple is included in such a group;
   (iv) Exactly two couples are included in such a group.

27. Let $S = \{1, 2, \ldots, n+1\}$ where $n \geq 2$, and let

$$T = \{(x, y, z) \in S^3 \mid x < z \quad \text{and} \quad y < z\}.$$

Show by counting $|T|$ in two different ways that

$$\sum_{k=1}^{n} k^2 = |T| = \binom{n+1}{2} + 2\binom{n+1}{3}.$$

28. Consider the following set of points in the $x - y$ plane:

$$A = \{(a, b) \mid a, b \in \mathbf{Z}, \ 0 \leq a \leq 9 \quad \text{and} \quad 0 \leq b \leq 5\}.$$

Find

(i) the number of rectangles whose vertices are points in A;

(ii) the number of squares whose vertices are points in A.

29. Fifteen points $P_1, P_2, \ldots, P_{15}$ are drawn in the plane in such a way that besides P_1, P_2, P_3, P_4, P_5 which are collinear, no other 3 points are collinear. Find

(i) the number of straight lines which pass through at least 2 of the 15 points;

(ii) the number of triangles whose vertices are 3 of the 15 points.

30. In each of the following 6-digit natural numbers:

$$333333, \ 225522, \ 118818, \ 707099,$$

every digit in the number appears at least twice. Find the number of such 6-digit natural numbers.

31. In each of the following 7-digit natural numbers:

$$1001011, \ 5550000, \ 3838383, \ 7777777,$$

every digit in the number appears at least 3 times. Find the number of such 7-digit natural numbers.

32. Let $X = \{1, 2, 3, \ldots, 1000\}$. Find the number of 2-element subsets $\{a, b\}$ of X such that the product $a \cdot b$ is divisible by 5.

33. Consider the following set of points in the $x - y$ plane:

$$A = \{(a, b) \mid a, b \in \mathbf{Z} \quad \text{and} \quad |a| + |b| \leq 2\}.$$

Find

(i) $|A|$;

(ii) the number of straight lines which pass through at least 2 points in A;   and

(iii) the number of triangles whose vertices are points in A.

34. Let P be a convex n-gon, where $n \geq 6$. Find the number of triangles formed by any 3 vertices of P that are pairwise nonadjacent in P.

35. 6 boys and 5 girls are to be seated around a table. Find the number of ways that this can be done in each of the following cases:

    (i) There are no restrictions;

    (ii) No 2 girls are adjacent;

    (iii) All girls form a single block;

    (iv) A particular girl G is adjacent to two particular boys B_1 and B_2.

36. Show that the number of r-circular permutations of n distinct objects, where $1 \leq r \leq n$, is given by $\frac{n!}{(n-r)! \cdot r}$.

37. Let $k, n \in \mathbf{N}$. Show that the number of ways to seat kn people around k distinct tables such that there are n people in each table is given by $\frac{(kn)!}{n^k}$.

38. Let $r \in \mathbf{N}$ such that

$$\frac{1}{\binom{9}{r}} - \frac{1}{\binom{10}{r}} = \frac{11}{6\binom{11}{r}}.$$

    Find the value of r.

39. Prove each of the following identities:

    (a) $\binom{n}{r} = \frac{n}{r}\binom{n-1}{r-1}$, where $n \geq r \geq 1$;

    (b) $\binom{n}{r} = \frac{n-r+1}{r}\binom{n}{r-1}$, where $n \geq r \geq 1$;

    (c) $\binom{n}{r} = \frac{n}{n-r}\binom{n-1}{r}$, where $n > r \geq 0$;

    (d) $\binom{n}{m}\binom{m}{r} = \binom{n}{r}\binom{n-r}{m-r}$, where $n \geq m \geq r \geq 0$.

40. Prove the identity $\binom{n}{r} = \binom{n}{n-r}$ by (BP).

41. Let $X = \{1, 2, ..., n\}$, $A = \{A \subseteq X \mid n \notin A\}$, and $B = \{A \subseteq X \mid n \in A\}$. Show that $|A| = |B|$ by (BP).

42. Let $r, n \in \mathbf{N}$. Show that the product

$$(n+1)(n+2)\cdots(n+r)$$

    of r consecutive positive integers is divisible by $r!$.

43. Let A be a set of kn elements, where $k, n \in \mathbf{N}$. A k-grouping of A is a partition of A into k-element subsets. Find the number of different k-groupings of A.

44. Twenty five of King Arthur's knights are seated at their customary round table. Three of them are chosen – all choices of three being equally likely – and are sent off to slay a troublesome dragon. Let P be the probability that at least two of the three had been sitting next to each other. If P is written as a fraction in lowest terms, what is the sum of the numerator and denominator? (AIME, 1983/7) (Readers who wish to get more information about the AIME may write to Professor Walter E. Mientka, AMC Executive Director, Department of Mathematics & Statistics, University of Nebraska, Lincohn, NE 68588-0322, USA.)

45. One commercially available ten-button lock may be opened by depressing – in any order – the correct five buttons. The sample shown below has $\{1, 2, 3, 6, 9\}$ as its combination. Suppose that these locks are redesigned so that sets of as many as nine buttons or as few as one button could serve as combinations. How many additional combinations would this allow? (AIME, 1988/1)

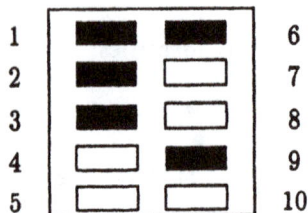

46. In a shooting match, eight clay targets are arranged in two hanging columns of three each and one column of two, as pictured. A marksman is to break all eight targets according to the following rules: (1) The marksman first chooses a column from which a target is to be broken. (2) The marksman must then break the lowest remaining unbroken target in the chosen column. If these rules are followed, in how many different orders can the eight targets be broken? (AIME, 1990/8)

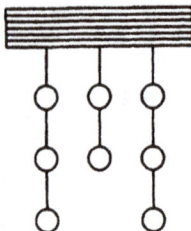

47. Using the numbers 1, 2, 3, 4, 5, we can form $5!(= 120)$ 5-digit numbers in which the 5 digits are all distinct. If these numbers are listed in increasing order:

$$\underset{\text{1st}}{12345}, \quad \underset{\text{2nd}}{12354}, \quad \underset{\text{3rd}}{12435}, \quad \dots, \quad \underset{\text{120th}}{54321},$$

find (i) the position of the number 35421; (ii) the 100th number in the list.

48. The $P_3^4(= 24)$ 3-permutations of the set $\{1, 2, 3, 4\}$ can be arranged in the following way, called the lexicographic ordering:

$$123, \ 124, \ 132, \ 134, \ 142, \ 143, \ 213, \ 214, \ 231, \ 234,$$

$$241, \ 243, \ 312, \ \dots, \ 431, \ 432.$$

Thus the 3-permutations "132" and "214" appear at the 3rd and 8th positions of the ordering respectively. There are $P_4^9(= 3024)$ 4-permutations of the set $\{1, 2, \dots, 9\}$. What are the positions of the 4-permutations "4567" and "5182" in the corresponding lexicographic ordering of the 4 permutations of $\{1, 2, \dots, 9\}$?

49. The $\binom{5}{3}(= 10)$ 3-element subsets of the set $\{1, 2, 3, 4, 5\}$ can be arranged in the following way, called the lexicographic ordering:

$$\{1, 2, 3\}, \ \{1, 2, 4\}, \ \{1, 2, 5\}, \ \{1, 3, 4\}, \ \{1, 3, 5\}, \ \{1, 4, 5\},$$

$$\{2, 3, 4\}, \ \{2, 3, 5\}, \ \{2, 4, 5\}, \ \{3, 4, 5\}.$$

Thus the subset $\{1, 3, 5\}$ appears at the 5th position of the ordering. There are $\binom{10}{4}$ 4-element subsets of the set $\{1, 2, \dots, 10\}$. What are the positions of the subsets $\{3, 4, 5, 6\}$ and $\{3, 5, 7, 9\}$ in the corresponding lexicographic ordering of the 4-element subsets of $\{1, 2, \dots, 10\}$?

50. Six scientists are working on a secret project. They wish to lock up the documents in a cabinet so that the cabinet can be opened when and only when three or more of the scientists are present. What is the smallest number of locks needed? What is the smallest number of keys each scientist must carry?

51. A 10-storey building is to be painted with some 4 different colours such that each storey is painted with one colour. It is not necessary that all 4 colours must be used. How many ways are there to paint the building if

(i) there are no other restrictions?

(ii) any 2 adjacent stories must be painted with different colours?

52. Find the number of all multi-subsets of $M = \{r_1 \cdot a_1, r_2 \cdot a_2, \cdots, r_n \cdot a_n\}$.

53. Let $r, b \in \mathbf{N}$ with $r \leq n$. A permutation $x_1 x_2 \cdots x_{2n}$ of the set $\{1, 2, ..., 2n\}$ is said to have property $P(r)$ if $|x_i - x_{i+1}| = r$ for at least one i in $\{1, 2, ..., 2n - 1\}$. Show that, for each n and r, there are more permutations with property $P(r)$ than without.

54. Prove by a combinatorial argument that each of the following numbers is always an integer for each $n \in \mathbf{N}$:

    (i) $\dfrac{(3n)!}{2^n \cdot 3^n}$,

    (ii) $\dfrac{(6n)!}{5^n \cdot 3^{2n} \cdot 2^{4n}}$,

    (iii) $\dfrac{(n^2)!}{(n!)^n}$,

    (iv) $\dfrac{(n!)!}{(n!)^{(n-1)!}}$.

55. Find the number of r-element multi-subsets of the multi-set

$$M = \{1 \cdot a_1, \infty \cdot a_2, \infty \cdot a_3, \ldots, \infty \cdot a_n\}.$$

56. Six distinct symbols are transmitted through a communication channel. A total of 18 blanks are to be inserted between the symbols with at least 2 blanks between every pair of symbols. In how many ways can the symbols and blanks be arranged?

57. In how many ways can the following 11 letters: A, B, C, D, E, F, X, X, X, Y, Y be arranged in a row so that every Y lies between two X's (not necessarily adjacent)?

58. Two n-digit integers (leading zero allowed) are said to be *equivalent* if one is a permutation of the other. For instance, 10075, 01057 and 00751 are equivalent 5-digit integers.

    (i) Find the number of 5-digit integers such that no two are equivalent.

    (ii) If the digits 5,7,9 can appear at most once, how many nonequivalent 5-digit integers are there?

59. How many 10-letter words are there using the letters a, b, c, d, e, f if

    (i) there are no restrictions?

    (ii) each vowel (a and e) appears 3 times and each consonant appears once?

(iii) the letters in the word appear in alphabetical order?

(iv) each letter occurs at least once and the letters in the word appear in alphabetical order?

60. Let $r, n, k \in \mathbf{N}$ such that $r \geq nk$. Find the number of ways of distributing r identical objects into n distinct boxes so that each box holds at least k objects.

61. Find the number of ways of arranging the 9 letters $r, s, t, u, v, w, x, y, z$ in a row so that y always lies between x and z (x and y, or y and z need not be adjacent in the row).

62. Three girls A, B and C, and nine boys are to be lined up in a row. In how many ways can this be done if B must lie between A and C, and A, B must be separated by exactly 4 boys?

63. Five girls and eleven boys are to be lined up in a row such that from left to right, the girls are in the order: G_1, G_2, G_3, G_4, G_5. In how many ways can this be done if G_1 and G_2 must be separated by at least 3 boys, and there is at most one boy between G_4 and G_5?

64. Given $r, n \in \mathbf{N}$ with $r \geq n$, let $L(r, n)$ denote the number of ways of distributing r distinct objects into n identical boxes so that no box is empty and the objects in each box are arranged in a row. Find $L(r, n)$ in terms of r and n.

65. Find the number of integer solutions to the equation:

$$x_1 + x_2 + x_3 + x_4 + x_5 + x_6 = 60$$

in each of the following cases:

(i) $x_i \geq i - 1$ for each $i = 1, 2, ..., 6$;

(ii) $x_1 \geq 2$, $x_2 \geq 5$, $2 \leq x_3 \leq 7$, $x_4 \geq 1$, $x_5 \geq 3$ and $x_6 \geq 2$.

66. Find the number of integer solutions to the equation:

$$x_1 + x_2 + x_3 + x_4 = 30$$

in each of the following cases:

(i) $x_i \geq 0$ for each $i = 1, 2, 3, 4$;

(ii) $2 \leq x_1 \leq 7$ and $x_i \geq 0$ for each $i = 2, 3, 4$;

(iii) $x_1 \geq -5$, $x_2 \geq -1$, $x_3 \geq 1$ and $x_4 \geq 2$.

67. Find the number of quadruples (w, x, y, z) of nonnegative integers which satisfy the inequality

$$w + x + y + z \leq 1992.$$

68. Find the number of nonnegative integer solutions to the equation:

$$5x_1 + x_2 + x_3 + x_4 = 14.$$

69. Find the number of nonnegative integer solutions to the equation:

$$rx_1 + x_2 + \cdots + x_n = kr,$$

where $k, r, n \in \mathbf{N}$.

70. Find the number of nonnegative integer solutions to the equation:

$$3x_1 + 5x_2 + x_3 + x_4 = 10.$$

71. Find the number of positive integer solutions to the equation:

$$(x_1 + x_2 + x_3)(y_1 + y_2 + y_3 + y_4) = 77.$$

72. Find the number of nonnegative integer solutions to the equation:

$$(x_1 + x_2 + \cdots + x_n)(y_1 + y_2 + \cdots + y_n) = p,$$

where $n \in \mathbf{N}$ and p is a prime.

73. There are 5 ways to express "4" as a sum of 2 nonnegative integers in which the order counts:

$$4 = 4 + 0 = 3 + 1 = 2 + 2 = 1 + 3 = 0 + 4.$$

Given $r, n \in \mathbf{N}$, what is the number of ways to express r as a sum of n nonnegative integers in which the order counts?

74. There are 6 ways to express "5" as a sum of 3 positive integers in which the order counts:

$$5 = 3 + 1 + 1 = 2 + 2 + 1 = 2 + 1 + 2 = 1 + 3 + 1 = 1 + 2 + 2 = 1 + 1 + 3.$$

Given $r, n \in \mathbf{N}$ with $r \geq n$, what is the number of ways to express r as a sum of n positive integers in which the order counts?

75. A positive integer d is said to be *ascending* if in its decimal representation: $d = d_m d_{m-1} \ldots d_2 d_1$ we have

$$0 < d_m \leq d_{m-1} \leq \cdots \leq d_2 \leq d_1.$$

For instance, 1337 and 2455566799 are ascending integers. Find the number of ascending integers which are less than 10^9.

76. A positive integer d is said to be *strictly ascending* if in its decimal representation: $d = d_m d_{m-1} \ldots d_2 d_1$ we have

$$0 < d_m < d_{m-1} < \cdots < d_2 < d_1.$$

For instance, 145 and 23689 are strictly ascending integers. Find the number of strictly ascending integers which are less than (i) 10^9, (ii) 10^5.

77. Let $A = \{1, 2, \ldots, n\}$, where $n \in \mathbf{N}$.

   (i) Given $k \in A$, show that the number of subsets of A in which k is the maximum number is given by 2^{k-1}.

   (ii) Apply (i) to show that

$$\sum_{i=0}^{n-1} 2^i = 2^n - 1.$$

78. In a given circle, $n \geq 2$ arbitrary chords are drawn such that no three are concurrent within the interior of the circle. Suppose m is the number of points of intersection of the chords within the interior. Find, in terms of n and m, the number r of line segments obtained through dividing the chords by their points of intersection. (In the following example, $n = 5, m = 3$ and $r = 11$.)

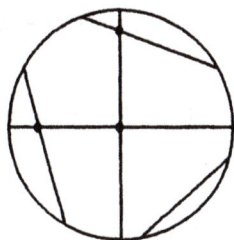

79. There are $p \geq 6$ points given on the circumference of a circle, and every two of the points are joined by a chord.

   (i) Find the number of such chords.

   Assume that no 3 chords are concurrent within the interior of the circle.

   (ii) Find the number of points of intersection of these chords within the interior of the circle.

   (iii) Find the number of line segments obtained through dividing the chords by their points of intersection.

   (iv) Find the number of triangles whose vertices are the points of intersection of the chords within the interior of the circle.

80. In how many ways can $n + 1$ different prizes be awarded to n students in such a way that each student has at least one prize?

81. (a) Let $n, m, k \in \mathbb{N}$, and let $\mathbf{N}_k = \{1, 2, ..., k\}$. Find

   (i) the number of mappings from $\mathbf{N}_n$ to $\mathbf{N}_m$.

   (ii) the number of 1-1 mappings from $\mathbf{N}_n$ to $\mathbf{N}_m$, where $n \leq m$.

   (b) A mapping $f : \mathbf{N}_n \rightarrow \mathbf{N}_m$ is *strictly increasing* if $f(a) < f(b)$ whenever $a < b$ in $\mathbf{N}_n$. Find the number of strictly increasing mappings from $\mathbf{N}_n$ to $\mathbf{N}_m$, where $n \leq m$.

   (c) Express the number of mappings from $\mathbf{N}_n$ *onto* $\mathbf{N}_m$ in terms of $S(n, m)$ (the Stirling number of the second kind).

82. Given $r, n \in \mathbb{Z}$ with $0 \leq n \leq r$, the Stirling number $s(r, n)$ of the first kind is defined as the number of ways to arrange r distinct objects around n identical circles such that each circle has at least one object. Show that

   (i) $s(r, 1) = (r - 1)!$ for $r \geq 1$;

   (ii) $s(r, 2) = (r - 1)!(1 + \frac{1}{2} + \frac{1}{3} + \cdots + \frac{1}{r-1})$ for $r \geq 2$;

   (iii) $s(r, r - 1) = \binom{r}{2}$ for $r \geq 2$;

   (iv) $s(r, r - 2) = \frac{1}{24}r(r - 1)(r - 2)(3r - 1)$ for $r \geq 2$;

   (v) $\sum_{n=0}^{r} s(r, n) = r!$.

83. The Stirling numbers of the first kind occur as the coefficients of x^n in the expansion of

$$x(x + 1)(x + 2) \cdots (x + r - 1).$$

For instance, when $r = 3$,

$$x(x+1)(x+2) = 2x + 3x^2 + x^3$$
$$= s(3,1)x + s(3,2)x^2 + s(3,3)x^3;$$

and when $r = 5$,

$$x(x+1)(x+2)(x+3)(x+4)$$
$$= 24x + 50x^2 + 35x^3 + 10x^4 + x^5$$
$$= s(5,1)x + s(5,2)x^2 + s(5,3)x^3 + s(5,4)x^4 + s(5,5)x^5.$$

Show that

$$x(x+1)(x+2)\cdots(x+r-1) = \sum_{n=0}^{r} s(r,n)x^n,$$

where $r \in \mathbf{N}$.

84. Given $r, n \in \mathbf{Z}$ with $0 \le n \le r$, the Stirling number $S(r,n)$ of the second kind is defined as the number of ways of distributing r distinct objects into n identical boxes such that no box is empty. Show that

(i) $S(r,2) = 2^{r-1} - 1$;

(ii) $S(r,3) = \frac{1}{2}(3^{r-1}+1) - 2^{r-1}$;

(iii) $S(r,r-1) = \binom{r}{2}$;

(iv) $S(r,r-2) = \binom{r}{3} + 3\binom{r}{4}$.

85. Let $(x)_0 = 1$ and for $n \in \mathbf{N}$, let

$$(x)_n = x(x-1)(x-2)\cdots(x-n+1).$$

The Stirling numbers of the second kind occur as the coefficients of $(x)_n$ when x^r is expressed in terms of $(x)_n$'s. For instance, when $r = 2, 3$ and 4, we have, respectively,

$$x^2 = x + x(x-1) = (x)_1 + (x)_2$$
$$= S(2,1)(x)_1 + S(2,2)(x)_2,$$
$$x^3 = x + 3x(x-1) + x(x-1)(x-2)$$
$$= S(3,1)(x)_1 + S(3,2)(x)_2 + S(3,3)(x)_3,$$
$$x^4 = x + 7x(x-1) + 6x(x-1)(x-2) + x(x-1)(x-2)(x-3)$$
$$= S(4,1)(x)_1 + S(4,2)(x)_2 + S(4,3)(x)_3 + S(4,4)(x)_4.$$

Show that for $r = 0, 1, 2, ...,$

$$x^r = \sum_{n=0}^{r} S(r,n)(x)_n.$$

86. Suppose that m chords of a given circle are drawn in such a way that no three are concurrent in the interior of the circle. If n denotes the number of points of intersection of the chords within the circle, show that the number of regions divided by the chords in the circle is $m + n + 1$.

87. For $n \geq 4$, let $r(n)$ denote the number of interior regions of a convex n-gon divided by all its diagonals if no three diagonals are concurrent within the n-gon. For instance, as shown in the following diagrams, $r(4) = 4$ and $r(5) = 11$. Prove that $r(n) = \binom{n}{4} + \binom{n-1}{2}$.

88. Let $n \in \mathbb{N}$. How many solutions are there in ordered positive integer pairs (x, y) to the equation

$$\frac{xy}{x + y} = n?$$

(Putnam, 1960)

89. Let $S = \{1, 2, 3, ..., 1992\}$. In each of the following cases, find the number of 3-element subsets $\{a, b, c\}$ of S satisfying the given condition:

(i) $3|(a + b + c)$;

(ii) $4|(a + b + c)$.

90. A sequence of 15 random draws, one at a time with replacement, is made from the set

$$\{A, B, C, ..., X, Y, Z\}$$

of the English alphabet. What is the probability that the string:

$$UNIVERSITY$$

occurs as a block in the sequence?

91. A set $S = \{a_1, a_2, \ldots, a_r\}$ of positive integers, where $r \in \mathbb{N}$ and $a_1 < a_2 < \ldots < a_r$, is said to be m-*separated* $(m \in \mathbb{N})$ if $a_i - a_{i-1} \geq m$, for each $i = 2, 3, \ldots, r$. Let $X = \{1, 2, \ldots, n\}$. Find the number of r-element subsets of X which are m-separated, where $0 \leq r \leq n - (m-1)(r-1)$.

92. Let $a_1, a_2, \ldots, a_n$ be positive real numbers, and let S_k be the sum of products of $a_1, a_2, \ldots, a_n$ taken k at a time. Show that

$$S_k S_{n-k} \geq \binom{n}{k}^2 a_1 a_2 \cdots a_n,$$

for $k = 1, 2, \ldots, n - 1$. (APMO, 1990)

93. For $\{1, 2, 3, \ldots, n\}$ and each of its nonempty subsets, a unique *alternating sum* is defined as follows: Arrange the numbers in the subset in decreasing order and then, beginning with the largest, alternately add and subtract successive numbers. (For example, the alternating sum for $\{1, 2, 4, 6, 9\}$ is $9 - 6 + 4 - 2 + 1 = 6$ and for $\{5\}$ it is simply 5.) Find the sum of all such alternating sums for $n = 7$. (AIME, 1983/13)

94. A gardener plants three maple trees, four oak trees and five birch trees in a row. He plants them in random order, each arrangement being equally likely. Let $\frac{m}{n}$ in lowest terms be the probability that no two birch trees are next to one another. Find $m + n$. (AIME, 1984/11)

95. In a tournament each player played exactly one game against each of the other players. In each game the winner was awarded 1 point, the loser got 0 points, and each of the two players earned 1/2 point if the game was a tie. After the completion of the tournament, it was found that exactly half of the points earned by each player were earned in games against the ten players with the least number of points. (In particular, each of the ten lowest scoring players earned half of her/his points against the other nine of the ten). What was the total number of players in the tournament? (AIME, 1985/14)

96. Let S be the sum of the base 10 logarithms of all of the proper divisors of 1,000,000. (By a proper divisor of a natural number we mean a positive integral divisor other than 1 and the number itself.) What is the integer nearest to S? (AIME, 1986/8)

97. In a sequence of coin tosses one can keep a record of the number of instances when a tail is immediately followed by a head, a head is immediately followed by a head, etc.. We denote these by TH, HH, etc.. For example, in the sequence $HHTTHHHHHTHHTTTT$ of 15 coin tosses we observe that there are five HH, three HT, two TH and four TT subsequences. How many different sequences of 15 coin tosses will contain exactly two HH, three HT, four TH and five TT subsequences? (AIME, 1986/13)

98. An ordered pair (m, n) of non-negative integers is called "simple" if the addition $m + n$ in base 10 requires no carrying. Find the number of simple ordered pairs of non-negative integers that sum to

    (i) 1492;   (AIME, 1987/1)   (ii) 1992.

99. Let m/n, in lowest terms, be the probability that a randomly chosen positive divisor of 10^{99} is an integer multiple of 10^{88}. Find $m + n$. (AIME, 1988/5)

100. A convex polyhedron has for its faces 12 squares, 8 regular hexagons, and 6 regular octagons. At each vertex of the polyhedron one square, one hexagon, and one octagon meet. How many segments joining vertices of the polyhedron lie in the interior of the polyhedron rather than along an edge or a face? (AIME, 1988/10)

101. Someone observed that $6! = 8 \cdot 9 \cdot 10$. Find the largest positive integer n for which $n!$ can be expressed as the product of $n - 3$ consecutive positive integers. (AIME, 1990/11)

102. Let $S = \{1, 2, ..., n\}$. Find the number of subsets A of S satisfying the following conditions:

    $A = \{a, a+d, \ldots, a+kd\}$ for some positive integers a, d and k,   and

    $A \cup \{x\}$ is no longer an A.P. with common difference d for each $x \in S \setminus A$.

    (Note that $|A| \geq 2$ and any sequence of two terms is considered as an A.P.) (Chinese Math. Competition, 1991)

103. Find all natural numbers $n > 1$ and $m > 1$ such that

    $$1!3!5! \cdots (2n - 1)! = m! \, .$$

    (Proposed by I. Cucurezeanu, see *Amer. Math. Monthly*, 94 (1987), 190.)

104. Show that for $n \in \mathbf{N}$,

$$\sum_{r=0}^{n} P_r^n = \lfloor n!e \rfloor,$$

where $\lfloor x \rfloor$ denotes the greatest integer $\leq x$ and $e = 2.718 \cdots$. (Proposed by D. Ohlsen, see *The College Math. J.* 20 (1989), 260.)

105. Let $S = \{1, 2, ..., 1990\}$. A 31-element subset A of S is said to be *good* if the sum $\sum_{a \in A} a$ is divisible by 5. Find the number of 31-element subsets of S which are good. (Proposed by the Indian Team at the 31st IMO.)

106. Let S be a 1990-element set and let $\mathcal{P}$ be a set of 100-ary sequences $(a_1, a_2, ..., a_{100})$, where a_i's are distinct elements of S. An ordered pair (x, y) of elements of S is said to *appear* in $(a_1, a_2, ..., a_{100})$ if $x = a_i$ and $y = a_j$ for some i, j with $1 \leq i < j \leq 100$. Assume that every ordered pair (x, y) of elements of S appears in at most one member in $\mathcal{P}$. Show that

$$|\mathcal{P}| \leq 800.$$

(Proposed by the Iranian Team at the 31st IMO.)

107. Let $M = \{r_1 \cdot a_1, r_2 \cdot a_2, \ldots, r_n \cdot a_n\}$ be a multi-set with $r_1 + r_2 + \cdots + r_n = r$. Show that the number of r-permutations of M is equal to the number of $(r-1)$-permutations of M.

108. Prove that it is impossible for seven distinct straight lines to be situated in the Euclidean plane so as to have at least six points where exactly three of these lines intersect and at least four points where exactly two of these lines intersect. (Putnam, 1973)

109. For what $n \in \mathbf{N}$ does there exist a permutation $(x_1, x_2, \ldots, x_n)$ of $(1, 2, ..., n)$ such that the differences $|x_k - k|$, $1 \leq k \leq n$, are all distinct? (Prosposed by M.J. Pelling, see *Amer. Math. Monthly*, 96 (1989), 843-844.)

110. Numbers $d(n, m)$, where n, m are integers and $0 \leq m \leq n$, are defined by

$$d(n, 0) = d(n, n) = 1 \quad \text{for all } n \geq 0$$

and

$$m \cdot d(n, m) = m \cdot d(n - 1, m) + (2n - m) \cdot d(n - 1, m - 1)$$

for $0 < m < n$. Prove that all the $d(n, m)$ are integers. (Great Britian, 1987)

111. A difficult mathematical competition consisted of a Part I and a Part II with a combined total of 28 problems. Each contestant solved 7 problems altogether. For each pair of problems, there were exactly two contestants who solved both of them. Prove that there was a contestant who, in Part I, solved either no problems or at least four problems. (USA MO, 1984/4)

112. Suppose that five points in a plane are situated so that no two of the straight lines joining them are parallel, perpendicular, or coincident. From each point perpendiculars are drawn to all the lines joining the other four points. Determine the maximum number of intersections that these perpendiculars can have. (IMO, 1964/5)

113. Let n distinct points in the plane be given. Prove that fewer than $2n^{\frac{3}{2}}$ pairs of them are at unit distance apart. (Putnam, 1978)

114. If c and m are positive integers each greater than 1, find the number $n(c, m)$ of ordered c-tuples $(n_1, n_2, ..., n_c)$ with entries from the initial segment $\{1, 2, ..., m\}$ of the positive integers such that $n_2 < n_1$ and $n_2 \leq n_3 \leq \cdots \leq n_c$. (Proposed by D. Spellman, see *Amer. Math. Monthly*, 94 (1987), 383-384.)

115. Let $X = \{x_1, x_2, ..., x_m\}$, $Y = \{y_1, y_2, ..., y_n\}$ ($m, n \in \mathbb{N}$) and $A \subseteq X \times Y$. For $x_i \in X$, let

$$A(x_i, \cdot) = (\{x_i\} \times Y) \cap A$$

and for $y_j \in Y$, let

$$A(\cdot, y_j) = (X \times \{y_j\}) \cap A.$$

(i) Prove the following *Fubini Principle*:

$$\sum_{i=1}^{m} |A(x_i, \cdot)| = |A| = \sum_{j=1}^{n} |A(\cdot, y_j)|.$$

(ii) Using (i), or otherwise, solve the following problem: There are $n \geq 3$ given points in the plane such that any three of them form a right-angled triangle. Find the largest possible value of n.

(23rd Moscow MO)

Chapter 2

Binomial Coefficients and Multinomial Coefficients

2.1. Introduction

Given $r, n \in \mathbf{Z}$ with $0 \le r \le n$, the number $\binom{n}{r}$ or C_r^n was defined in Chapter 1 as the number of r-element subsets of an n-element set. For convenience, we further define that $\binom{n}{r} = 0$ if $r > n$ or $r < 0$. Hence, by the result of (1.4.1), we have:

$$\binom{n}{r} = \begin{cases} \dfrac{n!}{r!(n-r)!} & \text{if } 0 \le r \le n, \\ 0 & \text{if } r > n \text{ or } r < 0, \end{cases}$$

for any $r, n \in \mathbf{Z}$ with $n \ge 0$.

In Chapter 1 and Exercise 1, we have learnt some basic identities governing the numbers $\binom{n}{r}$'s. These useful identities are summarized in the following list:

$$\binom{n}{r} = \binom{n}{n-r} \tag{2.1.1}$$

$$\binom{n}{r} = \frac{n}{r}\binom{n-1}{r-1} \quad \text{provided that } r \ge 1 \tag{2.1.2}$$

$$\binom{n}{r} = \frac{n-r+1}{r}\binom{n}{r-1} \quad \text{provided that } r \ge 1 \tag{2.1.3}$$

$$\binom{n}{r} = \binom{n-1}{r-1} + \binom{n-1}{r} \tag{2.1.4}$$

$$\binom{n}{m}\binom{m}{r} = \binom{n}{r}\binom{n-r}{m-r} \tag{2.1.5}$$

The numbers $\binom{n}{r}$'s are perhaps the most important and significant numbers in enumeration, and are often called *binomial coefficients* since they appear as the coefficients in the expansion of the binomial expression $(x+y)^n$. In this chapter, we shall derive some more fundamental and useful identities involving the binomial coefficients. Various techniques employed in the derivation of these identities will be discussed. We shall also introduce and study the notion of *multinomial coefficients* that are generalizations of the binomial coefficients.

2.2. The Binomial Theorem

We begin with the following simplest form of the binomial theorem discovered by Issac Newton (1646-1727) in 1676.

Theorem 2.2.1. *For any integer $n \geq 0$,*

$$(x+y)^n = \binom{n}{0}x^n + \binom{n}{1}x^{n-1}y + \cdots + \binom{n}{n-1}xy^{n-1} + \binom{n}{n}y^n$$

$$= \sum_{r=0}^{n} \binom{n}{r}x^{n-r}y^r.$$

First proof – mathematical induction. For $n = 0$, the result is trivial as $(x + y)^0 = 1 = \binom{0}{0}x^0y^0$. Assume that it holds when $n = k$ for some integer $k \geq 0$, that is,

$$(x+y)^k = \sum_{r=0}^{k} \binom{k}{r}x^{k-r}y^r.$$

Consider $n = k + 1$. Observe that

$$(x+y)^{k+1} = (x+y)(x+y)^k$$

$$= (x+y)\sum_{r=0}^{k} \binom{k}{r}x^{k-r}y^r \quad \text{(by the inductive hypothesis)}$$

$$= \sum_{r=0}^{k} \binom{k}{r}x^{k+1-r}y^r + \sum_{r=0}^{k} \binom{k}{r}x^{k-r}y^{r+1}$$

$$= \binom{k}{0}x^{k+1} + \binom{k}{1}x^k y + \binom{k}{2}x^{k-1}y^2 + \cdots + \binom{k}{k}xy^k$$

$$\quad + \binom{k}{0}x^k y + \binom{k}{1}x^{k-1}y^2 + \cdots + \binom{k}{k-1}xy^k + \binom{k}{k}y^{k+1}.$$

Applying (2.1.4) and the trivial results that $\binom{k}{0} = 1 = \binom{k+1}{0}$ and $\binom{k}{k} = 1 = \binom{k+1}{k+1}$, we have

$$(x+y)^{k+1} = \binom{k+1}{0}x^{k+1} + \binom{k+1}{1}x^k y + \cdots + \binom{k+1}{k}xy^k + \binom{k+1}{k+1}y^{k+1}$$

as desired. The result thus follows by induction. ∎

Second proof – combinatorial method. It suffices to prove that the coefficient of $x^{n-r}y^r$ in the expansion of $(x+y)^n$ is $\binom{n}{r}$.

To expand the product $(x+y)^n = \underbrace{(x+y)(x+y)\cdots(x+y)}_{n}$, we choose either x or y from each factor $(x+y)$ and then multiply them together. Thus to form a term $x^{n-r}y^r$, we first select r of the n factors $(x+y)$ and then pick "y" from the r factors chosen (and of course pick "x" from the remaining $(n-r)$ factors). The first step can be done in $\binom{n}{r}$ ways while the second in 1 way. Thus, the number of ways to form the term $x^{n-r}y^r$ is $\binom{n}{r}$ as required. ∎

2.3. Combinatorial Identities

The binomial theorem is a fundamental result in mathematics that has many applications. In this section, we shall witness how Theorem 2.2.1 yields easily a set of interesting identities involving the binomial coefficients. For the sake of comparison, some alternative proofs of these identities will be given.

Example 2.3.1. Show that for all integers $n \geq 0$,

$$\sum_{r=0}^{n}\binom{n}{r} = \binom{n}{0} + \binom{n}{1} + \cdots + \binom{n}{n} = 2^n. \tag{2.3.1}$$

First proof. By letting $x = y = 1$ in Theorem 2.2.1, we obtain immediately

$$\sum_{r=0}^{n}\binom{n}{r} = (1+1)^n = 2^n. \ \blacksquare$$

Second proof. Let X be an n-element set and $\mathcal{P}(X)$ be the set of all subsets of X. We shall count $|\mathcal{P}(X)|$ in two ways.

For each $r = 0, 1, ..., n$, the number of r-element subsets of X is $\binom{n}{r}$ by definition. Thus

$$|\mathcal{P}(X)| = \binom{n}{0} + \binom{n}{1} + \cdots + \binom{n}{n}.$$

On the other hand, by the result of Example 1.5.2, $|\mathcal{P}(X)| = 2^n$. The identity thus follows. ∎

Example 2.3.2. Show that for all integers $n \geq 1$,

(i) $\sum_{r=0}^{n}(-1)^r \binom{n}{r} = \binom{n}{0} - \binom{n}{1} + \binom{n}{2} - \cdots + (-1)^n \binom{n}{n} = 0,$ \hfill (2.3.2)

(ii) $\binom{n}{0} + \binom{n}{2} + \cdots + \binom{n}{2k} + \cdots = \binom{n}{1} + \binom{n}{3} + \cdots + \binom{n}{2k+1} + \cdots = 2^{n-1}.$ (2.3.3)

Proof. By letting $x = 1$ and $y = -1$ in Theorem 2.2.1, we obtain

$$\sum_{r=0}^{n} \binom{n}{r}(-1)^r = (1-1)^n = 0,$$

which is (i). The identity (ii) now follows from (i) and identity (2.3.1). ∎

Remark. A subset A of a non-empty set X is called an *even-element* (resp. *odd-element*) subset of X if $|A|$ is even (resp. odd). Identity (2.3.3) says that given an n-element set X, the number of even-element subsets of X is the same as the number of odd-element subsets of X. The reader is encouraged to establish a bijection between the family of even-element subsets of X and that of odd-element subsets of X (see Problem 2.10).

Example 2.3.3. Show that for all integers $n \in \mathbb{N}$,

$$\sum_{r=1}^{n} r\binom{n}{r} = \binom{n}{1} + 2\binom{n}{2} + 3\binom{n}{3} + \cdots + n\binom{n}{n} = n \cdot 2^{n-1}. \quad (2.3.4)$$

First proof. Letting $x = 1$ in Theorem 2.2.1 yields

$$(1+y)^n = \sum_{r=0}^{n} \binom{n}{r} y^r.$$

Differentiating both sides of the above identity with respect to y gives

$$n(1+y)^{n-1} = \sum_{r=1}^{n} r \binom{n}{r} y^{r-1}.$$

Finally, by putting $y = 1$, we have

$$\sum_{r=1}^{n} r \binom{n}{r} = n(1+1)^{n-1} = n \cdot 2^{n-1}. \quad \blacksquare$$

Second proof. Identity (2.1.2) can be rewritten as

$$r \binom{n}{r} = n \binom{n-1}{r-1}.$$

It thus follows that

$$\sum_{r=1}^{n} r \binom{n}{r} = \sum_{r=1}^{n} n \binom{n-1}{r-1} = n \sum_{r=1}^{n} \binom{n-1}{r-1}$$

$$= n \sum_{s=0}^{n-1} \binom{n-1}{s} \quad \text{(letting } s = r - 1)$$

$$= n \cdot 2^{n-1} \quad \text{(by (2.3.1)).} \quad \blacksquare$$

Remark. Extending the techniques used in the two proofs above, one can also show that

$$\sum_{r=1}^{n} r^2 \binom{n}{r} = n(n+1)2^{n-2},$$

$$\sum_{r=1}^{n} r^3 \binom{n}{r} = n^2(n+3)2^{n-3}$$

for all $n \in \mathbf{N}$ (see Problem 2.47).

In general, what can be said about the summation

$$\sum_{r=1}^{n} r^k \binom{n}{r},$$

where $k \in \mathbf{N}$ and $k \geq 4$ (see Problem 2.48)?

The next result was published by the French mathematician A.T. Vandermonde (1735-1796) in 1772.

Example 2.3.4. **(Vandermonde's Identity)** Show that for all $m, n, r \in N$,

$$\sum_{i=0}^{r} \binom{m}{i}\binom{n}{r-i} = \binom{m}{0}\binom{n}{r} + \binom{m}{1}\binom{n}{r-1} + \cdots + \binom{m}{r}\binom{n}{0}$$

$$= \binom{m+n}{r}. \tag{2.3.5}$$

First proof. Expanding the expressions on both sides of the identity

$$(1+x)^{m+n} = (1+x)^m(1+x)^n,$$

we have by Theorem 2.2.1,

$$\sum_{k=0}^{m+n} \binom{m+n}{k} x^k$$

$$= \left(\sum_{i=0}^{m}\binom{m}{i}x^i\right)\left(\sum_{j=0}^{n}\binom{n}{j}x^j\right)$$

$$= \binom{m}{0}\binom{n}{0} + \left\{\binom{m}{0}\binom{n}{1} + \binom{m}{1}\binom{n}{0}\right\}x$$

$$+ \left\{\binom{m}{0}\binom{n}{2} + \binom{m}{1}\binom{n}{1} + \binom{m}{2}\binom{n}{0}\right\}x^2 + \cdots + \binom{m}{m}\binom{n}{n}x^{m+n}.$$

Now, comparing the coefficients of x^r on both sides yields

$$\binom{m+n}{r} = \binom{m}{0}\binom{n}{r} + \binom{m}{1}\binom{n}{r-1} + \cdots + \binom{m}{r}\binom{n}{0}. \quad \blacksquare$$

Second proof. Let $X = \{a_1, a_2, ..., a_m, b_1, b_2, ..., b_n\}$ be a set of $m+n$ objects. We shall count the number of r-combinations A of X.

Assuming that A contains exactly i a's, where $i = 0, 1, ..., r$, then the other $r - i$ elements of A are b's; and in this case, the number of ways to form A is given by $\binom{m}{i}\binom{n}{r-i}$. Thus, by (AP), we have

$$\sum_{i=0}^{r} \binom{m}{i}\binom{n}{r-i} = \binom{m+n}{r}. \quad \blacksquare$$

Remark. If we put $m = n = r$ in identity (2.3.5) and apply identity (2.1.1), we obtain the following

$$\sum_{i=0}^{n}\binom{n}{i}^2 = \binom{n}{0}^2 + \binom{n}{1}^2 + \cdots + \binom{n}{n}^2 = \binom{2n}{n}. \qquad (2.3.6)$$

We now give an example to show an application of the Vandermonde's identity. In Section 1.6, we showed that H_r^n, the number of r-element multi-subsets of $M = \{\infty \cdot a_1, \infty \cdot a_2, \ldots, \infty \cdot a_n\}$, is given by

$$H_r^n = \binom{r+n-1}{r}.$$

Consider the following 3×3 matrix A whose entries are H_r^n's:

$$A = \begin{pmatrix} H_1^1 & H_2^1 & H_3^1 \\ H_1^2 & H_2^2 & H_3^2 \\ H_1^3 & H_2^3 & H_3^3 \end{pmatrix}.$$

What is the value of the determinant $\det(A)$ of A? We observe that

$$A = \begin{pmatrix} \binom{1}{1} & \binom{2}{2} & \binom{3}{3} \\ \binom{2}{1} & \binom{3}{2} & \binom{4}{3} \\ \binom{3}{1} & \binom{4}{2} & \binom{5}{3} \end{pmatrix} = \begin{pmatrix} 1 & 1 & 1 \\ 2 & 3 & 4 \\ 3 & 6 & 10 \end{pmatrix}$$

and it is easy to check that $\det(A) = 1$.

In general, we have the following interesting result, which can be found in [N] (pp.167 and 256).

Example 2.3.5. Let $A = (H_r^n)$ be the square matrix of order k, where $n, r \in \{1, 2, \ldots, k\}$, in which the (n, r)-entry is H_r^n. Show that $\det(A) = 1$.

Proof. Let $B = (b_{ij})$ and $C = (c_{ij})$ be the square matrices of order k defined by

$$b_{ij} = \binom{i}{j} \quad \text{and} \quad c_{ij} = \binom{j-1}{j-i};$$

i.e.,

$$B = \begin{pmatrix} \binom{1}{1} & 0 & 0 & \cdots & 0 \\ \binom{2}{1} & \binom{2}{2} & 0 & \cdots & 0 \\ \binom{3}{1} & \binom{3}{2} & \binom{3}{3} & \cdots & 0 \\ \vdots & \vdots & \vdots & \ddots & \vdots \\ \binom{k}{1} & \binom{k}{2} & \binom{k}{3} & \cdots & \binom{k}{k} \end{pmatrix}$$

and

$$
C = \begin{pmatrix}
\binom{0}{0} & \binom{1}{1} & \binom{2}{2} & \cdots & \binom{k-1}{k-1} \\
0 & \binom{1}{0} & \binom{2}{1} & \cdots & \binom{k-1}{k-2} \\
0 & 0 & \binom{2}{0} & \cdots & \binom{k-1}{k-3} \\
\vdots & \vdots & \vdots & \ddots & \vdots \\
0 & 0 & 0 & \cdots & \binom{k-1}{0}
\end{pmatrix}.
$$

Claim. $A = BC$.

Indeed, if a_{nr} denotes the (n,r)-entry of the product BC, then

$$
a_{nr} = \sum_{i=1}^{k} b_{ni} c_{ir} = \sum_{i=1}^{k} \binom{n}{i}\binom{r-1}{r-i}
$$

$$
= \sum_{i=1}^{r} \binom{n}{i}\binom{r-1}{r-i} \quad \left(\binom{r-1}{r-i} = 0 \text{ if } i > r \right)
$$

$$
= \binom{r+n-1}{r} \quad \text{(by Vandermonde's identity)}
$$

$$
= H_r^n .
$$

Thus, $BC = A$, as claimed.

Now,

$$
\det(A) = \det(BC) = \det(B)\det(C)
$$

$$
= \left[\binom{1}{1} \cdot \binom{2}{2} \cdots \binom{k}{k} \right] \cdot \left[\binom{0}{0} \cdot \binom{1}{0} \cdots \binom{k-1}{0} \right] = 1. \quad \blacksquare
$$

2.4. The Pascal's Triangle

The set of binomial coefficients $\binom{n}{r}$'s can be conveniently arranged in a triangular form from top to bottom and left to right in increasing order of the values of n and r respectively, as shown in Figure 2.4.1. This diagram, one of the most influential number patterns in the history of mathematics, is called the *Pascal triangle*, after the renown French mathematician Blaise Pascal (1623-1662) who discovered it and made significant contributions to the understanding of it in 1653. The triangle is also called Yang Hui's triangle in China as it was discovered much earlier by the Chinese mathematician Yang Hui in 1261. The same triangle was also included in the

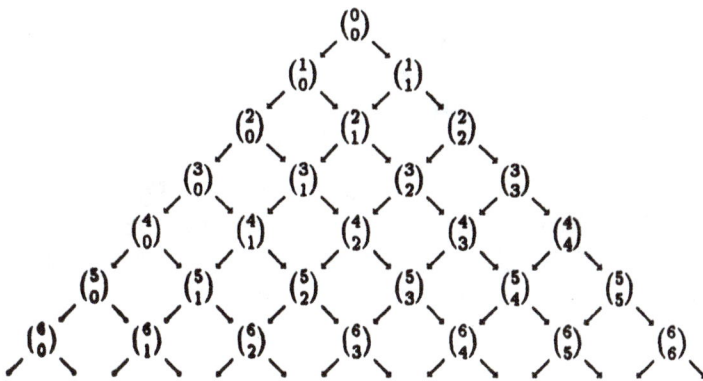

Figure 2.4.1.

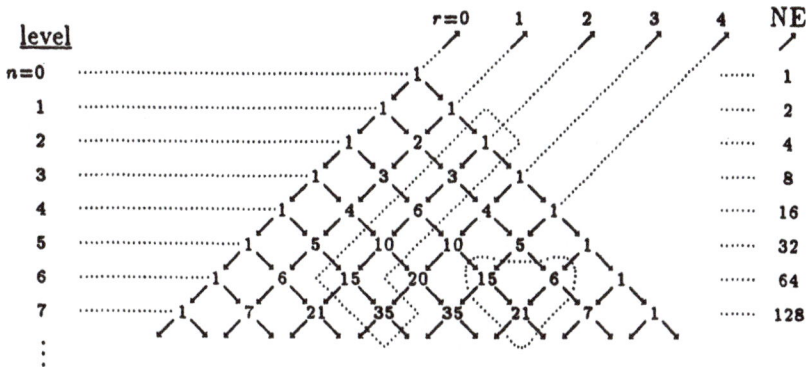

Figure 2.4.2.

book "Precious Mirror of the Four Elements" by another Chinese mathematician Chu Shih-Chieh in 1303. For the history of the Pascal's triangle, the reader may refer to the book [E].

We now make some simple observations with reference to Figure 2.4.2.

(1) The binomial coefficient $\binom{n}{r}$, located at the nth level from the top and rth position from the left, is the number of shortest routes from the top vertex representing $\binom{0}{0}$ to the vertex representing $\binom{n}{r}$. This is identical to what we observed in Example 1.5.1.

(2) As $\binom{n}{r} = \binom{n}{n-r}$, the entries of the triangle are symmetric with respect to the vertical line passing through the vertex $\binom{0}{0}$.

(3) Identity (2.3.1) says that the sum of the binomial coefficients at the nth level is equal to 2^n, and identity (2.3.6) says that the sum of the squares of the binomial coefficients at the nth level is equal to $\binom{2n}{n}$.

(4) Identity (2.1.4), namely $\binom{n}{r} = \binom{n-1}{r-1} + \binom{n-1}{r}$, simply says that each binomial coefficient in the interior of the triangle is equal to the sum of the two binomial coefficients on its immediate left and right "shoulders". For instance, $21 = 15 + 6$ as shown in Figure 2.4.2.

2.5. Chu Shih-Chieh's Identity

We proceed with another observation in Figure 2.4.2. Consider the 5 consecutive binomial coefficients:

$$\binom{2}{2} = 1, \ \binom{3}{2} = 3, \ \binom{4}{2} = 6, \ \binom{5}{2} = 10 \text{ and } \binom{6}{2} = 15$$

along the NE line when $r = 2$ from the right side of the triangle as shown. The sum of these 5 number is $1 + 3 + 6 + 10 + 15 = 35$, which is the immediate number we reach after turning left from the route 1-3-6-10-15. Why is this so? Replacing $\binom{2}{2}$ by $\binom{3}{3}$ (they all equal 1) and applying the above observation (4) successively, we have

$$\binom{2}{2} + \binom{3}{2} + \binom{4}{2} + \binom{5}{2} + \binom{6}{2}$$

$$= \underbrace{\binom{3}{3} + \binom{3}{2}} + \binom{4}{2} + \binom{5}{2} + \binom{6}{2}$$

$$= \underbrace{\binom{4}{3} + \binom{4}{2}} + \binom{5}{2} + \binom{6}{2}$$

$$= \underbrace{\binom{5}{3} + \binom{5}{2}} + \binom{6}{2}$$

$$= \underbrace{\binom{6}{3} + \binom{6}{2}}$$

$$= \binom{7}{3} = 35.$$

Evidently, this argument can be used in a general way to obtain the following identity (2.5.1), which was also discovered by Chu Shih-Chieh in 1303.

Example 2.5.1. Show that

(i) $$\binom{r}{r} + \binom{r+1}{r} + \cdots + \binom{n}{r} = \binom{n+1}{r+1} \qquad (2.5.1)$$

for all $r, n \in \mathbf{N}$ with $n \geq r$;

(ii) $$\binom{r}{0} + \binom{r+1}{1} + \cdots + \binom{r+k}{k} = \binom{r+k+1}{k} \qquad (2.5.2)$$

for all $r, k \in \mathbf{N}$.

Identities (2.5.1) and (2.5.2) can be remembered easily with the help of the patterns as shown in Figure 2.5.1. Due to the symmetry of the Pascal's triangle, identities (2.5.1) and (2.5.2) are equivalent; i.e., (2.5.1) $\Leftrightarrow$ (2.5.2).

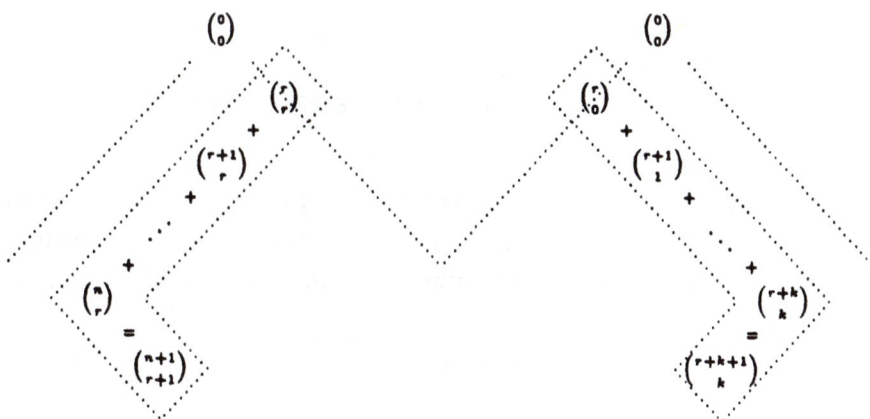

Figure 2.5.1.

We now give a combinatorial proof for identity (2.5.1).

Proof of (i). Let $X = \{a_1, a_2, ..., a_{n+1-r}, ..., a_{n+1}\}$ be a set of $n+1$ elements. We shall count the number of $(r+1)$-element subsets A of X. Consider the following $n+1-r$ cases:

(1): $a_1 \in A$. We need another r elements from $X\backslash\{a_1\}$ to form A. There are $\binom{n}{r}$ ways that A can be formed.

(2): $a_1 \notin A$ and $a_2 \in A$. We need another r elements from $X\backslash\{a_1, a_2\}$ to form A. There are $\binom{n-1}{r}$ ways that A can be formed.

$\cdots$

$(n-r)$: $a_1, a_2, ..., a_{n-1-r} \notin A$ and $a_{n-r} \in A$. We need another r elements from $X\backslash\{a_1, a_2, ..., a_{n-r}\}$ to form A. There are $\binom{(n+1)-(n-r)}{r} = \binom{r+1}{r}$ ways that A can be formed.

$(n+1-r)$: $a_1, a_2, ..., a_{n-r} \notin A$. In this case, there is $\binom{r}{r} = 1$ way to form A, namely, $A = \{a_{n-r+1}, a_{n-r+2}, ..., a_{n+1}\}$.

We note that all the above $n+1-r$ cases are pairwise disjoint and exhaustive. Thus we have by (AP),

$$\binom{n}{r} + \binom{n-1}{r} + \cdots + \binom{r+1}{r} + \binom{r}{r} = \binom{n+1}{r+1},$$

proving identity (2.5.1). ∎

We shall present two examples showing some applications of identity (2.5.1).

Example 2.5.2. (IMO, 1981/2) Let $1 \le r \le n$ and consider all r-element subsets of the set $\{1, 2, ..., n\}$. Each of these subsets has a smallest member. Let $F(n, r)$ denote the arithmetic mean of these smallest numbers. Prove that

$$F(n, r) = \frac{n+1}{r+1}.$$

Before proving the result, we give an illustrating example to help us understand the problem better. Take $n = 5$ and $r = 3$. All the 3-element subsets of $\{1, 2, 3, 4, 5\}$ and their respective smallest members are shown in Table 2.5.1.

3-element subsets of $\{1,2,3,4,5\}$	Smallest members
$\{1,2,3\}$	1
$\{1,2,4\}$	1
$\{1,2,5\}$	1
$\{1,3,4\}$	1
$\{1,3,5\}$	1
$\{1,4,5\}$	1
$\{2,3,4\}$	2
$\{2,3,5\}$	2
$\{2,4,5\}$	2
$\{3,4,5\}$	3

Table 2.5.1.

Thus $F(5,3) = \frac{1}{10}(6 \cdot 1 + 3 \cdot 2 + 1 \cdot 3) = \frac{3}{2}$, while $\frac{n+1}{r+1} = \frac{6}{4} = \frac{3}{2}$, and they are equal.

Two questions are in order. First, which numbers in the set $\{1, 2, ..., n\}$ could be the smallest members of some r-element subsets of $\{1, 2, ..., n\}$? How many times does each of these smallest members contribute to the sum? Observe that $\{n-r+1, n-r+2, ..., n\}$ consists of $n-(n-r+1)+1 = r$ elements; and it is the r-element subset of $\{1, 2, ..., n\}$ consisting of the largest possible members. Thus the numbers $1, 2, ..., n - r + 1$ are all the possible smallest members of the r-element subsets of $\{1, 2, ..., n\}$. This answers the first question. Let $m = 1, 2, ..., n - r + 1$. The number of times that m contributes to the sum is the number of r-element subsets of $\{1, 2, ..., n\}$ which contain m as the smallest member. This, however, is equal to the number of ways to form $(r - 1)$-element subsets from the set $\{m+1, m+2, ..., n\}$. Thus the desired number of times that m contributes to the sum is $\binom{n-m}{r-1}$, which answers the second question. We are now ready to see how identity (2.5.1) can be applied to prove the statement of Example 2.5.2.

Proof. For $m = 1, 2, ..., n - r + 1$, the number of r-element subsets of $\{1, 2, ..., n\}$ which contain m as the smallest member is given by $\binom{n-m}{r-1}$. Thus the sum S of the smallest members of all the r-element subsets of $\{1, 2, ..., n\}$ is given by

$$S = 1\binom{n-1}{r-1} + 2\binom{n-2}{r-1} + 3\binom{n-3}{r-1} + \cdots + (n-r+1)\binom{r-1}{r-1}$$

$$
\left.
\begin{aligned}
= \quad &\binom{n-1}{r-1} + \binom{n-2}{r-1} + \binom{n-3}{r-1} + \cdots + \binom{r-1}{r-1} \\
&+ \binom{n-2}{r-1} + \binom{n-3}{r-1} + \cdots + \binom{r-1}{r-1} \\
&\qquad\qquad + \binom{n-3}{r-1} + \cdots + \binom{r-1}{r-1} \\
&\qquad\qquad\qquad\qquad + \cdots + \binom{r-1}{r-1} \\
&\qquad\qquad\qquad\qquad\qquad\quad + \binom{r-1}{r-1}
\end{aligned}
\right\} \; (n-r+1) \text{ rows}
$$

Applying identity (2.5.1) to each row yields

$$S = \binom{n}{r} + \binom{n-1}{r} + \binom{n-2}{r} + \cdots + \binom{r}{r},$$

which is equal to $\binom{n+1}{r+1}$, applying (2.5.1) once more. Since the number of r-element subsets of $\{1, 2, ..., n\}$ is $\binom{n}{r}$, it follows that

$$F(n, r) = \frac{\binom{n+1}{r+1}}{\binom{n}{r}} = \frac{(n+1)!}{(r+1)!(n-r)!} \cdot \frac{r!(n-r)!}{n!} = \frac{n+1}{r+1}. \quad \blacksquare$$

We now consider another example. For $n \in \mathbb{N}$, the nth *subdivision* of an equilateral triangle ABC is the configuration obtained by (i) dividing each side of $\triangle ABC$ into $n + 1$ equal parts by n points; and (ii) adding $3n$ line segments to join the $3n$ pairs of such points on adjacent sides so that the line segments are parallel to the third side. The configurations for $n = 1, 2, 3$ are shown in Figure 2.5.2.

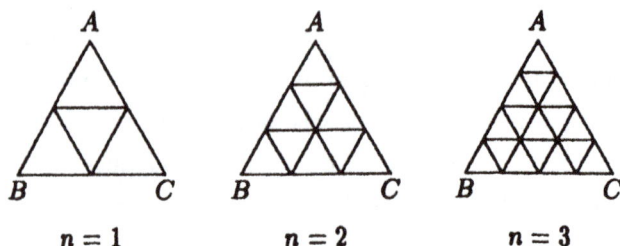

Figure 2.5.2.

Let $g(n)$ denote the number of parallelograms contained in the nth subdivision of an equilateral triangle. It can be checked from Figure 2.5.2 that

$$g(1) = 3, \quad g(2) = 15, \quad \text{and} \quad g(3) = 45.$$

The general case is discussed below.

Example 2.5.3. For each $n \in \mathbb{N}$, evaluate $g(n)$.

Remark. This problem, which can be found, for instance, in [MM], was given to the trainees in the 1990 Singapore Mathematical Olympiad Team as a test problem on 15 June, 1989. Lin Ziwei, a member in the team, of age 14 then, was able to solve the problem within an hour. His solution is presented below

Solution. There are 3 types of parallelograms:

Type 1   Type 2   Type 3

By symmetry, the number of parallelograms of each type is the same. Thus we need only to count the number of parallelograms of one type, say Type 1.

Any parallelogram of Type 1 is formed by 4 line segments ℓ_1, ℓ_2, ℓ_3 and ℓ_4 as shown in Figure 2.5.3.

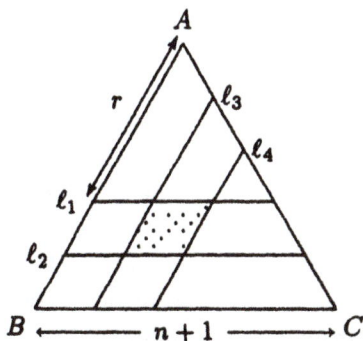

Figure 2.5.3

Each side of $\triangle ABC$ is of length $n+1$ units. When ℓ_1 is r units from the vertex A, the number of choices for ℓ_2 is $n+1-r$, and the number of ways of choosing the pair $\{\ell_3, \ell_4\}$ is $\binom{r+1}{2}$. Thus the total number of parallelograms of Type 1 is given by

$$\sum_{r=1}^{n}(n+1-r)\binom{r+1}{2}$$

$$= \binom{2}{2}n + \binom{3}{2}(n-1) + \binom{4}{2}(n-2) + \cdots + \binom{n+1}{2}1$$

$$\left.\begin{array}{l} \binom{2}{2} + \binom{3}{2} + \binom{4}{2} + \cdots + \binom{n}{2} + \binom{n+1}{2} \\[2mm] + \binom{2}{2} + \binom{3}{2} + \binom{4}{2} + \cdots + \binom{n}{2} \\[2mm] = \qquad \vdots \\[2mm] + \binom{2}{2} + \binom{3}{2} \\[2mm] + \binom{2}{2} \end{array}\right\} n \text{ rows}$$

$$= \binom{n+2}{3} + \binom{n+1}{3} + \cdots + \binom{4}{3} + \binom{3}{3} \quad \text{(by identity (2.5.1))}$$

$$= \binom{n+3}{4} \quad \text{(by identity (2.5.1) again).}$$

Hence $g(n) = 3\binom{n+3}{4}$. ∎

Remark. Since the above answer for $g(n)$ is a simple binomial coefficient, one may wonder whether there is any shorter or more direct combinatorial argument proving the result. We present one below

First, extend the sides AB and AC of the equilateral triangle ABC to AB' and AC' respectively such that $\frac{AB}{AB'} = \frac{AC}{AC'} = \frac{n+1}{n+2}$. Thus the nth subdivision of $\triangle ABC$ is part of the $(n+1)$th subdivision of $\triangle AB'C'$ (see Figure 2.5.4(a)). Note that including B' and C', there are exactly $n+3$ subdivision points on $B'C'$ with respect to the $(n+1)$th subdivision of $\triangle AB'C'$. Now, observe that any parallelogram of Type 2 in the nth subdivision of $\triangle ABC$ corresponds to a unique set of four subdivision points of $B'C'$ as shown in Figure 2.5.4(b). It can be shown that this correspondence

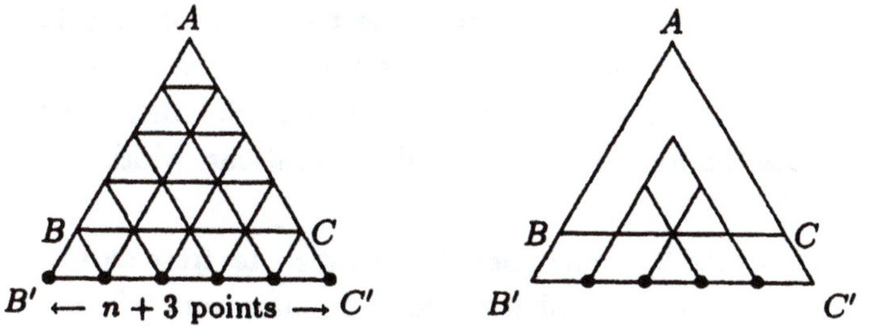

Figure 2.5.4.

is a bijection. Thus by (BP), the number of parallelograms of Type 2 in the nth subdivision of $\triangle ABC$ is equal to the number of 4-element subsets of the set of $n + 3$ subdivision points on $B'C'$. Since the latter is equal to $\binom{n+3}{4}$, we have $g(n) = 3\binom{n+3}{4}$. ∎

2.6. Shortest Routes in a Rectangular Grid

A point (a, b) in the x-y plane is called a *lattice point* if both a and b are integers. Figure 2.6.1 shows a rectangular grid in the x-y plane consisting of $(m + 1) \times (n + 1)$ lattice points, and a shortest route from the lattice point $(0, 0)$ to the lattice point (m, n), where $m, n \in \mathbf{N}$. It follows from Example 1.5.1 that the number of shortest routes from $(0, 0)$ to (m, n) is given by $\binom{m+n}{m}$ or $\binom{m+n}{n}$.

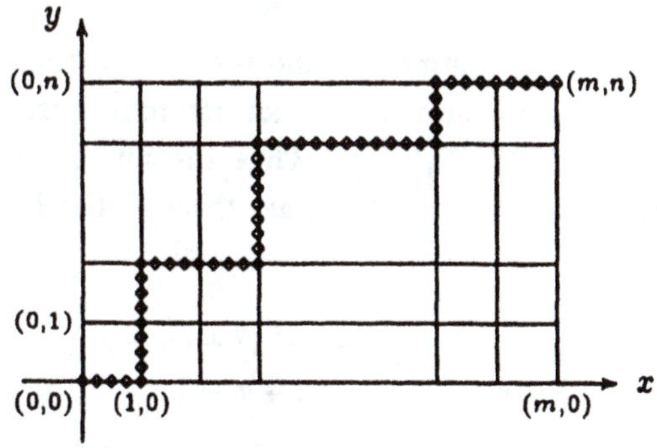

Figure 2.6.1.

In this section, we shall see that the technique of counting shortest routes between two lattice points in a rectangular grid can serve as a way of deriving combinatorial identities involving binomial coefficients. To begin with, we state the following two useful observations, which are related to Problem 1.25.

1° In Figure 2.6.2, the number of shortest routes from $O(0,0)$ to $A(x,y)$ is $\binom{x+y}{x}$, and the number of shortest routes from $A(x,y)$ to $P(m,n)$ is $\binom{(m-x)+(n-y)}{m-x}$. Thus the number of shortest routes from $O(0,0)$ to $P(m,n)$ that pass through $A(x,y)$ is given by

$$\binom{x+y}{x}\binom{(m-x)+(n-y)}{m-x}.$$

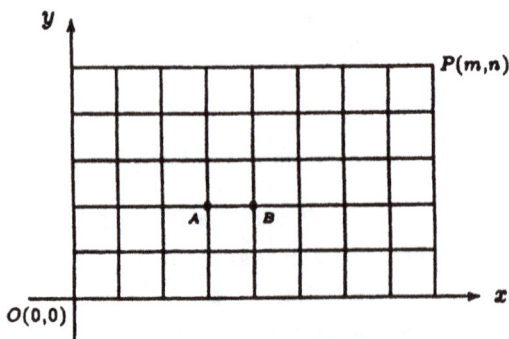

$$A = (x,y),\ B = (x+1,y)$$

Figure 2.6.2.

2° In Figure 2.6.2, the number of shortest routes from $O(0,0)$ to $A(x,y)$ is $\binom{x+y}{x}$, and the number of shortest routes from $B(x+1,y)$ to $P(m,n)$ is $\binom{(m-x-1)+(n-y)}{m-x-1}$. Thus the number of shortest routes from $O(0,0)$ to $P(m,n)$ that pass through the line segment AB is given by

$$\binom{x+y}{x}\binom{(m-x-1)+(n-y)}{m-x-1}.$$

As the first example, we derive the Vandermonde's identity using the technique of counting shortest routes.

Example 2.6.1. Show that

$$\binom{m}{0}\binom{n}{r} + \binom{m}{1}\binom{n}{r-1} + \cdots + \binom{m}{r}\binom{n}{0} = \binom{m+n}{r}$$

where $m, n, r \in \mathbb{N}$ with $m, n \geq r$.

Proof. Consider the rectangular grid shown in Figure 2.6.3.

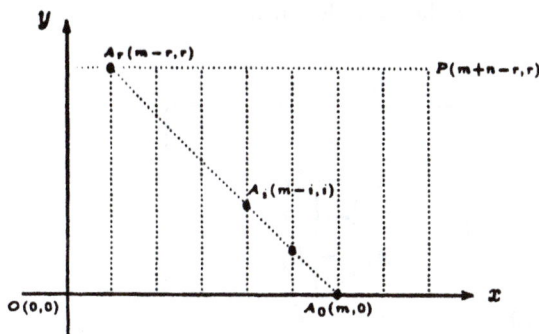

Figure 2.6.3.

The number of shortest routes from $O(0,0)$ to $P(m+n-r,r)$ is equal to

$$\binom{m+n-r+r}{r} = \binom{m+n}{r}.$$

We now count this number in a different way. Consider the line segment joining $A_0(m,0), A_1(m-1,1), \ldots,$ and $A_r(m-r,r)$ as shown in Figure 2.6.3. We note that each shortest route from O to P passes through one and only one A_i ($i = 0, 1, \ldots, r$) on the line segment. The number of such shortest routes passing through $A_i(m-i, i)$ is, by observation 1°, given by

$$\binom{m-i+i}{i}\binom{(m+n-r-m+i)+(r-i)}{r-i} = \binom{m}{i}\binom{n}{r-i}.$$

The identity now follows by (AP). ∎

The next example makes use of observation 2°.

Example 2.6.2. Show that for all integers $p, q, r \geq 0$,

$$\binom{p+q}{q}\binom{r}{r} + \binom{p+q-1}{q}\binom{r+1}{r} + \cdots + \binom{q}{q}\binom{r+p}{r}$$

$$= \binom{p+q+r+1}{q+r+1} = \binom{p+q+r+1}{p}. \tag{2.6.1}$$

Proof.   Consider the grid shown in Figure 2.6.4.

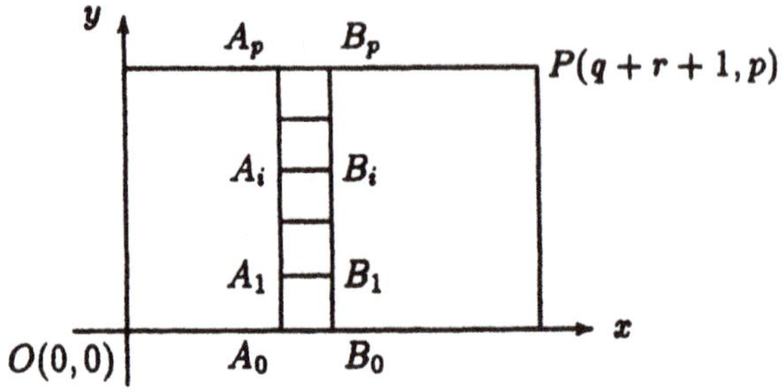

$$A_i = (r, i), \quad B_i = (r+1, i), \quad i = 0, 1, ..., p$$

Figure 2.6.4.

The number of shortest routes from $O(0,0)$ to $P(q + r + 1, p)$ is given by

$$\binom{q+r+1+p}{p}.$$

Another way of counting this number is as follows: Consider the sequence of unit line segments $A_0B_0, A_1B_1, \ldots, A_pB_p$, where $A_i = (r, i)$ and $B_i = (r+1, i)$, $i = 0, 1, ..., p$, as shown in Figure 2.6.4. We note that each shortest route from O to P must pass through one and only one unit line segment A_iB_i. The number of such shortest routes passing through A_iB_i is, by observation 2°, given by

$$\binom{r+i}{r}\binom{(q+r+1-r-1)+(p-i)}{q} = \binom{r+i}{r}\binom{p+q-i}{q}.$$

Identity (2.6.1) thus follows by (AP).   ∎

From now on, let $N_k = \{1, 2, ..., k\}$, where $k \in N$. In Problem 1.81, we counted the number of mappings $\alpha : N_n \to N_m$ $(n, m \in N)$ that may satisfy some additional conditions. These results are summarized in the following table.

$\alpha : \mathbf{N}_n \to \mathbf{N}_m$	Number of α
α is a mapping	m^n
α is injective ($n \leq m$)	$P_n^m = m(m-1)\cdots(m-n+1)$
α is surjective ($n \geq m$)	$m!S(n,m)$
α is strictly increasing	$\binom{m}{n}$

Our next aim is to apply the technique of counting shortest routes to enumerate two special types of mappings.

A mapping $\alpha : \mathbf{N}_n \to \mathbf{N}_m$ is said to be *increasing* if $\alpha(a) \leq \alpha(b)$ whenever $a \leq b$ in $\mathbf{N}_n$. The first problem we shall study is the enumeration of increasing mappings $\alpha : \mathbf{N}_n \to \mathbf{N}_m$.

Given an increasing mapping $\alpha : \mathbf{N}_n \to \mathbf{N}_m$, we construct a shortest route $R(\alpha)$ from $(1,1)$ to $(n+1, m)$ as follows:

(i) Join $(1,1)$ to $(1, \alpha(1))$ if $\alpha(1) > 1$;

(ii) For each $i = 1, 2, ..., n-1$,

join $(i, \alpha(i))$ to $(i+1, \alpha(i+1))$ if $\alpha(i) = \alpha(i+1)$,

join $(i, \alpha(i))$ to $(i+1, \alpha(i))$ and $(i+1, \alpha(i))$ to $(i+1, \alpha(i+1))$ if $\alpha(i) < \alpha(i+1)$;

(iii) Join $(n, \alpha(n))$ to $(n+1, m)$ if $\alpha(n) = m$;

Join $(n, \alpha(n))$ to $(n+1, \alpha(n))$ and $(n+1, \alpha(n))$ to $(n+1, m)$ if $\alpha(n) < m$.

For instance, if $\alpha : \mathbf{N}_6 \to \mathbf{N}_5$ is the increasing mapping defined in Figure 2.6.5(a), then $R(\alpha)$ is the shortest route shown in Figure 2.6.5(b).

On the other hand, if R is the shortest route form $(1,1)$ to $(7,5)$ as shown in Figure 2.6.6(a), then $R = R(\alpha)$, where $\alpha : \mathbf{N}_6 \to \mathbf{N}_5$ is the increasing mapping shown in Figure 2.6.6(b), by reversing the above procedure.

We are now ready to deal with the following:

Example 2.6.3. Show that the number of increasing mappings from $\mathbf{N}_n$ to $\mathbf{N}_m$ ($m, n \in \mathbf{N}$) equals the number of shortest routes from the lattice point $(1,1)$ to the lattice point $(n+1, m)$, which is $\binom{m+n-1}{n}$.

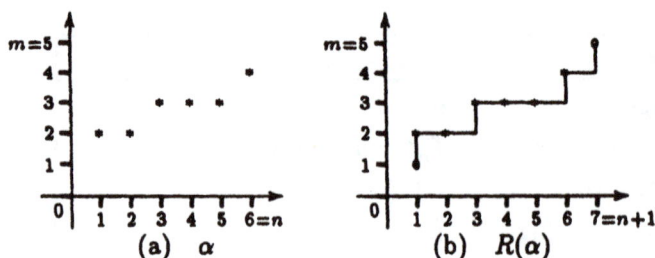

Figure 2.6.5.

i	$\alpha(i)$
1	2
2	2
3	3
4	3
5	3
6	4

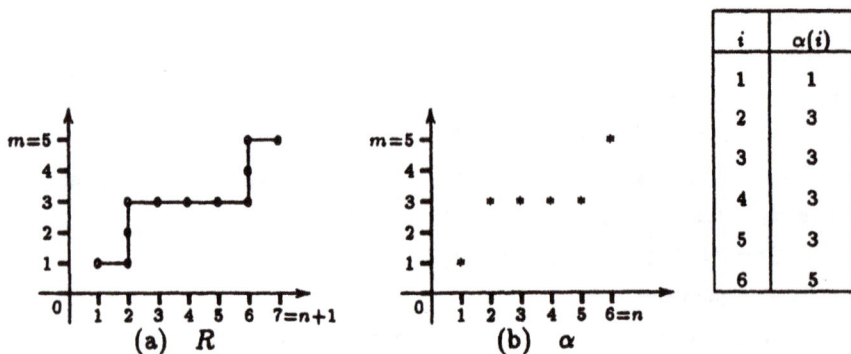

Figure 2.6.6.

i	$\alpha(i)$
1	1
2	3
3	3
4	3
5	3
6	5

Proof. Let X be the set of increasing mappings $\alpha : \mathbf{N}_n \to \mathbf{N}_m$, and Y be the set of shortest routes from $(1,1)$ to $(n+1,m)$. Define a mapping $f : X \to Y$ by putting for each $\alpha \in X$, $f(\alpha) = R(\alpha)$, which is the shortest route associated with α as defined above. It can be checked that f is indeed a bijection between X and Y. Hence we have by (BP),

$$|X| = |Y| = \binom{(n+1-1)+(m-1)}{n} = \binom{n+m-1}{n}. \quad \blacksquare$$

Remarks. (1) The reader should understand why we choose the lattice point $(n+1,m)$ but not (n,m) as a terminus in the above argument.

(2) The answer in Example 2.6.3, which is $H_n^m = \binom{m+n-1}{n}$, suggests another way to enumerate $|X|$. Indeed, given an increasing mapping $\alpha : N_n \to N_m$, there corresponds a unique n-element multi-subset $\{\alpha(1), \alpha(2), ..., \alpha(n)\}$ of the multi-set $M = \{\infty \cdot 1, \infty \cdot 2, ..., \infty \cdot m\}$ (thus the mapping of Figure 2.6.5(a) is associated with the 6-element multi-subset $\{2 \cdot 2, 3 \cdot 3, 1 \cdot 4\}$ of $M = \{\infty \cdot 1, \infty \cdot 2, ..., \infty \cdot 5\}$ and the mapping of Figure 2.6.6(b) is associated with $\{1 \cdot 1, 4 \cdot 3, 1 \cdot 5\}$ of M), and conversely, every n-element multi-subset of M corresponds to a unique increasing mapping from N_n to N_m. The existence of this one-to-one correspondence shows that $|X| = H_n^m$.

Let $N_k^* = \{0\} \cup N_k$. Our next problem is to enumerate the number of increasing mappings $\alpha : N_n \to N_{n-1}^*$ such that $\alpha(a) < a$ for each $a \in N_n$. First of all, we establish a useful principle about shortest routes in a grid, called the *reflection principle*.

Let $L : y = x + k \ (k \in Z)$ be a line of slope 1 on the x-y plane. Suppose P and Q are two lattice points on one side of L and P' is the reflection of P with respect to L as shown in Figure 2.6.7. Then we have:

Reflection Principle (RP). The number of shortest routes from P to Q that meet the line L is equal to the number of shortest routes from P' to Q.

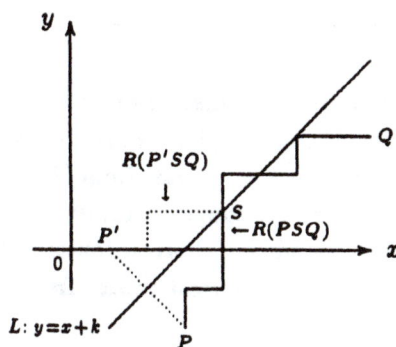

Figure 2.6.7.

Proof. Let X be the set of shortest routes from P to Q which meet L and Y be the set of shortest routes from P' to Q. The equality $|X| = |Y|$ will be proved by establishing a bijection between X and Y.

Let $R(PSQ)$ be a member in X where S is the first lattice point that $R(PSQ)$ meets L as it traverses from P to Q (see Figure 2.6.7). Let $R(P'SQ)$ be the union of (1) the shortest route from P' to S, which is the reflection of the portion from P to S in $R(PSQ)$ with respect to L, and (2) the shortest route from S to Q contained in $R(PSQ)$. Obviously, $R(P'SQ)$ is a member in Y. It can be checked that the correspondence

$$R(PSQ) \rightarrow R(P'SQ)$$

is indeed a bijection between X and Y. Thus $|X| = |Y|$ and so (RP) follows. ∎

Example 2.6.4. Show that the number of increasing mappings α : $\mathbf{N}_n \rightarrow \mathbf{N}_{n-1}^*$, $n \in \mathbf{N}$, such that $\alpha(a) < a$ is given by $\frac{1}{n+1}\binom{2n}{n}$.

For instance, if $n = 3$, there are $\frac{1}{3+1}\binom{6}{3} = 5$ such mappings from $\mathbf{N}_3$ to $\mathbf{N}_2^*$. They are exhibited in the table below.

i	$\alpha_1(i)$	$\alpha_2(i)$	$\alpha_3(i)$	$\alpha_4(i)$	$\alpha_5(i)$
1	0	0	0	0	0
2	0	0	0	1	1
3	0	1	2	1	2

Proof. It follows from the discussion in the proof of Example 2.6.3 that the number of increasing mappings $\alpha : \mathbf{N}_n \rightarrow \mathbf{N}_{n-1}^*$ such that $\alpha(a) < a$ is equal to the number of shortest routes from $(1,0)$ to $(n+1, n-1)$ which do not meet the line $y = x$. For convenience, let δ_1 denote this number; and further let δ_2 denote the number of shortest routes from $(1,0)$ to $(n+1, n-1)$ and δ_3 denote the number of shortest routes from $(1,0)$ to $(n+1, n-1)$ which meet the line $y = x$.

It is clear that $\delta_1 = \delta_2 - \delta_3$ and $\delta_2 = \binom{(n+1-1)+(n-1)}{n} = \binom{2n-1}{n}$.

It remains to evaluate δ_3. First we note that the mirror image of the lattice point $(1,0)$ with respect to the line $y = x$ is $(0,1)$. Thus by (RP),

δ_3 is equal to the number of shortest routes from $(0, 1)$ to $(n + 1, n - 1)$, which is given by

$$\delta_3 = \binom{(n + 1) + (n - 1 - 1)}{n + 1} = \binom{2n - 1}{n + 1}.$$

Thus,

$$\delta_1 = \delta_2 - \delta_3 = \binom{2n - 1}{n} - \binom{2n - 1}{n + 1} = \frac{1}{n + 1}\binom{2n}{n}. \quad \blacksquare$$

Remarks. (1) Both the ideas of (RP) and the above argument are essentially due to the French combinatorist Désiré André (1840-1917), who made use of them to solve a problem in 1887, called the *ballot problem*, which was posed and also solved by Joseph Louis Francois Bertrand (1822-1900) in the same year. Readers may refer to the interesting survey article [BM] for the history and some generalizations of the problem.

(2) The first few terms of the numbers $C_n = \frac{1}{n+1}\binom{2n}{n}$ just obtained are $1, 2, 5, 14, 42, 132, 429, 1430, \ldots$. They are called *Catalan numbers* after the Belgium mathematician Eugene Charles Catalan (1814-1894) who found the sequence of numbers in 1838 when he enumerated the number of ways of putting brackets in the product $x_1 x_2 \cdots x_n$ of n numbers. (Thus 1 way for $n = 2$: $(x_1 x_2)$; 2 ways for $n = 3$: $((x_1 x_2)x_3), (x_1(x_2 x_3))$; 5 ways for $n = 4$: $(((x_1 x_2)x_3)x_4), ((x_1(x_2 x_3))x_4), ((x_1 x_2)(x_3 x_4)), (x_1((x_2 x_3)x_4)), (x_1(x_2(x_3 x_4)))$ and so on). Some other problems related to Catalan numbers will be discussed in Chapter 6.

2.7. Some Properties of Binomial Coefficients

In the previous sections, we studied several identities involving binomial coefficients and introduced different techniques used to derive them. In this section, we shall state without proof some useful and striking properties about the binomial coefficients.

First of all, we have the following *unimodal* property:

1° For even $n \in \mathbb{N}$,

$$\binom{n}{0} < \binom{n}{1} < \cdots < \binom{n}{\frac{n}{2}} > \cdots > \binom{n}{n - 1} > \binom{n}{n}. \qquad (2.7.1)$$

and for odd $n \in \mathbb{N}$,

$$\binom{n}{0} < \binom{n}{1} < \cdots < \binom{n}{\frac{n-1}{2}} = \binom{n}{\frac{n+1}{2}} > \cdots > \binom{n}{n-1} > \binom{n}{n}. \quad (2.7.2)$$

$2°$ Let $n \geq 2$ be an integer. Mann and Shanks [MS] showed that

$$n \text{ is a prime} \quad \text{iff} \quad n | \binom{n}{r} \text{ for all } r = 1, 2, ..., n-1.$$

Recently, this result has been improved by Z. Hao who showed (via private communication) that an integer $n > 2$ is prime iff

$$n \left| \binom{n}{6k \pm 1} \right.,$$

for all k with $1 \leq k \leq \lfloor \frac{\sqrt{n}}{6} \rfloor$, where $\lfloor x \rfloor$ denotes the greatest integer not exceeding the real number x.

$3°$ For $a, b, c \in \mathbb{Z}$, we write $a \equiv b \pmod{c}$ iff $c \mid (a - b)$. The following results are due to the 19th-century French mathematician E. Lucas (1842-1891).

Let p be a prime. Then

(i) $\binom{n}{p} \equiv \lfloor \frac{n}{p} \rfloor \pmod{p}$ for every $n \in \mathbb{N}$,

(ii) $\binom{p}{r} \equiv 0 \pmod{p}$ for every r such that $1 \leq r \leq p - 1$,

(iii) $\binom{p+1}{r} \equiv 0 \pmod{p}$ for every r such that $2 \leq r \leq p - 1$,

(iv) $\binom{p-1}{r} \equiv (-1)^r \pmod{p}$ for every r such that $0 \leq r \leq p - 1$,

(v) $\binom{p-2}{r} \equiv (-1)^r (r + 1) \pmod{p}$ for every r such that $0 \leq r \leq p - 2$,

(vi) $\binom{p-3}{r} \equiv (-1)^r \binom{r+2}{2} \pmod{p}$ for every r such that $0 \leq r \leq p - 3$.

$4°$ Given a prime p, one can always find an $n \in \mathbb{N}^* = \mathbb{N} \cup \{0\}$ such that

$$p \nmid \binom{n}{r} \quad \text{for every } r = 0, 1, ..., n.$$

For instance, take $n = 0, 1, 2, ..., p - 1$ (see properties (iv)–(vi) above). Besides these, there are other such numbers n, and so the problem is:

Given a prime p, determine the set

$$A = \{n \in \mathbb{N} \mid p \nmid \binom{n}{r}, \quad \text{for every } r = 0, 1, ..., n\}.$$

According to Honsberger [H2], this problem was posed and also solved by two Indian mathematicians M.R. Railkar and M.R. Modak in 1976. They proved that

$$n \in A \quad \text{iff} \quad n = kp^m - 1$$

where m is a nonnegative integer and $k = 1, 2, ..., p - 1$.

5° Let $n, r \in \mathbf{N}$ and p be a prime. Write n and r with base p as follows:

$$n = n_0 + n_1 p + n_2 p^2 + \cdots + n_k p^k,$$
$$r = r_0 + r_1 p + r_2 p^2 + \cdots + r_k p^k,$$

where k is a nonnegative integer and $n_i, r_i \in \{0, 1, ..., p - 1\}$ for every $i = 0, 1, ..., k$. In 1878, Lucas proved the following important result:

$$\binom{n}{r} \equiv \binom{n_0}{r_0} \binom{n_1}{r_1} \cdots \binom{n_k}{r_k} \pmod{p}.$$

In particular, if we take $p = 2$ and write n and r in binary system:

$$n = (n_k n_{k-1} \cdots n_1 n_0)_2$$
$$r = (r_k r_{k-1} \cdots r_1 r_0)_2$$

where $n_i, r_i \in \{0, 1\}$ for every $i = 0, 1, ..., k$, then we have the following interesting result:

$$\binom{n}{r} \text{ is odd} \quad \text{iff} \quad n_i \geq r_i \quad \text{for every } i = 0, 1, ..., k. \qquad (2.7.3)$$

For instance, take $a = 11 = (a_3 a_2 a_1 a_0)_2 = (1011)_2$, $b = 9 = (b_3 b_2 b_1 b_0)_2 = (1001)_2$, and $c = 6 = (c_3 c_2 c_1 c_0)_2 = (0110)_2$. Since $a_i \geq b_i$ for every $i = 0, 1, 2, 3$, $\binom{a}{b} = \binom{11}{9}$ is odd; and since $a_2 \not\geq c_2$, $\binom{a}{c} = \binom{11}{6}$ is even.

6° According to Honsberger [H1], the following problem had been studied and solved by Fine [F]: Fix $n \in \mathbf{N}$, how many odd binomial coefficients $\binom{n}{r}$ are there at the nth level of the Pascal's triangle? We shall apply result (2.7.3) to answer this question.

Write $n = (n_k n_{k-1} \cdots n_1 n_0)_2$ in binary system and let $w(n) = \sum_{i=0}^{k} n_i$, which is equal to the number of 1's in the multi-set $\{n_0, n_1, ..., n_k\}$. Given $r \in \mathbf{Z}$ such that $0 \leq r \leq n$, write $r = (r_k r_{k-1} \cdots r_1 r_0)_2$. By result (2.7.3), $\binom{n}{r}$ is odd iff $r_i \leq n_i$. In order that $r_i \leq n_i$, we have $r_i = 0$ if $n_i = 0$, and $r_i \in \{0, 1\}$ if $n_i = 1$. Thus the number of choices for r is $2^{w(n)}$. We therefore conclude that given $n \in \mathbf{N}$, the number of odd binomial coefficients $\binom{n}{r}$'s at the nth level is given by $2^{w(n)}$. For instance, if $n = 11 = (1011)_2$, then $w(11) = 3$, and among the 12 binomial coefficients $\binom{11}{0}, \binom{11}{1}, \ldots, \binom{11}{11}$ at 11th level, the following $8 (= 2^3)$ are odd:

$$\binom{11}{0} = \binom{11}{11} = 1, \quad \binom{11}{1} = \binom{11}{10} = 11, \quad \binom{11}{2} = \binom{11}{9} = 55, \quad \binom{11}{3} = \binom{11}{8} = 165.$$

2.8. Multinomial Coefficients and the Multinomial Theorem

By changing the symbols x, y to x_1, x_2 respectively, the binomial expansion may be written as

$$(x_1 + x_2)^n = \sum_{r=0}^{n} \binom{n}{r} x_1^r x_2^{n-r},$$

where $n \in \mathbf{N}$. Naturally, one may wish to find the coefficients in the expansion of the following more general product:

$$(x_1 + x_2 + \cdots + x_m)^n \tag{2.8.1}$$

where $n, m \in \mathbf{N}$ and $m \geq 2$.

To do this, let us first introduce a family of numbers, that can be regarded as extensions of binomial coefficients. Let

$$\binom{n}{n_1, n_2, \ldots, n_m} \tag{2.8.2}$$

denote the number of ways to distribute n distinct objects into m distinct boxes such that n_1 of them are in box 1, n_2 in box 2, ..., and n_m in box m, where $n, m, n_1, n_2, ..., n_m$ are nonnegative integers with

$$n_1 + n_2 + \cdots + n_m = n. \tag{2.8.3}$$

What can be said about the number (2.8.2) when $m = 2$? Since there are $\binom{n}{n_1}$ ways to select n_1 of n distinct objects and put them in box 1, and 1 way to put the remaining $n_2 = n - n_1$ objects in box 2, we see that $\binom{n}{n_1, n_2} = \binom{n}{n_1}$, which is the usual binomial coefficient. Actually, in general, numbers of the form (2.8.2) can be expressed as a product of a sequence of binomial coefficients as follows: From the given n distinct objects, there are

$\binom{n}{n_1}$ ways to select n_1 objects and put them in box 1,

$\binom{n-n_1}{n_2}$ ways to select n_2 objects from the remaining objects and put them in box 2,

$\vdots$

$\binom{n-(n_1+\cdots+n_{m-2})}{n_{m-1}}$ ways to select n_{m-1} objects from the remaining objects and put them in box $(m-1)$, and

$\binom{n-(n_1+\cdots+n_{m-1})}{n_m} = 1$ way to put the remaining objects in box m.

Thus we have

$$\binom{n}{n_1, n_2, ..., n_m}$$
$$= \binom{n}{n_1}\binom{n-n_1}{n_2}\cdots\binom{n-(n_1+n_2+\cdots n_{m-1})}{n_m}. \qquad (2.8.4)$$

Note that, as proved in Section 1.6, the right-hand product of (2.8.4) is equal to $\frac{n!}{n_1!n_2!\cdots n_m!}$. Thus we have:

$$\binom{n}{n_1, n_2, ..., n_m} = \frac{n!}{n_1!n_2!\cdots n_m!}. \qquad (2.8.5)$$

We shall see the role played by the family of numbers (2.8.2) in the expansion of the product (2.8.1).

In expanding the product,

$$(x_1 + x_2 + \cdots + x_m)^n = \underbrace{(x_1 + x_2 + \cdots + x_m)\cdots(x_1 + x_2 + \cdots + x_m)}_{n},$$

we choose, for each of the above n factors, a symbol x_i from $\{x_1, x_2, ..., x_m\}$ and then multiply them together. Thus each term in the expansion is of the form:

$$x_1^{n_1} x_2^{n_2} \cdots x_m^{n_m} \qquad (2.8.6)$$

for some nonnegative integers $n_1, n_2, ..., n_m$ with $\sum_{i=1}^{m} n_i = n$. If the like terms are grouped together, then the coefficient of (2.8.6) can be found. Let A be the set of ways that (2.8.6) can be formed, and B the set of ways of distributing n distinct objects into m distinct boxes such that n_i objects are put in box i for each $i = 1, 2, ..., m$, where $\sum_{i=1}^{m} n_i = n$. We claim that $|A| = |B|$. Define a mapping $f : A \to B$ as follows. For each member of the form $a = x_1^{n_1} x_2^{n_2} \cdots x_m^{n_m}$ in A, let $f(a)$ be the way of putting n_i objects in box i (corresponding to x_i). It is evident that f is a bijection between A and B and so $|A| = |B|$, as claimed.

We thus conclude that the coefficient of (2.8.6) in the expansion is given by

$$|A| = |B| = \binom{n}{n_1, n_2, ..., n_m}.$$

Combining this with identity (2.8.5), we arrive at the following generalization of the binomial theorem, that was first formulated by G.W. Leibniz (1646-1716) and later on proved by Johann Bernoulli (1667-1748).

Theorem 2.8.1 (The Multinomial Theorem). *For $n, m \in \mathbb{N}$,*

$$(x_1 + x_2 + \cdots + x_m)^n = \sum \binom{n}{n_1, n_2, ..., n_m} x_1^{n_1} x_2^{n_2} \cdots x_m^{n_m}$$

where the sum is taken over all m-ary sequences $(n_1, n_2, ..., n_m)$ of nonnegative integers with $\sum_{i=1}^{m} n_i = n$, and

$$\binom{n}{n_1, n_2, ..., n_m} = \frac{n!}{n_1! n_2! \cdots n_m!}.$$

Example 2.8.1. For $n = 4$ and $m = 3$, we have by Theorem 2.8.1,

$$(x_1 + x_2 + x_3)^4 = \binom{4}{4,0,0}x_1^4 + \binom{4}{3,1,0}x_1^3x_2 + \binom{4}{3,0,1}x_1^3x_3$$

$$+ \binom{4}{2,2,0}x_1^2x_2^2 + \binom{4}{2,1,1}x_1^2x_2x_3 + \binom{4}{2,0,2}x_1^2x_3^2$$

$$+ \binom{4}{1,3,0}x_1x_2^3 + \binom{4}{1,2,1}x_1x_2^2x_3 + \binom{4}{1,1,2}x_1x_2x_3^2$$

$$+ \binom{4}{1,0,3}x_1x_3^3 + \binom{4}{0,4,0}x_2^4 + \binom{4}{0,3,1}x_2^3x_3$$

$$+ \binom{4}{0,2,2}x_2^2x_3^2 + \binom{4}{0,1,3}x_2x_3^3 + \binom{4}{0,0,4}x_3^4$$

$$= x_1^4 + 4x_1^3x_2 + 4x_1^3x_3 + 6x_1^2x_2^2 + 12x_1^2x_2x_3 + 6x_1^2x_3^2$$

$$+ 4x_1x_2^3 + 12x_1x_2^2x_3 + 12x_1x_2x_3^2 + 4x_1x_3^3 + x_2^4$$

$$+ 4x_2^3x_3 + 6x_2^2x_3^2 + 4x_2x_3^3 + x_3^4.$$

Because of Theorem 2.8.1, the numbers of the form (2.8.2) are usually called the *multinomial coefficients*. Since multinomial coefficients are generalizations of binomial coefficients, it is natural to ask whether some results about binomial coefficients can be generalized to multinomial coefficients. We end this chapter with a short discussion on this.

$1°$ The identity $\binom{n}{n_1} = \binom{n}{n-n_1}$ for binomial coefficients may be written as $\binom{n}{n_1,n_2} = \binom{n}{n_2,n_1}$ (here of course $n_1 + n_2 = n$). By identity (2.8.5), it is easy to see in general that

$$\binom{n}{n_1, n_2, ..., n_m} = \binom{n}{n_{\alpha(1)}, n_{\alpha(2)}, \cdots n_{\alpha(m)}} \tag{2.8.7}$$

where $\{\alpha(1), \alpha(2), ..., \alpha(m)\} = \{1, 2, ..., m\}$.

$2°$ The identity $\binom{n}{n_1} = \binom{n-1}{n_1-1} + \binom{n-1}{n_1}$ for binomial coefficients may be written:

$$\binom{n}{n_1, n_2} = \binom{n-1}{n_1 - 1, n_2} + \binom{n-1}{n_1, n_2 - 1}.$$

In general, we have:

$$\binom{n}{n_1, n_2, ..., n_m} = \binom{n-1}{n_1 - 1, n_2, ..., n_m} + \binom{n-1}{n_1, n_2 - 1, ..., n_m} + \cdots$$

$$+ \binom{n-1}{n_1, n_2, ..., n_m - 1}. \tag{2.8.8}$$

3° For binomial coefficients, we have the identity $\sum_{r=0}^{n} \binom{n}{r} = 2^n$. By letting $x_1 = x_2 = \cdots = x_m = 1$ in the multinomial theorem, we have

$$\sum \binom{n}{n_1, n_2, ..., n_m} = m^n \qquad (2.8.9)$$

where the sum is taken over all m-ary sequences $(n_1, n_2, ..., n_m)$ of nonnegative integers with $\sum_{i=1}^{m} n_i = n$.

Identity (2.8.9) simply says that the sum of the coefficients in the expansion of $(x_1 + x_2 + \cdots + x_m)^n$ is given by m^n. Thus, in Example 2.8.1, the sum of the coefficients in the expansion of $(x_1 + x_2 + x_3)^4$ is 81, which is 3^4.

4° In the binomial expansion $(x_1 + x_2)^n = \sum_{r=0}^{n} \binom{n}{r} x_1^r x_2^{n-r}$, the number of distinct terms is $n + 1$. How many distinct terms are there in the expansion of $(x_1 + x_2 + \cdots + x_m)^n$? To answer this question, let us first look at Example 2.8.1. The distinct terms obtained in the expansion of $(x_1 + x_2 + x_3)^4$ are shown on the left column below:

$$
\begin{aligned}
x_1^4 &\rightarrow \{4 \cdot x_1\} \\
x_1^3 x_2 &\rightarrow \{3 \cdot x_1, x_2\} \\
x_1^3 x_3 &\rightarrow \{3 \cdot x_1, x_3\} \\
x_1^2 x_2^2 &\rightarrow \{2 \cdot x_1, 2 \cdot x_2\} \\
x_1^2 x_2 x_3 &\rightarrow \{2 \cdot x_1, x_2, x_3\} \\
x_1^2 x_3^2 &\rightarrow \{2 \cdot x_1, 2 \cdot x_3\} \\
x_1 x_2^3 &\rightarrow \{x_1, 3 \cdot x_2\} \\
x_1 x_2^2 x_3 &\rightarrow \{x_1, 2 \cdot x_2, x_3\} \\
x_1 x_2 x_3^2 &\rightarrow \{x_1, x_2, 2 \cdot x_3\} \\
x_1 x_3^3 &\rightarrow \{x_1, 3 \cdot x_3\} \\
x_2^4 &\rightarrow \{4 \cdot x_2\} \\
x_2^3 x_3 &\rightarrow \{3 \cdot x_2, x_3\} \\
x_2^2 x_3^2 &\rightarrow \{2 \cdot x_2, 2 \cdot x_3\} \\
x_2 x_3^3 &\rightarrow \{x_2, 3 \cdot x_3\} \\
x_3^4 &\rightarrow \{4 \cdot x_3\}.
\end{aligned}
$$

Observe that each of them corresponds to a unique 4-element multi-subset of $M = \{\infty \cdot x_1, \infty \cdot x_2, \infty \cdot x_3\}$, and vice versa, as shown on the right column above. Thus by (BP), the number of distinct terms in the expansion of $(x_1 + x_2 + x_3)^4$ is equal to the number of 4-element multi-subsets of M, which is $H_4^3 = \binom{4+3-1}{4} = \binom{6}{4} = 15$. In general, one can prove that (see Problem 2.62)

the number of distinct terms in the expansion of $(x_1 + x_2 + \cdots + x_m)^n$

is given by $H_n^m = \binom{n+m-1}{n}$.

In particular, for binomial expansion, we have $H_n^2 = \binom{2+n-1}{n} = n+1$, which agrees with what we mentioned before.

$5°$ It follows from (2.7.1) and (2.7.2) that for a given positive integer n, the maximum value of the binomial coefficients $\binom{n}{r}$, $r = 0, 1, ..., n$, is equal to

$$\begin{cases} \dbinom{n}{\frac{n}{2}} & \text{if } n \text{ is even,} \\[2ex] \dbinom{n}{\frac{n-1}{2}} = \dbinom{n}{\frac{n+1}{2}} & \text{if } n \text{ is odd.} \end{cases}$$

What can we say about the maximum value of multinomial coefficients $\binom{n}{n_1, n_2, ..., n_m}$? This problem has recently been solved by Wu [W]. For $n, m \geq 2$, let

$$M(n, m) = \max\left\{ \binom{n}{n_1, n_2, \ldots, n_m} \middle| n_i \in \mathbf{N}^* \text{ and } \sum_{i=1}^{m} n_i = n \right\}.$$

Case 1. $m \mid n$.

Let $n = mr$ for some $r \in \mathbf{N}$. Then

$$M(n, m) = \binom{n}{\underbrace{r, r, \ldots, r}_{m}} = \frac{n!}{(r!)^m},$$

and $\binom{n}{\underbrace{r, r, \ldots, r}_{m}}$ is the only term attaining this maximum value.

Case 2. $m \nmid n$.

Suppose that $n = mr + k$ for some $r, k \in \mathbf{N}$ with $1 \leq k \leq m - 1$. Then

$$M(n, m) = \binom{n}{\underbrace{r, r, \ldots, r,}_{m-k} \underbrace{(r + 1), (r + 1), \ldots, (r + 1)}_{k}}$$

$$= \frac{n!}{(r!)^{m-k}((r + 1)!)^k} = \frac{n!}{(r + 1)^k (r!)^m},$$

and $\binom{n}{n_1,n_2,\ldots,n_m}$, where $\{n_1,n_2,\ldots,n_m\} = \{(m-k)\cdot r, k\cdot(r+1)\}$ as multi-sets, are the $\binom{m}{k}$ terms attaining this maximum value.

For instance, in Example 2.8.1, we have

$$n = 4, \quad m = 3, \quad r = 1 \quad \text{and} \quad k = 1.$$

Thus the maximum coefficient is

$$M(4,3) = \frac{4!}{2!(1!)^3} = 12,$$

which is attained by the following $\binom{m}{k} = 3$ terms:

$$\binom{4}{1,1,2}, \quad \binom{4}{1,2,1} \quad \text{and} \quad \binom{4}{2,1,1}.$$

Exercise 2

1. The number 4 can be expressed as a sum of one or more positive integers, taking order into account, in 8 ways:

$$4 = 1+3 = 3+1 = 2+2 = 1+1+2$$
$$= 1+2+1 = 2+1+1 = 1+1+1+1.$$

In general, given $n \in \mathbf{N}$, in how many ways can n be so expressed?

2. Find the number of $2n$-digit binary sequences in which the number of 0's in the first n digits is equal to the number of 1's in the last n digits.

3. Let $m, n, r \in \mathbf{N}$. Find the number of r-element multi-subsets of the multi-set

$$M = \{a_1, a_2, \ldots, a_n, m \cdot b\}$$

in each of the following cases:

(i) $r \le m,\, r \le n$;

(ii) $n \le r \le m$;

(ii) $m \le r \le n$.

4. Ten points are marked on a circle. How many distinct convex polygons of three or more sides can be drawn using some (or all) of the ten points as vertices? (Polygons are distinct unless they have exactly the same vertices.) (AIME, 1989/2)

5. Find the coefficient of x^5 in the expansion of $(1 + x + x^2)^8$.

6. Find the coefficient of x^6 in the expansion of $(1 + x + x^2)^9$.

7. Find the coefficient of x^{18} in the expansion of

$$(1 + x^3 + x^5 + x^7)^{100}.$$

8. Find the coefficient of x^{29} in the expansion of

$$(1 + x^5 + x^7 + x^9)^{1000}.$$

9. In the expansion of

$$(1 + x + x^2 + \cdots + x^{10})^3,$$

what is the coefficient of

(i) x^5?   (ii) x^8?

10. Given an n-element set X, where $n \in \mathbf{N}$, let $\mathcal{O} = \{A \subseteq X \mid |A| \text{ is odd}\}$ and $\mathcal{E} = \{A \subseteq X \mid |A| \text{ is even}\}$. Show that $|\mathcal{O}| = |\mathcal{E}|$ by establishing a bijection between $\mathcal{O}$ and $\mathcal{E}$.

11. Find the number of permutations of the multi-set $\{m \cdot 1, n \cdot 2\}$, where $m, n \in \mathbf{N}$, which must contain the m 1's.

12. Let $1 \leq r \leq n$ and consider all r-element subsets of the set $\{1, 2, \ldots, n\}$. Each of these subsets has a *largest* member. Let $H(n, r)$ denote the arithmetic mean of these largest members. Find $H(n, r)$ and simplify your result (see Example 2.5.2).

13. For $n \in \mathbf{N}$, let $\Delta(n)$ denote the number of triangles XYZ in the nth subdivision of an equilateral triangle ABC (see Figure 2.5.2) such that $YZ // BC$, and X and A are on the same side of YZ. Evaluate $\Delta(n)$. (For other enumeration problems relating to this, see M.E. Larsen, The eternal triangle – A history of a counting problem, *The College Math. J.* **20** (1989), 370-384.)

14. Find the coefficients of x^n and x^{n+r} $(1 \leq r \leq n)$ in the expansion of

$$(1 + x)^{2n} + x(1 + x)^{2n-1} + x^2(1 + x)^{2n-2} + \cdots + x^n(1 + x)^n.$$

15. A polynomial in x is defined by

$$a_0 + a_1 x + a_2 x^2 + \cdots + a_{2n} x^{2n} = (x + 2x^2 + \cdots + nx^n)^2.$$

Show that

$$\sum_{i=n+1}^{2n} a_i = \frac{n(n+1)(5n^2 + 5n + 2)}{24}.$$

16. Show that

$$P_r^r + P_r^{r+1} + \cdots + P_r^{2r} = P_r^{2r+1},$$

where r is a nonnegative integer.

17. Given $r, n, m \in \mathbb{N}^*$ with $r < n$, show that

$$P_r^n + P_r^{n+1} + \cdots + P_r^{n+m} = \frac{1}{r+1}(P_{r+1}^{n+m+1} - P_{r+1}^n).$$

(See Problem 2.35.)

18. Show that

(i) for even $n \in \mathbb{N}$,

$$\binom{n}{i} < \binom{n}{j} \quad \text{if } 0 \le i < j \le \frac{n}{2};$$

and

$$\binom{n}{i} > \binom{n}{j} \quad \text{if } \frac{n}{2} \le i < j \le n.$$

(ii) for odd $n \in \mathbb{N}$,

$$\binom{n}{i} < \binom{n}{j} \quad \text{if } 0 \le i < j \le \frac{1}{2}(n-1);$$

and

$$\binom{n}{i} > \binom{n}{j} \quad \text{if } \frac{1}{2}(n+1) \le i < j \le n.$$

19. Give three different proofs for each of the following identities:

(i) $\binom{2(n+1)}{n+1} = \binom{2n}{n+1} + 2\binom{2n}{n} + \binom{2n}{n-1}$;

(ii) $\binom{n+1}{m} = \binom{n}{m-1} + \binom{n-1}{m} + \binom{n-1}{m-1}$.

20. Give a combinatorial proof for the identity

$$\binom{n}{m}\binom{m}{r} = \binom{n}{r}\binom{n-r}{m-r}.$$

21. Show that for $n \in \mathbf{N}^*$,

$$\sum_{r=0}^{n} \frac{(2n)!}{(r!)^2((n-r)!)^2} = \binom{2n}{n}^2.$$

22. By using the identity $(1 - x^2)^n = (1 + x)^n(1 - x)^n$, show that for each $m \in \mathbf{N}^*$ with $m \le n$,

$$\sum_{i=0}^{2m}(-1)^i\binom{n}{i}\binom{n}{2m-i} = (-1)^m\binom{n}{m},$$

and

$$\sum_{i=0}^{2m+1}(-1)^i\binom{n}{i}\binom{n}{2m+1-i} = 0.$$

Deduce that

$$\sum_{i=0}^{n}(-1)^i\binom{n}{i}^2 = \begin{cases} (-1)^{\frac{n}{2}}\binom{n}{\frac{n}{2}} & \text{if } n \text{ is even} \\ 0 & \text{if } n \text{ is odd.} \end{cases}$$

23. What is the value of the sum

$$S = m! + \frac{(m+1)!}{1!} + \frac{(m+2)!}{2!} + \cdots + \frac{(m+n)!}{n!} ?$$

(Beijing Math. Contest (1962))

Prove each of the following identities in Problems 24–43, where $m, n \in \mathbf{N}^*$:

24. $\sum\limits_{r=0}^{n} 3^r \binom{n}{r} = 4^n$,

25. $\sum\limits_{r=0}^{n}(r+1)\binom{n}{r} = (n+2)2^{n-1}$,

26. $\sum\limits_{r=0}^{n} \frac{1}{r+1}\binom{n}{r} = \frac{1}{n+1}(2^{n+1} - 1)$,

27. $\sum\limits_{r=0}^{n} \frac{(-1)^r}{r+1}\binom{n}{r} = \frac{1}{n+1}$,

28. $\displaystyle\sum_{r=m}^{n} \binom{n}{r}\binom{r}{m} = 2^{n-m}\binom{n}{m}$ for $m \le n$,

29. $\displaystyle\sum_{r=0}^{m}(-1)^r \binom{n}{r} = \begin{cases} (-1)^m \binom{n-1}{m} & \text{if } m < n \\ 0 & \text{if } m = n > 0, \end{cases}$

30. $\displaystyle\sum_{r=0}^{m}(-1)^{m-r}\binom{n}{r} = \binom{n-1}{m}$ for $m \le n - 1$,

31. $\displaystyle\sum_{r=0}^{n}(-1)^r r\binom{n}{r} = 0$ for $n > 1$,

32. $\displaystyle\sum_{r=0}^{n-1}\binom{2n-1}{r} = 2^{2n-2}$,

33. $\displaystyle\sum_{r=0}^{n}\binom{2n}{r} = 2^{2n-1} + \frac{1}{2}\binom{2n}{n}$,

34. $\displaystyle\sum_{r=0}^{n} r\binom{2n}{r} = n2^{2n-1}$,

35. $\displaystyle\sum_{r=k}^{m}\binom{n+r}{n} = \binom{n+m+1}{n+1} - \binom{n+k}{n+1}$ for $k \in \mathbf{N}^*$ and $k \le m$,

36. $\displaystyle\sum_{r=1}^{n}\binom{n}{r}\binom{n-1}{r-1} = \binom{2n-1}{n-1}$,

37. $\displaystyle\sum_{r=m}^{n}(-1)^r\binom{n}{r}\binom{r}{m} = \begin{cases} (-1)^m & \text{if } m = n \\ 0 & \text{if } m < n, \end{cases}$

38. $\displaystyle\sum_{r=1}^{n-1}(n-r)^2\binom{n-1}{n-r} = n(n-1)2^{n-3}$,
(See Problem 2.47(i).)

39. $\displaystyle\sum_{r=0}^{n}\binom{2n}{r}^2 = \frac{1}{2}\left\{\binom{4n}{2n} + \binom{2n}{n}^2\right\}$,

40. $\displaystyle\sum_{r=0}^{n}\binom{n}{r}^2\binom{r}{n-k} = \binom{n}{k}\binom{n+k}{k}$ for $k \in \mathbf{N}^*$, $0 \le k \le n$,

41. $\displaystyle\sum_{r=0}^{n}\binom{n}{r}\binom{m+r}{n} = \sum_{r=0}^{n}\binom{n}{r}\binom{m}{r}2^r$,

42. $\displaystyle\sum_{r=0}^{m}\binom{m}{r}\binom{n}{r}\binom{p+r}{m+n} = \binom{p}{m}\binom{p}{n}$, for $p \in \mathbf{N}$, $p \ge m, n$;
(Li Shanlan, 1811-1882)

43. $\displaystyle\sum_{r=0}^{m}\binom{m}{r}\binom{n}{r}\binom{p+m+n-r}{m+n} = \binom{p+m}{m}\binom{p+n}{n}$, for $p \in \mathbf{N}$.

(Li Shanlan)

---

44. Prove the following identities using the technique of counting shortest routes in a grid:

    (i) $\sum_{r=0}^{n} \binom{n}{r} = 2^n$,

    (ii) $\sum_{k=0}^{n} \binom{r+k}{r} = \binom{r+n+1}{r+1}$.

45. Use the technique of finding the number of shortest routes in rectangular grid to prove the following identity:

$$\binom{p}{q}\binom{r}{0} + \binom{p-1}{q-1}\binom{r+1}{1} + \cdots + \binom{p-q}{0}\binom{r+q}{q} = \binom{p+r+1}{q}.$$

46. Give a combinatorial proof for the following identity:

$$\sum_{r=1}^{n} r\binom{n}{r} = n \cdot 2^{n-1}.$$

47. Given $n \in \mathbf{N}$, show that

    (i) $\sum_{r=1}^{n} r^2\binom{n}{r} = n(n+1)2^{n-2}$;

    (Putnam, 1962)

    (ii) $\sum_{r=1}^{n} r^3\binom{n}{r} = n^2(n+3)2^{n-3}$;

    (iii) $\sum_{r=1}^{n} r^4\binom{n}{r} = n(n+1)(n^2+5n-2)2^{n-4}$.

48. (i) Prove that for $r, k \in \mathbf{N}$,

$$r^k = \sum_{i=0}^{k} \binom{k}{i}(r-1)^{k-i}.$$

(ii) For $n, k \in \mathbf{N}$, let

$$R(n,k) = \sum_{r=1}^{n} r^k\binom{n}{r} \quad \text{and} \quad R(n,0) = \sum_{r=0}^{n} \binom{n}{r}.$$

Show that

$$R(n,k) = n \cdot \sum_{j=0}^{k-1} \binom{k-1}{j} R(n-1,j).$$

Remark. Two Chinese teachers, Wei Guozhen and Wang Kai (1988) showed that

$$\sum_{r=1}^{n} r^k \binom{n}{r} = \sum_{i=1}^{k} S(k,i) \cdot P_i^n \cdot 2^{n-i},$$

where $k \le n$ and $S(k,i)$'s are the Stirling numbers of the second kind.

49. Prove that

$$\sum_{r=1}^{n} \frac{1}{r} \binom{n}{r} = \sum_{r=1}^{n} \frac{1}{r}(2^r - 1).$$

50. Give two different proofs for the following identity:

$$\sum_{r=1}^{n} r \binom{n}{r}^2 = n\binom{2n-1}{n-1},$$

where $n \in \mathbf{N}$.

51. Let p be a prime. Show that

$$\binom{p}{r} \equiv 0 \pmod{p}$$

for all r such that $1 \le r \le p-1$. Deduce that $(1+x)^p \equiv (1+x^p)$ $\pmod{p}$.

52. Let p be an odd prime. Show that

$$\binom{2p}{p} \equiv 2 \pmod{p}.$$

53. Let n, m, p be integers such that $1 \le p \le m \le n$.
    (i) Express, in terms of $S(n,p)$, the number of mappings $f : \mathbf{N}_n \to \mathbf{N}_m$ such that $|f(\mathbf{N}_n)| = p$.
    (ii) Express, in terms of $S(n,k)$'s, where $p \le k \le m$, the number of mappings $f : \mathbf{N}_n \to \mathbf{N}_m$ such that $\mathbf{N}_p \subseteq f(\mathbf{N}_n)$.

54. Recall that for nonnegative integers n, r, $H_r^n = \binom{r+n-1}{r}$. Prove each of the following identities:
    (a) $H_r^n = \frac{n}{r} H_{r-1}^{n+1}$;
    (b) $H_r^n = \frac{n+r-1}{r} H_{r-1}^n$;
    (c) $H_r^n = H_{r-1}^n + H_r^{n-1}$;

(d) $\sum_{k=0}^{r} H_k^n = H_r^{n+1}$;

(e) $\sum_{k=1}^{r} kH_k^n = nH_{r-1}^{n+2}$;

(f) $\sum_{k=0}^{r} H_k^m H_{r-k}^n = H_r^{m+n}$.

55. For $n, k \in \mathbf{N}$ with $n \geq 2$ and $1 \leq k \leq n$, let

$$d_k(n) = \left| \binom{n}{k} - \binom{n}{k-1} \right|,$$

$$d_{\min}(n) = \min\{d_k(n) \mid 1 \leq k \leq n\}.$$

Show that

(i) $d_{\min}(n) = 0$ iff n is odd;

(ii) For odd n, $d_k(n) = 0$ iff $k = \frac{1}{2}(n+1)$.

Let $d_{\min}^*(n) = \min\{d_k(n) \mid 1 \leq k \leq n, \ k \neq \frac{1}{2}(n+1)\}$. Show that

(iii) For $n \neq 4$, $d_{\min}^*(n) = n - 1$;

(iv) For $n \neq 4$ and $n \neq 6$,

$$d_k(n) = n - 1 \quad \text{iff} \quad k = 1 \text{ or } k = n;$$

(v) For $n = 6$, $d_k(6) = 5$ iff $k = 1, 3, 4$ or 6.

(See Z. Shan and E.T.H. Wang, The gaps between consecutive binomial coefficients, *Math. Magazine*, **63** (1990), 122-124.)

56. Prove that

(i) $\left(\binom{n}{2} \right) = 3\binom{n+1}{4}$ for $n \in \mathbf{N}$;

(ii) $\left(\binom{n}{3} \right) > \left(\binom{n}{2} \right)$ for $n \in \mathbf{N}, n \geq 3$;

(iii) $\left(\binom{r}{2} \right) = \sum_{j=1}^{r} \left(\binom{r}{j} + \epsilon_j \atop 2 \right) \binom{n+r-j}{2r}$,

where $\epsilon_j = \begin{cases} 1 & \text{if } j \text{ is odd} \\ 0 & \text{if } j \text{ is even,} \end{cases}$ and $n, r \in \mathbf{N}$ with $r \leq n$;

(iv) $\left(\binom{n}{r} \right) = \sum_{j=1}^{r} \binom{2j-1}{j} \binom{r+j}{2j} \binom{n}{r+j}$,

for $n, r \in \mathbf{N}$ with $r \leq n$.

(For more results on these iterated binomial coefficients, see S.W. Golomb, Iterated binomial coefficients, *Amer. Math. Monthly*, **87** (1980), 719-727.)

57. Let $a_n = 6^n + 8^n$. Determine the remainder on dividing a_{83} by 49. (AIME, 1983/6)

58. The increasing sequence 1, 3, 4, 9, 10, 12, 13, ... consists of all those positive integers which are powers of 3 or sums of distinct powers of 3. Find the 100th term of this sequence (where 1 is the 1st term, 3 is the 2nd term, and so on). (AIME, 1986/7)

59. The polynomial $1 - x + x^2 - x^3 + \cdots + x^{16} - x^{17}$ may be written in the form $a_0 + a_1 y + a_2 y^2 + a_3 y^3 + \cdots + a_{16} y^{16} + a_{17} y^{17}$, where $y = x + 1$ and the a_i's are constants. Find the value of a_2. (AIME, 1986/11)

60. In an office, at various times during the day, the boss gives the secretary a letter to type, each time putting the letter on top of the pile in the secretary's in-box. When there is time, the secretary takes the top letter off the pile and types it. There are nine letters to be typed during the day, and the boss delivers them in the order 1, 2, 3, 4, 5, 6, 7, 8, 9.

    While leaving for lunch, the secretary tells a colleague that letter 8 has already been typed, but says nothing else about the morning's typing. The colleague wonders which of the nine letters remain to be typed after lunch and in what order they will be typed. Based upon the above information, how many such *after-lunch typing orders* are possible? (That there are no letters left to be typed is one of the possibilities.) (AIME, 1988/15)

61. Expanding $(1 + 0.2)^{1000}$ by the binomial theorem and doing no further manipulation gives

    $$\binom{1000}{0}(0.2)^0 + \binom{1000}{1}(0.2)^1 + \binom{1000}{2}(0.2)^2 + \cdots + \binom{1000}{1000}(0.2)^{1000}$$
    $$= A_0 + A_1 + A_2 + \cdots + A_{1000},$$

    where $A_k = \binom{1000}{k}(0.2)^k$ for $k = 0, 1, 2, \ldots, 1000$. For which k is A_k the largest? (AIME, 1991/3)

62. Prove that the number of distinct terms in the expansion of

    $$(x_1 + x_2 + \cdots + x_m)^n$$

    is given by $H_n^m = \binom{n+m-1}{n}$.

63. Show by two different methods that

$$\binom{n}{n_1, n_2, \ldots, n_m} = \sum_{i=1}^{m} \binom{n-1}{n_1, \ldots, n_i - 1, n_{i+1}, \ldots, n_m}.$$

64. For $n, m \in \mathbf{N}$, show that

$$\sum \binom{n}{n_1, n_2, \ldots, n_m} = m! S(n, m),$$

where the sum is taken over all m-ary sequences $(n_1, n_2, \ldots, n_m)$ such that $n_i \neq 0$ for all i, and $S(n, m)$ is a Stirling number of the second kind.

65. Prove that

$$\sum \binom{n}{n_1, n_2, \ldots, n_m} (-1)^{n_2 + n_4 + n_6 + \cdots} = \begin{cases} 1 & \text{if } m \text{ is odd} \\ 0 & \text{if } m \text{ is even,} \end{cases}$$

where the sum is taken over all m-ary sequences $(n_1, n_2, \ldots, n_m)$ of nonnegative integers with $\sum_{i=1}^{m} n_i = n$.

66. Prove the following generalized Vandermonde's identity for multinomial coefficients: for $p, q \in \mathbf{N}$,

$$\binom{p+q}{k_1, k_2, \ldots, k_m}$$
$$= \sum \binom{p}{j_1, j_2, \ldots, j_m} \binom{q}{k_1 - j_1, k_2 - j_2, \ldots, k_m - j_m},$$

where the sum is taken over all m-ary sequences $(j_1, j_2, \ldots, j_m)$ of non-negative integers with $j_1 + j_2 + \cdots + j_m = p$.

67. Given any prime p and $m \in \mathbf{N}$, show that

$$\binom{p}{n_1, n_2, \cdots, n_m} \equiv 0 \pmod{p},$$

if $p \neq n_i$ for any $i = 1, 2, \ldots, m$.

Deduce that

$$\left(\sum_{i=1}^{m} x_i \right)^p \equiv \sum_{i=1}^{m} x_i^p \pmod{p}.$$

68. Let p be a prime, and $n \in \mathbf{N}$. Write n in base p as follows:

$$n = n_0 + n_1 p + n_2 p^2 + \cdots + n_k p^k,$$

where $n_i \in \{0, 1, \ldots, p-1\}$ for each $i = 1, 2, \ldots, k$.

Given $m \in \mathbf{N}$, show that the number of terms in the expansion of $(x_1 + x_2 + \cdots + x_m)^n$ whose coefficients are not divisible by p is

$$\prod_{i=0}^{k} \binom{n_i + m - 1}{m - 1}.$$

(See F.T. Howard, The number of multinomial coefficients divisible by a fixed power of a prime, *Pacific J. Math.*, **50** (1974), 99-108.)

69. Show that

$$\sum_{r=0}^{n} \binom{n}{r}^2 \binom{2n + m - r}{2n} = \binom{m+n}{n}^2.$$

(Li Jen Shu)

70. Show that

$$\sum_{r=1}^{n} \frac{(-1)^{r-1}}{r} \binom{n}{r} = \sum_{k=1}^{n} \frac{1}{k},$$

where $n \in \mathbf{N}$.

71. Given $r \in \mathbf{N}$ with $r \geq 2$, show that

$$\sum_{n=r}^{\infty} \frac{1}{\binom{n}{r}} = \frac{r}{r - 1}.$$

(see H.W. Gould, *Combinatorial Identities*, Morgantown, W.V. (1972), 18-19)

72. Let $S = \{1, 2, \ldots, n\}$. For each $A \subseteq S$ with $A \neq \emptyset$, let $M(A) = \max\{x \mid x \in A\}$, $m(A) = \min\{x \mid x \in A\}$ and $\alpha(A) = M(A) + m(A)$. Evaluate the arithmetic mean of all the $\alpha(A)$'s when A runs through all nonempty subsets of S.

73. Given $a_n = \sum_{k=0}^{n} \binom{n}{k}^{-1}$, $n \in \mathbf{N}$,

show that

$$\lim_{n \to \infty} a_n = 2.$$

(Putnam, November 1958)

74. Let $(z)_0 = 1$ and for $n \in \mathbb{N}$, let

$$(z)_n = z(z-1)(z-2)\cdots(z-n+1).$$

Show that

$$(x+y)_n = \sum_{i=0}^{n} \binom{n}{i} (x)_i (y)_{n-i},$$

for all $n \in \mathbb{N}^*$. (Putnam, 1962)

75. In how many ways can the integers from 1 to n be ordered subject to the condition that, except for the first integer on the left, every integer differs by 1 from some integer to the left of it? (Putnam, 1965)

76. Show that, for any positive integer n,

$$\sum_{r=0}^{\lfloor \frac{n-1}{2} \rfloor} \left\{ \frac{n-2r}{n} \binom{n}{r} \right\}^2 = \frac{1}{n} \binom{2n-2}{n-1}.$$

(Putnam, 1965)

77. Show that for $n \in \mathbb{N}$ with $n \geq 2$,

$$\sum_{r=1}^{n} r \sqrt{\binom{n}{r}} < \sqrt{2^{n-1} n^3}.$$

(Spanish MO, 1988)

78. Let $n, r \in \mathbb{N}$ with $r \leq n$ and let k be the HCF of the following numbers:

$$\binom{n}{r}, \binom{n+1}{r}, \cdots, \binom{n+r}{r}.$$

Show that $k = 1$.

79. Show that there are no four consecutive binomial coefficients $\binom{n}{r}$, $\binom{n}{r+1}$, $\binom{n}{r+2}$, $\binom{n}{r+3}$ ($n, r \in \mathbb{N}$ with $r+3 \leq n$) which are in arithmetic progression. (Putnam, 1972)

80. Find the greatest common divisor (i.e., HCF) of

$$\binom{2n}{1}, \binom{2n}{3}, \cdots, \binom{2n}{2n-1}.$$

(Proposed by N.S. Mendelsohn, see *Amer. Math. Monthly*, **78** (1971), 201.)

81. Let $n \in \mathbb{N}$. Show that $\binom{n}{r}$ is odd for each $r \in \{0, 1, 2, \ldots, n\}$ iff $n = 2^k - 1$ for some $k \in \mathbb{N}$.

82. An unbiased coin is tossed n times. What is the expected value of $|H - T|$, where H is the number of heads and T is the number of tails? In other words, evaluate in *closed form*:

$$\frac{1}{2^{n-1}} \sum_{k < \frac{n}{2}} (n - 2k) \binom{n}{k}.$$

("closed form" means a form not involving a series.) (Putnam, 1974)

83. Prove that

$$\binom{pa}{pb} \equiv \binom{a}{b} \pmod{p}$$

for all integers p, a and b with p a prime, and $a \geq b \geq 0$. (Putnam, 1977)

84. The geometric mean (G.M.) of k positive numbers $a_1, a_2, \ldots, a_k$ is defined to be the (positive) kth root of their product. For example, the G.M. of 3, 4, 18 is 6. Show that the G.M. of a set S of n positive numbers is equal to the G.M. of the G.M.'s of all nonempty subsets of S. (Canadian MO, 1983)

85. For $n, k \in \mathbb{N}$, let $S_k(n) = 1^k + 2^k + \cdots + n^k$. Show that

(i)

$$\sum_{k=0}^{m-1} \binom{m}{k} S_k(n) = (n + 1)^m - 1,$$

(ii)

$$S_m(n) - \sum_{k=0}^{m} (-1)^{m-k} \binom{m}{k} S_k(n) = n^m,$$

where $m \in \mathbb{N}$.

86. Let $P(x)$ be a polynomial of degree n, $n \in \mathbb{N}$, such that $P(k) = 2^k$ for each $k = 1, 2, \ldots, n+1$. Determine $P(n+2)$. (Proposed by M. Klamkin, see *Pi Mu Epsilon*, 4 (1964), 77, Problem 158.)

87. Let $X = \{1, 2, \ldots, 10\}$, $\mathcal{A} = \{A \subset X \mid |A| = 4\}$, and $f : \mathcal{A} \to X$ be an arbitrary mapping. Show that there exists $S \subset X$, $|S| = 5$ such that

$$f(S - \{r\}) \neq r$$

for each $r \in S$.

88. (i)   Applying the arithmetic-geometric mean inequality on

$$\binom{n+1}{1}, \binom{n+1}{2}, \cdots, \binom{n+1}{n},$$

show that

$$(2^{n+1} - 2)^n \geq n^n \prod_{r=1}^{n} \binom{n+1}{r},$$

where $n \in \mathbb{N}$.

(ii)   Show that

$$(n!)^{n+1} = \left(\prod_{r=1}^{n} r^r\right) \left(\prod_{r=1}^{n} (r!)\right).$$

(iii)   Deduce from (i) and (ii) or otherwise, that

$$\left(\frac{n(n+1)!}{2^{n+1} - 2}\right)^{\frac{n}{2}} \leq \frac{(n!)^{n+1}}{\prod_{r=1}^{n} r^r}.$$

(iv)   Show that the equality in (iii) holds iff $n = 1$ or $n = 2$. (See *The College Math. J.* **20** (1989), 344.)

89. Find, with proof, the number of positive integers whose base-n representation consists of distinct digits with the property that, except for the leftmost digit, every digit differs by ± 1 from some digit further to the left. (Your answer should be an explicit function of n in simplest form.) (USA MO, 1990/4)

90. Let $S_n = \sum_{k=0}^{n} \binom{3n}{3k}$. Prove that

$$\lim_{n \to \infty} (S_n)^{\frac{1}{3n}} = 2.$$

(Bulgarian Spring Competition, 1985)

91. (i)   If $f(n)$ denotes the number of 0's in the decimal representation of the positive integer n, what is the value of the sum

$$S = 2^{f(1)} + 2^{f(2)} + \cdots + 2^{f(\overbrace{9999999999}^{10})} ?$$

(ii)   Let a be a nonzero real number, and $b, k, m \in \mathbf{N}$. Denote by $f(k)$ the number of zeros in the base $b+1$ representation of k. Compute

$$S_n = \sum_{k=1}^{n} a^{f(k)},$$

where $n = (b+1)^m - 1$.

Remark. Part (i) was a 1981 Hungarian Mathematical Competition problem. Part (ii) is a generalization of part (i), and was formulated by M.S. Klamkin (see *Crux Mathematicorum*, **9** (1983), 17-18).

92. Prove that the number of binary sequences of length n which contain exactly m occurrences of "01" is $\binom{n+1}{2m+1}$. (Great Britain MO, 1982/6)

93. There are n people in a gathering, some being acquaintances, some strangers. It is given that every 2 strangers have exactly 2 common friends, and every 2 acquaintances have no common friends. Show that everyone has the same number of friends in the gathering. (23rd Moscow MO)

94. Let $n \in \mathbf{N}^*$. For $p = 1, 2, \ldots$, define

$$A_p(n) = \sum_{0 \le k \le \frac{n}{2}} (-1)^k \left\{ \binom{n}{k} - \binom{n}{k-1} \right\}^p.$$

Prove that, whenever n is odd, $A_2(n) = nA_1(n)$. (Proposed by H.W. Gould, see *Amer. Math. Monthly*, **80** (1973), 1146.)

95. Let $n \in \mathbf{N}^*$. For $p = 1, 2, \ldots$, define

$$B_p(n) = \sum_{k=0}^{\lfloor \frac{n}{2} \rfloor} \left\{ \binom{n}{k} - \binom{n}{k-1} \right\}^p.$$

Evaluate $B_2(n)$. (Proposed by E.T. Ordman, see *Amer. Math. Monthly*, **80** (1973), 1066.)

96. Show that
   (i) $\binom{2n-1}{r}^{-1} = \frac{2n}{2n+1} \left\{ \binom{2n}{r}^{-1} + \binom{2n}{r+1}^{-1} \right\}$, where $r, n \in \mathbf{N}$;
   (ii) $\sum_{r=1}^{2n-1} (-1)^{r-1} \binom{2n-1}{r}^{-1} \sum_{j=1}^{r} \frac{1}{j} = \frac{2n}{2n+1} \sum_{r=1}^{2n} \frac{1}{r}$.
   (Proposed by I. Kaucký, see *Amer. Math. Monthly*, **78** (1971), 908.)

97. Given $\ell, m, n \in \mathbb{N}^*$ with $\ell, n \leq m$, evaluate the double sum

$$\sum_{i=0}^{\ell}\sum_{j=0}^{i}(-1)^{j}\binom{m-i}{m-\ell}\binom{n}{j}\binom{m-n}{i-j}.$$

(Proposed by D.B. West, see *Amer. Math. Monthly*, **97** (1990), 428-429.)

98. Show that

$$\sum_{r=0}^{n}\binom{n}{r}\binom{p}{r+s}\binom{q+r}{m+n}=\sum_{r=0}^{n}\binom{n}{r}\binom{q}{m+r}\binom{p+r}{n+s},$$

where $m, n, p, q, s \in \mathbb{N}^*$. (See R.C. Lyness, The mystery of the double sevens, *Crux Mathematicorum*, **9** (1983), 194-198.)

References.

[BM] D.E. Barton and C.L. Mallows, Some aspects of the random sequence, *Annals of Math. Stat.* **36** (1965), 236-260.

[E] A.W.F. Edwards, *Pascal's Arithmetical Triangle*, Oxford University Press, 1987.

[F] N.J. Fine, Binomial coefficients modulo a prime, *Amer. Math. Monthly*, **54** (1947), 589.

[H1] R. Honsberger, *Mathematical Gems II*, The Mathematical Association of America, 1976.

[H2] R. Honsberger, Mathematical Gems, *Two-Year College Mathematics Journal*, **11** (1980), 116-119.

[MM] *Mathematics Magazine*, **51** (1978), 246.

[MS] H.B. Mann and D. Shanks, A necessary and sufficient condition for primality, and its source, *J. Combinatorial Theory (A)*, **13** (1972), 131-134.

[N] E.A. Netto, *Lehrbuch der Kombinatorik*, Leipzig, 1901.

[W] Q. Wu, Maximal coefficient of the multinomial $(x_2 + x_2 + \cdots + x_k)^n$, *Southeast Asian Bulletin of Maths.* **15** (1991), 77-82.

Chapter 3

The Pigeonhole Principle and Ramsey Numbers

3.1. Introduction

You may have come across the following statements which are of the same mathematical nature:

"*Among any group of two or more people, there are two who have the same number of friends in the group.*"

"*Among any 5 points in an equilateral triangle of unit length, there are two whose distance is at most half a unit apart.*"

"*Given any set A of 5 numbers, there are 3 distinct elements in A whose sum is divisible by 3.*"

"*Given a sequence of 10 distinct numbers, there exists either a decreasing subsequence of 4 terms or an increasing subsequence of 4 terms.*"

This type of problems concerns with the existence of a certain kind of quantity, pattern or arrangement. In this chapter, we shall introduce a fundamental principle in combinatorics, known as the Pigeonhole Principle, which deals with a class of problems of this type. We shall also see how the principle can be applied to study some problems that give rise to a class of numbers, called Ramsey numbers.

3.2. The Pigeonhole Principle

If three pigeons are to be put into two compartments, then you will certainly agree that one of the compartments will accommodate at least two pigeons. A much more general statement of this simple observation, known as the *Pigeonhole Principle*, is given below.

> **The Pigeonhole Principle (PP).** Let k and n be any two posi-
> tive integers. If at least $kn+1$ objects are distributed among n boxes,
> then one of the boxes must contain at least $k+1$ objects. In particular,
> if at least $n+1$ objects are to be put into n boxes, then one of the
> boxes must contain at least two objects.

The proof of (PP) is easy. If no boxes contain $k+1$ or more objects, then
every box contains at most k objects. This implies that the total number
of objects put into the n boxes is at most kn, a contradiction. ∎

(PP) is also known as the *Dirichlet Drawer Principle*, after the German mathematician Peter G.L. Dirichlet (1805-1859) who had used it to
prove some results in number theory. (PP) looks almost trivial; however,
as we shall witness in this and the following two sections, it is a surprisingly useful and powerful device that proves many "existence" statements
in mathematics.

Example 3.2.1. Among any group of 7 people, there must be at least
4 of the same sex.

Let us see how (PP) can be applied to this example. We treat the
7 people as 7 objects, and create two "boxes": box (1) for "female" and
box (2) for "male".

$$(1) \quad \lfloor\;\;\;\rfloor \qquad (2) \quad \lfloor\;\;\;\rfloor$$

        female   male

If a person of the group is a lady (resp., gentleman), then she (resp., he) is
put into box (1) (resp., box (2)). Thus the $7(= 3 \cdot 2 + 1 = kn + 1)$ "objects"
are put into $2(= n)$ "boxes" and so by (PP), there is a box which contains
at least $4(= 3 + 1 = k + 1)$ objects; i.e., there are at least 4 people among
the group who are of the same sex. ∎

By applying (PP) in a similar way, you should be able to prove the
following.

Example 3.2.2. Among any group of 13 people, there must be at
least 2 whose birthdays are in the same month.

Example 3.2.3. Among any group of 3000 people, there are at least 9 who have the same birthday.

As we have just seen, in applying (PP), we have to identify what the "objects" and what the "boxes" are. Moreover, we must know the values of k and n (number of boxes) involved in (PP), and to make sure that the number of objects is at least $kn + 1$.

Example 3.2.4. Show that for any set of 10 points chosen within a square whose sides are of length 3 units, there are two points in the set whose distance apart is at most $\sqrt{2}$.

What are the objects? What are the boxes? These are the two questions we have to ask beforehand. It is fairly clear that we should treat the 10 given points in the set as our "objects". The conclusion we wish to arrive at is the existence of "2 points" from the set which are "close" to each other (i.e. their distance apart is at most $\sqrt{2}$ units). This indicates that "$k + 1 = 2$" (i.e., $k = 1$), and suggests also that we should partition the 3×3 square into n smaller regions, $n < 10$, so that the distance between any 2 points in a region is at most $\sqrt{2}$.

Solution. Divide the 3×3 square into 9 unit squares as shown below:

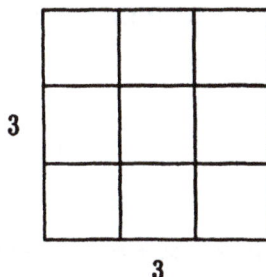

Let A be any set of 10 points (our objects) chosen from the 3×3 square. Since each point in A is contained in (at least) one of the 9 unit squares (our boxes), and since $10 > 9$, by (PP), there is a unit square (box) which contains at least 2 points (objects) of A. Let these 2 points be u and v. It is easy to verify that the distance between u and v does not exceed the length of a diagonal of the unit square, which is $\sqrt{1^2 + 1^2} = \sqrt{2}$. ∎

Remarks. **(1)** If the hypothesis of (PP) is satisfied, then the conclusion of (PP) guarantees that there is a (certain) box which contains at least $k+1$ objects. It should be noted, however, that (PP) does not tell us "which box it is" and "which $k+1$ objects it contains".

(2) In Example 3.2.4, one might divide the 3×3 square into the 9 rectangles as shown below, and apply (PP) to reach the conclusion that there are 2 points in A contained in one of the 9 rectangles.

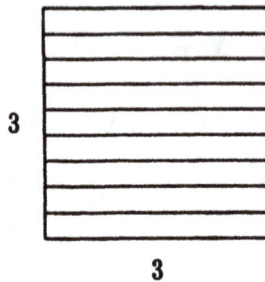

In this case, however, one would not be able to draw the conclusion that the distance between these 2 points is at most $\sqrt{2}$. So, does it mean that (PP) is invalid? Certainly not! It simply reveals the fact that the "boxes" we create here are not appropriate!

3.3. More Examples

In the preceding section, we gave some simple examples where (PP) can be applied. They are "simple" since the identification of the "objects" and "boxes" in these problems is rather straightforward. This is not always the case in general. In this section, we shall present more difficult and sophisticated problems from different areas where (PP) can be applied (but in a nontrivial way). Through the discussion of these problems, it is hoped that readers will appreciate, as a mathematical tool in problem solving, how powerful and useful (PP) is.

Example 3.3.1. Let $A = \{a_1, a_2, ..., a_5\}$ be a set of 5 positive integers. Show that for any permutation $a_{i_1} a_{i_2} a_{i_3} a_{i_4} a_{i_5}$ of A, the product

$$(a_{i_1} - a_1)(a_{i_2} - a_2) \cdots (a_{i_5} - a_5)$$

is always even.

For instance, if

$$a_1 = 2, \quad a_2 = 5, \quad a_3 = 7, \quad a_4 = 3, \quad a_5 = 8,$$
$$a_{i_1} = a_4, \quad a_{i_2} = a_3, \quad a_{i_3} = a_5, \quad a_{i_4} = a_1, \quad a_{i_5} = a_2,$$

then the product

$$(a_4 - a_1)(a_3 - a_2)(a_5 - a_3)(a_1 - a_4)(a_2 - a_5)$$
$$= (3 - 2)(7 - 5)(8 - 7)(2 - 3)(5 - 8) = 6,$$

which is even.

Unlike those examples given in Section 3.2, it is not apparent how (PP) can be applied here. Let us first analyze the problem. To show that the product is even, it suffices to show the "existence" of an even factor, say $(a_{i_k} - a_k)$. We note that the number $a_{i_k} - a_k$ is even if and only if a_{i_k} and a_k are both even or both odd (in this case, we say that a_{i_k} and a_k have the same parity). Thus we see that it may have something to do with the parity of the 5 numbers in A. In view of this, we create 2 "boxes", one for "even numbers" and one for "odd numbers".

Solution. We have $|A| = 5$. By (PP), there exist at least 3 elements of A (say, a_1, a_2, a_3) which are of the same parity (in this case $k = n = 2$).

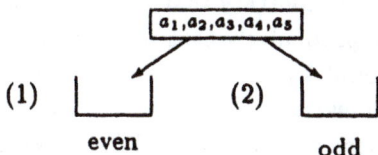

$$(1) \quad \text{even} \qquad (2) \quad \text{odd}$$

Observe that $\{a_{i_1}, a_{i_2}, a_{i_3}\} \cap \{a_1, a_2, a_3\} \neq \emptyset$ (otherwise, $|A|$ will be at least $6 = |\{a_{i_1}, a_{i_2}, a_{i_3}, a_1, a_2, a_3\}|$). Thus we may assume, say $a_1 = a_{i_3}$. This implies that $a_{i_3} - a_3 = a_1 - a_3$, the latter being even as a_1 and a_3 are of the same parity. Thus the factor $(a_{i_3} - a_3)$ is even, which completes the proof. ∎

Remarks. (1) The above proof can be extended in a natural way to prove the same result for any odd number of positive integers $a_1, a_2, ..., a_{2p+1}$ (see Problem 3.6).

(2) The conclusion of Example 3.3.1 is no longer true if $|A|$ is even.

Example 3.3.2. Ten players took part in a round robin chess tournament (i.e., each player must play exactly one game against every other player). According to the rules, a player scores 1 point if he wins a game; -1 point if he loses; and 0 point if the game ends in a draw. When the tournament was over, it was found that more than 70% of the games ended in a draw. Show that there were two players who had the same total score.

Judging from the last statement of the problem, it seems that we should treat the 10 players as our "10 objects", and create "boxes" for "total scores". However, what are the possible total scores? How many different total scores are there? (Don't forget, we have to ensure that the number of objects is bigger than the number of boxes.) These questions seem not easy to answer. Let us try an "indirect" way.

Solution. Since every 2 players played one and only one game against each other, there were $\binom{10}{2} = 45$ games held during the tournament. Among these games, there were at least

$$\lceil 45 \times 70\% \rceil = \lceil 31.5 \rceil = 32$$

games that ended in a draw, where $\lceil x \rceil$ denotes the least integer not less than the real x. Hence

(∗) there were at most $45 - 32 = 13$ games which did not end in a draw.

Now, suppose to the contrary that the 10 players had 10 different total scores. This implies particularly that at most one of the players had total score "0". Thus at least 9 players had either "positive" or "negative" total scores. Treat these players as our "objects", and create 2 "boxes", one for "positive" and one for "negative". By (PP), at least 5 players had positive total scores or at least 5 players had negative total scores.

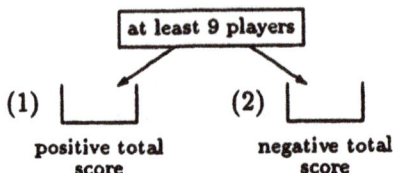

By symmetry, we may assume the former. Since the total scores are assumed to be different, the sum of these positive total scores must be at least

$$1 + 2 + 3 + 4 + 5 = 15.$$

But this implies that there must be at least 15 games which did not end in a draw, contradicting the statement (*). Hence there were 2 players who had the same total score. ∎

Example 3.3.3. Let A be a set of m positive integers where $m \geq 1$. Show that there exists a nonempty subset B of A such that the sum $\sum(x \mid x \in B)$ is divisible by m.

For example, if $A = \{3, 9, 14, 18, 23\}$, then $m = |A| = 5$, and we take $B = \{3, 14, 18\}$ (there are other choices for B). Observe that

$$\sum(x \mid x \in B) = 3 + 14 + 18 = 35,$$

which is divisible by 5.

Since the conclusion of the problem involves the divisibility of m, one possible way to tackle the problem is to make use of the congruence relation modulo m. (Recall that $a \equiv b \pmod{m}$ iff $m|(a - b)$.) A basic property of "$\equiv$" says that if $a \equiv r \pmod{m}$ and $b \equiv r \pmod{m}$, then $a \equiv b \pmod{m}$, i.e., $m|(a - b)$. This observation suggests the following solution.

Solution. Let $A = \{a_1, a_2, ..., a_m\}$. Consider the following m subsets of A and their respective sums:

$$A_1 = \{a_1\}, \quad A_2 = \{a_1, a_2\}, \quad \cdots, \quad A_m = \{a_1, a_2, ..., a_m\};$$
$$a_1, \qquad a_1 + a_2, \qquad \cdots, \qquad a_1 + a_2 + \cdots + a_m.$$

If one of the sums (say $a_1 + a_2 + a_3$) is divisible by m, then we take B to be the respective set (in this case, $B = A_3$), and we are through. Thus we may assume that no sums above are divisible by m, and we have

$$a_1 \equiv r_1 \pmod{m},$$

$$a_1 + a_2 \equiv r_2 \pmod{m},$$

$$\vdots$$

$$a_1 + a_2 + \cdots + a_m \equiv r_m \pmod{m},$$

where $r_i \in \{1, 2, ..., m-1\}$ for each $i = 1, 2, ..., m$.

Now, treat the m sums as our m "objects" and create $m-1$ "boxes" for the $m-1$ residue classes modulo m:

$$(1) \quad\boxed{} \qquad (2) \quad\boxed{} \qquad \cdots \qquad (m-1)\boxed{}$$

$$x \equiv 1 (\bmod\ m) \qquad x \equiv 2 (\bmod\ m) \qquad\qquad x \equiv m-1 (\bmod\ m)$$

By (PP), there are 2 sums, say

$$a_1 + a_2 + \cdots + a_i \quad \text{and} \quad a_1 + a_2 + \cdots + a_i + \cdots + a_j,$$

where $i < j$, that are in the same residue class modulo m; i.e.,

$$a_1 + a_2 + \cdots + a_i \equiv r \ (\bmod\ m)$$

$$\text{and} \quad a_1 + a_2 + \cdots + a_i + \cdots + a_j \equiv r \ (\bmod\ m)$$

for some $r \in \{1, 2, ..., m-1\}$. This implies that

$$a_1 + a_2 + \cdots + a_i + \cdots + a_j \equiv a_1 + a_2 + \cdots + a_i \ (\bmod\ m),$$

i.e. $m | ((a_1 + \cdots + a_i + \cdots + a_j) - (a_1 + a_2 + \cdots + a_i))$

or $m | (a_{i+1} + a_{i+2} + \cdots + a_j)$.

Thus, $B = \{a_{i+1}, a_{i+2}, ..., a_j\}$ $(= A_j \backslash A_i)$ is a required subset of A. ∎

The following example is an IMO problem (IMO, 1972/1) with the original statement rephrased.

Example 3.3.4. Let $X \subseteq \{1, 2, ..., 99\}$ and $|X| = 10$. Show that it is possible to select two disjoint nonempty proper subsets Y, Z of X such that $\sum(y \mid y \in Y) = \sum(z \mid z \in Z)$.

For instance, if $X = \{2, 7, 15, 19, 23, 50, 56, 60, 66, 99\}$, take $Y = \{19, 50\}$ and $Z = \{2, 7, 60\}$, and check that

$$\sum(y \mid y \in Y) = 19 + 50 = 2 + 7 + 60 = \sum(z \mid z \in Z).$$

The required conclusion suggests that we may treat the nonempty proper subsets of X as our "objects", and create the "boxes" for their possible sums. If the number of "objects" is larger than the number of "boxes", then there are two nonempty proper subsets of X which have the same sum. This conclusion is very close to what we want. Now, how are we going to estimate the number of "objects" and the number of "boxes"? These are two crucial questions that we have to answer.

Solution. Since $|X| = 10$, by Example 1.5.2, the number of nonempty proper subsets of X (excluding $\emptyset$, X) is

$$2^{10} - 2 = 1022.$$

On the other hand, for each nonempty proper subset A of X,

$$1 \leq \sum (a \mid a \in A) \leq 91 + 92 + \cdots + 99 = 855;$$

that is, the sum of numbers in each A lies inclusively between 1 and 855.

Now, treat the 1022 nonempty proper subsets of X as our "1022 objects", and create "855 boxes" for the sums "$1, 2, ..., 855$". Since $1022 > 855$, by (PP), there are two distinct nonempty proper subsets B, C of X which have the same sum; i.e.,

$$\sum (b \mid b \in B) = \sum (c \mid c \in C).$$

(Note that B and C need not be disjoint and thus they may not be the desired subsets of X.) Clearly, $B \not\subseteq C$ and $C \not\subseteq B$. Let $Y = B \backslash (B \cap C)$ and $Z = C \backslash (B \cap C)$. Then we have $\sum (y \mid y \in Y) = \sum (z \mid z \in Z)$ (why?) and so Y and Z are two desired subsets of X. ∎

Example 3.3.5. **(IMO, 1983/4)** Let ABC be an equilateral triangle and $\mathcal{E}$ the set of all points contained in the 3 segments AB, BC, CA (including A, B and C). Show that, for every partition of $\mathcal{E}$ into 2 disjoint subsets, at least one of the 2 subsets contains the vertices of a right-angled triangle.

For instance, if the set $\mathcal{E}$ is partitioned into 2 subsets $\mathcal{E}_1$ and $\mathcal{E}_2$ as shown in Figure 3.3.1(a), then it is not difficult to find 3 points all in $\mathcal{E}_1$ or $\mathcal{E}_2$ (in this case both) which form a right-angled triangle (see Figure 3.3.1(b)).

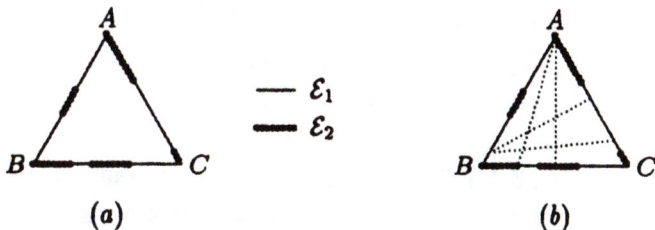

(a)   (b)

Figure 3.3.1.

Solution. We prove it by contradiction. Suppose to the contrary that there is a partition of $\mathcal{E}$ into 2 disjoint subsets $\mathcal{E}_1$ and $\mathcal{E}_2$ such that

(*) no three points in $\mathcal{E}_1$ (resp., $\mathcal{E}_2$) form a right-angled triangle.

Let X, Y and Z be the points on AB, BC and CA respectively such that
$$\frac{AX}{XB} = \frac{BY}{YC} = \frac{CZ}{ZA} = 2.$$
Consider $\triangle AZX$. We claim that $\angle AZX = 90°$ (see Figure 3.3.2.).

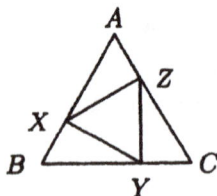

Figure 3.3.2

By cosine law,

$$
\begin{aligned}
(XZ)^2 &= (AZ)^2 + (AX)^2 - 2(AX)(AZ)\cos\angle XAZ \\
&= (\tfrac{1}{3}AC)^2 + (\tfrac{2}{3}AB)^2 - 2(\tfrac{1}{3}AC)(\tfrac{2}{3}AB)\cos 60° \\
&= \frac{1}{3}(AB)^2.
\end{aligned}
$$

Thus $(XZ)^2 + (AZ)^2 = \frac{1}{3}(AB)^2 + \frac{1}{9}(AC)^2 = (\frac{2}{3}AB)^2 = (AX)^2$, and by Pythagolas's theorem, $\angle AZX = 90°$, as claimed.

Similarly, we have $\angle BXY = \angle CYZ = 90°$.

Treat the points X, Y and Z as "3 objects", and create "2 boxes": one for $\mathcal{E}_1$ and one for $\mathcal{E}_2$. By (PP), at least 2 of the points are all in $\mathcal{E}_1$ or all in $\mathcal{E}_2$. By symmetry, say $X, Y \in \mathcal{E}_1$.

Since $YX \perp AB$ and since we assume the condition (*), no points in $AB\backslash\{X\}$ can be in $\mathcal{E}_1$; i.e., all points in $AB\backslash\{X\}$ must be in $\mathcal{E}_2$. The latter, in turn, implies that $C \notin \mathcal{E}_2$ and $Z \notin \mathcal{E}_2$ (why?); i.e., $C, Z \in \mathcal{E}_1$. But then we have $\{C, Z, Y\} \subseteq \mathcal{E}_1$, and they form a right-angled triangle. This, however, contradicts (*). The proof is thus complete. ∎

For more examples and a special application of (PP) to map-colouring problems, the reader may like to read the excellent expository article [Re] by Rebman.

3.4. Ramsey Type Problems and Ramsey Numbers

In this section, we shall continue to apply (PP) to solve a class of problems that are of a different flavour from the previous ones. The study of these problems leads to the introduction of a famous class of numbers, called Ramsey numbers.

To begin with, we first state an IMO problem, that was proposed by Hungarian representatives in the 6th IMO, held in Russia in 1964.

Example 3.4.1 (IMO, 1964/4) Seventeen people correspond by mail with one another – each one with all the rest. In their letters only three different topics are discussed. Each pair of correspondents deals with only one of these topics. Prove that there are at least three people who write to one another about the same topic.

We shall solve this problem later on. To make it easier to follow the solution, let us first mention two simpler but related problems.

Example 3.4.2. Prove that at a gathering of any six people. Some three of them are either mutual acquaintances or complete strangers to one another.

The above problem was proposed by Bostwick of Maryland, USA, in 1958 as Problem E 1321 in the American Mathematical Monthly, **65** (1958), 446. As shown in the American Mathematical Monthly, **66** (1959), 141-142, Example 3.4.2 received much attention, and various solutions were provided. It was further pointed out by someone there that Example 3.4.2 could indeed be reduced to the following problem.

Example 3.4.3. Six points are in general position in space (no three in a line, no four in a plane). The fifteen line segments joining them in pairs are drawn, and then painted with some segments red and the rest blue. Prove that some triangle has all its sides the same colour.

Example 3.4.3 first appeared as a competition problem in Hungary in 1947, and was also a problem in the William Lowell Putnam Mathematical Competition (for undergraduates in North America) that was held in 1953.

Let us first prove Example 3.4.3 by apply (PP).

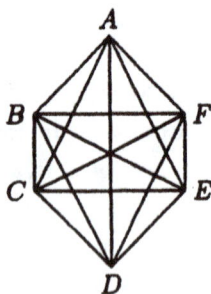

Figure 3.4.1.

Proof of Example 3.4.3. Figure 3.4.1 shows a configuration with 6 vertices (or points) in which every two are joined by an edge (or a line segment). Each of these $\binom{6}{2} = 15$ edges is coloured by one of the two colours: blue and red.

Consider the vertex A. The 5 edges incident with A (namely, AB, AC, AD, AE and AF) are each coloured by either blue or red. By (PP), one of the colours, say blue, is used to colour at least 3 of these 5 edges. By symmetry, assume that AB, AC and AD are coloured blue. Consider now the 3 edges BC, BD and CD. If any one of them (say BC) is coloured blue, then we have a "blue triangle" (namely, ABC). If none of them is coloured blue, then the 3 edges must be coloured red, and in this case, we have a "red triangle" BCD. ∎

We now proceed to prove Example 3.4.2.

Proof of Example 3.4.2. Represent the 6 people by 6 vertices $A, B, ..., F$ as shown in the configuration of Figure 3.4.1. Given any 2 people X and Y, the edge joining X and Y is coloured blue (resp., red) if X and Y are acquaintances (resp., strangers). By Example 3.4.3, there exists in the resulting configuration either a "blue triangle" or a "red triangle". In other words, there are 3 mutual acquaintances or 3 mutual strangers. ∎

We are now in a position to solve the IMO problem mentioned earlier.

Proof of Example 3.4.1. We represent the 17 people by 17 vertices $A, B, C, ...,$ in which every two are joined by an edge. An edge joining two vertices X and Y is coloured blue (resp., red and yellow) if X and Y discuss topic I (resp., II and II). Consider the vertex A. By assumption, the 16 edges incident with A are each coloured by exactly one of the 3 colours: blue, red and yellow. Since $16 = 5 \cdot 3 + 1$, by (PP), one of the colours, say blue, is used to colour at least $5 + 1 (= 6)$ edges. By symmetry, assume that AB, AC, AD, AE, AF and AG are coloured blue. Consider now the configuration consisting of 6 vertices $B, C, \ldots, G$, together with the 15 edges joining all pairs of the 6 vertices. If any one these edges, say BC, is coloured blue, then we have a "blue triangle", namely ABC. If none of them is coloured blue, then the 15 edges must be coloured red or yellow. But then by Example 3.4.3, there is in this configuration a "red triangle" or a "yellow triangle". In any event, there is a triangle having all its edges the same colour. This means that there are at least 3 people who discuss the same topic with one another. ∎

Though the IMO problem has been solved, we cannot help but carry on the story.

Let us revisit Example 3.4.3. Suppose now we have only 5 vertices (instead of 6) in the problem. Is the conclusion still valid? To see this, consider the configuration of Figure 3.4.2 which consists of 5 vertices and 10 edges. If the edges AB, BC, CD, DE and EA are coloured blue while the rest red as shown, then the resulting configuration contains neither blue triangles nor red triangles. This shows that 6 is the minimum number of vertices that are needed in a configuration in order to ensure the existence of a triangle coloured by the same colour if each edge of the configuration is coloured by one of the two given colours.

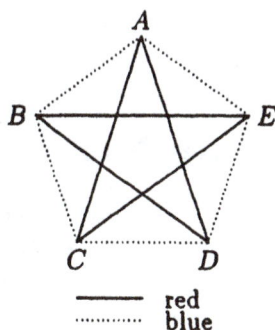

Figure 3.4.2.

The above discussion serves as a motivation for us to introduce a class of numbers, known as Ramsey numbers.

A *clique* is a configuration consisting of a finite set of vertices together with edges joining all pairs of vertices. A *k-clique* is a clique which has exactly k vertices. Thus a 1-clique is a vertex, a 2-clique is an edge joining 2 vertices and a 3-clique looks like a triangle. The configuration of Figure 3.4.2 is a 5-clique and that of Figure 3.4.1 is a 6-clique. Given $p, q \in \mathbb{N}$, let $R(p, q)$ denote the smallest natural number "n" such that for any colouring of the edges of an n-clique by 2 colours: blue or red (one colour for each edge), there exists either a "blue p-clique" or a "red q-clique".

Thus, as shown above, we have $R(3, 3) = 6$. The following equalities follow directly from the definition:

$$\begin{cases} R(p, q) = R(q, p) \\ R(1, q) = 1 \\ R(2, q) = q. \end{cases} \qquad (3.4.1)$$

The numbers $R(p, q)$ are called *Ramsey numbers*, in honour of the English philosopher Frank P. Ramsey (1903-1930), who proved around 1928 a remarkable existence theorem [Ra] that includes the following as a special case.

Theorem 3.4.1. (Ramsey's Theorem) *For all integers $p, q \geq 2$, the number $R(p, q)$ always exists.*

Ramsey died of complications following an abdominal operation in 1930 before his 27th birthday. In 1983, a special issue of the Journal of Graph Theory (Vol.7 No.1) was dedicated to the memory of Ramsey on the occasion of the 80th anniversary of his birth.

3.5. Bounds for Ramsey Numbers

The determination of the exact values of $R(p, q)$, where p and q are large, is far beyond our research. In this section, we present some bounds for $R(p, q)$ that may be useful in estimating these numbers. The following recursive upper bound for $R(p, q)$ was obtained by two Hungarian mathematicians Erdös and Szekeres [ES] (see also Greenwood and Gleason [GG]).

Theorem 3.5.1. *For all integers* $p, q \geq 2$,

$$R(p, q) \leq R(p - 1, q) + R(p, q - 1).$$

Before proving this theorem, we state the following *Generalized Pigeon-hole Principle*:

The Generalized Pigeonhole Principle (GPP).

Let $n, k_1, k_2, ..., k_n \in \mathbf{N}$. If $k_1 + k_2 + \cdots k_n - (n - 1)$ or more objects are put into n boxes, then either the first box contains at least k_1 objects, or the second box contains at least k_2 objects, ..., or the n th box contains at least k_n objects.

Proof of Theorem 3.5.1. Let $n = R(p - 1, q) + R(p, q - 1)$. Since $R(p, q)$ always exists by Theorem 3.4.1, to show that $R(p, q) \leq n$, we need only to prove that for any colouring of the edges of an n-clique K_n by 2 colours: blue and red, there exists either a "blue p-clique" or a "red q-clique".

Fix a vertex, say v in K_n. Then v is incident with $n - 1 = R(p - 1, q) + R(p, q - 1) - 1$ edges in K_n. By (GPP), either $R(p - 1, q)$ of the edges are coloured blue or $R(p, q - 1)$ of the edges are coloured red, say the former.

Let X be the set of vertices of K_n, other than v, which are incident with these $R(p - 1, q)$ blue edges. Since $|X| = R(p - 1, q)$, by definition, the clique induced by X contains either a blue $(p - 1)$-clique or a red q-clique. If it contains a red q-clique, then we are through. If it contains a blue $(p - 1)$-clique, then the clique induced by $X \cup \{v\}$ contains a blue p-clique. ∎

The inequality in Theorem 3.5.1 can be slightly improved under an additional condition.

Theorem 3.5.2. **[GG]** *For all integers* $p, q \geq 2$, *if* $R(p - 1, q)$ *and* $R(p, q - 1)$ *are even, then*

$$R(p, q) \leq R(p - 1, q) + R(p, q - 1) - 1.$$

Proof. Let $m = R(p-1,q) + R(p,q-1) - 1$ and let K_m be an m-clique in which the $\binom{m}{2}$ edges are coloured blue or red. Fix an arbitrary vertex w in K_m. Then w is incident with $m - 1$ edges. If $R(p-1,q)$ or more of the edges are blue, then as shown in the above proof, there is either a blue p-clique or a red q-clique in K_m. Likewise, if $R(p,q-1)$ or more of the edges are red, then we are again through. It remains to consider the following case: there are exactly $R(p-1,q) - 1$ blue edges and $R(p,q-1) - 1$ red edges incident with *each* vertex v in K_m. We claim that this is impossible. Indeed, if this were the case, then the number of blue edges in K_m would be

$$\frac{m}{2} \cdot \{R(p-1,q) - 1\}.$$

Since $R(p-1,q)$ and $R(p,q-1)$ are even, both m and $R(p-1,q) - 1$ are odd, and so the above number is not an integer, a contradiction. The proof is thus complete. ∎

By applying Theorem 3.5.1, it is not hard to prove, by induction on $p + q$, the following result:

$$\text{If } p,q \geq 2, \text{ then } R(p,q) \leq \binom{p+q-2}{p-1}. \tag{3.5.1}$$

When $p = 3$, inequality (3.5.1) becomes

$$\dot{R}(3,q) \leq \frac{1}{2}(q^2 + q).$$

However, by applying Theorems 3.5.1 and 3.5.2, the following sharper bound can be derived (see Problem 3.33):

$$\text{For } q \in \mathbf{N}, \; R(3,q) \leq \tfrac{1}{2}(q^2 + 3). \tag{3.5.2}$$

When $p = q \geq 3$, we also have:

$$\frac{p \cdot 2^{\frac{5}{2}}}{\sqrt{2}e} < R(p,p) \leq 4R(p-2,p) + 2. \tag{3.5.3}$$

The above upper bound for $R(p,p)$ was given by Walker [W] while the lower bound was proved by Erdös [E] using a probabilistic method.

As an example, let us show how Theorem 3.5.2 can be applied to obtain the exact value of $R(3,4)$.

We know that $R(2,4) = 4$ by (3.4.1) and $R(3,3) = 6$. Since both numbers are even, we have by Theorem 3.5.2

$$R(3,4) \leq R(2,4) + R(3,3) - 1 = 9.$$

We claim that $R(3,4) \geq 9$. To see this, consider the 8-clique of Figure 3.5.1. By colouring the edges $AB, BC, CD, DE, EF, FG, GH, HA, AE, BF, CG$ and DH blue and the rest red, it can be checked that the resulting configuration contains neither a "blue 3-clique" nor a "red 4-clique". This shows that $R(3,4) \geq 9$. Hence we have $R(3,4) = 9$.

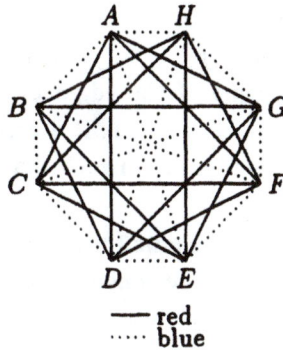

Figure 3.5.1.

Note. The following points should be borne in mind. To show that $R(p,q) \leq n$, we may apply known inequalities or show by definition that every n-clique in which the edges are coloured blue or red contains either a blue p-clique or a red q-clique. On the other hand, to show that $R(p,q) > n$, we may construct an n-clique K_n and colour the $\binom{n}{2}$ edges blue or red in a specific way so that K_n contains neither blue p-clique nor red q-clique.

Some known exact values or bounds for $R(p,q)$ when p and q are small are contained in Table 3.5.1 (see [CG], [GRS] and [MZ]). Grinstead and Roberts [GR] showed that $28 \leq R(3,8) \leq 29$. In the recent article [MZ], McKay and Zhang proved that $R(3,8) = 28$. It was also reported in [CL] that $R(4,8) \geq 52$.

p \ q	3	4	5	6	7	8	9	10
3	6	9	14	18	23	28	36	40-43
4		18	25-28	34-44				
5			42-55	57-94				
6				102-169				
7					126-586			

Table 3.5.1

A Generalization. The definition of the Ramsey number $R(p,q)$ with 2 parameters can be generalized in a natural way to the Ramsey number $R(p_1, p_2, ..., p_k)$ with k parameters as follows. Let $k, p_1, p_2, ..., p_k \in \mathbb{N}$ with $k \geq 3$. The *Ramsey number* $R(p_1, p_2, ..., p_k)$ is the smallest natural number n such that for any colouring of the edges of an n-clique by k colours: colour 1, colour 2, ..., colour k, there exist a colour i $(i = 1, 2, ..., k)$ and a p_i-clique in the resulting configuration such that all edges in the p_i-clique are coloured by colour i.

The result of Example 3.4.1 shows that $R(3,3,3) \leq 17$. In 1955, Greenwood and Gleason [GG] proved by construction that $R(3,3,3) \geq 17$. Thus $R(3,3,3) = 17$. Surprisingly enough, this is the only exact value known up to date for $R(p_1, p_2, ..., p_k)$ when $k \geq 3$ and $p_i \geq 3$ for each $i = 1, 2, ..., k$.

Final remarks. We have by now introduced some very basic knowledge of Ramsey numbers and shown how they are linked to (PP) and (GPP). The theory of Ramsey numbers forms in fact a tiny part of the more profound and more general Ramsey theory of structures. One may obtain a rough scope of this general theory from the book [GRS] by Graham, Rothschild and Spencer. Just like other theories in combinatorics, the theory of Ramsey numbers can also find applications in other areas. An introduction of applications of Ramsey numbers to areas such as number theory, geometry, computer science, communication, decision making, etc. can be found in Chapter 8 of Roberts' book [12]. Readers are also encouraged to read the two expository articles [G] and [GS] on Ramsey Theory.

As a result of numerous contributions from Ramsey theoreticians, Ramsey theory has now been recognized as a cohesive, established and growing branch of combinatorics and graph theory, that in no way could have been anticipated by Frank Ramsey when he read to the London Mathematical Society his celebrated article [Ra] in 1928 at the age of 24, two years before he left the world.

Exercise 3

1. Show that among any 5 points in an equilateral triangle of unit side length, there are 2 whose distance is at most $\frac{1}{2}$ units apart.

2. Given any set C of $n + 1$ distinct points ($n \in \mathbf{N}$) on the circumference of a unit circle, show that there exist $a, b \in C, a \neq b$, such that the distance between them does not exceed $2 \sin \frac{\pi}{n}$.

3. Given any set S of 9 points within a unit square, show that there always exist 3 distinct points in S such that the area of the triangle formed by these 3 points is less than or equal to $\frac{1}{8}$. (Beijing Math. Competition, 1963)

4. Show that given any set of 5 numbers, there are 3 numbers in the set whose sum is divisible by 3.

5. Let A be a set of $n + 1$ elements, where $n \in \mathbf{N}$. Show that there exist $a, b \in A$ with $a \neq b$ such that $n | (a - b)$.

6. Let $A = \{a_1, a_2, \cdots, a_{2k+1}\}$, where $k \geq 1$, be a set of $2k + 1$ positive integers. Show that for any permutation $a_{i_1} a_{i_2} \ldots a_{i_{2k+1}}$ of A, the product

$$\prod_{j=1}^{2k+1} (a_{i_j} - a_j)$$

is always even.

7. Let $A \subseteq \{1, 2, \ldots, 2n\}$ such that $|A| = n + 1$, where $n \in \mathbf{N}$. Show that there exist $a, b \in A$, with $a \neq b$ such that $a | b$.

8. Let A be a subset of $\{1, 2, \ldots, 2n\}$ such that $|A| = n + 1$. Show that there exist $a, b \in A$ such that a and b are coprime.

9. Show that among any group of n people, where $n \geq 2$, there are at least two people who know exactly the same number of people in the group (assuming that "knowing" is a symmetry relation).

10. Let $C = \{r_1, r_2, \ldots, r_{n+1}\}$ be a set of $n + 1$ real numbers, where $0 \leq r_i < 1$ for each $i = 1, 2, \ldots, n + 1$. Show that there exist r_p, r_q in C, where $p \neq q$, such that $|r_p - r_q| < \frac{1}{n}$.

11. Show that given any set A of 13 distinct real numbers, there exist $x, y \in A$ such that
$$0 < \frac{x - y}{1 + xy} \leq 2 - \sqrt{3}.$$

12. Consider a set of $2n$ points in space, $n > 1$. Suppose they are joined by at least $n^2 + 1$ segments. Show that at least one triangle is formed. Show that for each n it is possible to have $2n$ points joined by n^2 segments without any triangles being formed. (Putnam, 1956)

13. Let there be given nine lattice points (points with integral coordinates) in the three dimensional Euclidean space. Show that there is a lattice point on the interior of one of the line segments joining two of these points. (Putnam, 1971)

14. (i) A point (a_1, a_2) in the $x - y$ plane is called a *lattice point* if both a_1 and a_2 are integers. Given any set L_2 of 5 lattice points in the $x - y$ plane, show that there exist 2 distinct members in L_2 whose midpoint is also a lattice point (not necessarily in L_2).

    More generally, we have:

    (ii) A point $(a_1, a_2, \ldots, a_n)$ in the space $\mathbf{R}^n$, where $n \geq 2$ is an integer, is called a *lattice point* if all the a_i's are integers. Show that given any set L_n of $2^n + 1$ lattice points in $\mathbf{R}^n$, there exist 2 distinct members in L_n whose midpoint is also a lattice point (but not necessarily in L_n).

15. Let A be any set of 20 distinct integers chosen from the arithmetic progression $1, 4, 7, \ldots, 100$. Prove that there must be two distinct integers in A whose sum is 104. (Putnam, 1978)

16. Let A be a set of 6 points in a plane such that no 3 are collinear. Show that there exist 3 points in A which form a triangle having an interior angle not exceeding $30°$. (26th Moscow MO)

17. Let $n \geq 3$ be an odd number. Show that there is a number in the set
$$\{2^1 - 1, 2^2 - 1, \ldots, 2^{n-1} - 1\}$$
which is divisible by n. (USSR MO, 1980)

18. There are n people at a party. Prove that there are two people such that, of the remaining $n - 2$ people, there are at least $\lfloor n/2 \rfloor - 1$ of them, each of whom either knows both or else knows neither of the two. Assume that "knowing" is a symmetric relation, and that $\lfloor x \rfloor$ denotes the greatest integer less than or equal to x. (USA MO, 1985/4)

19. For a finite set A of integers, denote by $s(A)$ the sum of numbers in A. Let S be a subset of $\{1, 2, 3, \ldots, 14, 15\}$ such that $s(B) \neq s(C)$ for any 2 disjoint subsets B, C of S. Show that $|S| \leq 5$. (USA MO, 1986)

20. In the rectangular array

$$\begin{array}{cccc}
a_{11} & a_{12} & \cdots & a_{1n} \\
a_{21} & a_{22} & \cdots & a_{2n} \\
\vdots & \vdots & & \vdots \\
a_{m1} & a_{m2} & \cdots & a_{mn}
\end{array}$$

of $m \times n$ real numbers, the difference between the maximum and the minimum element in each row is at most d, where $d > 0$. Each column is then rearranged in decreasing order so that the maximum element of the column occurs in the first row, and the minimum element occurs in the last row. Show that in the rearranged array the difference between the maximum and the minimum elements in each row is still at most d. (Swedish Math. Competition, 1986)

21. We are given a regular decagon with all diagonals drawn. The number "+1" is attached to each vertex and to each point where diagonals intersect (we consider only internal points of intersection). We can decide at any time to simultaneously change the sign of all such numbers along a given side or a given diagonal. Is it possible after a certain number of such operations to have changed all the signs to negative? (International Mathematics Tournament of the Towns, Senior, 1984)

22. In a football tournament of one round (each team plays each other once, 2 points for win, 1 point for draw and 0 points for loss), 28 teams compete. During the tournament more than 75% of the matches finished in a draw. Prove that there were two teams who finished with the same number of points. (International Mathematics Tournament of the Towns, Junior, 1986)

23. Fifteen problems, numbered 1 through 15, are posed on a certain exami-
    nation. No student answers two consecutive problems correctly. If 1600
    candidates sit the test, must at least two of them have the identical an-
    swer patterns? (Assume each question has only 2 possible answers, right
    or wrong, and assume that no student leaves any question unanswered.)
    (24th Spanish MO, 1989)

24. Suppose that $a_1 \leq a_2 \leq \cdots \leq a_n$ are natural numbers such that $a_1 +
    \cdots + a_n = 2n$ and such that $a_n \neq n+1$. Show that if n is even, then for
    some subset K of $\{1, 2, \ldots, n\}$ it is true that $\sum_{i \in K} a_i = n$. Show that
    this is true also if n is odd when we make the additional assumption
    that $a_n \neq 2$. (Proposed by J. Q. Longyear, see *Amer. Math. Monthly*,
    80 (1973), 946-947.)

25. Let X be a nonempty set having n elements and C be a colour set with
    $p \geq 1$ elements. Find the greatest number p satisfying the following
    property: If we colour in an arbitrary way each subset of X with colours
    from C such that each subset receives only one colour, then there exist
    two distinct subsets A, B of X such that the sets $A, B, A \cup B, A \cap B$ have
    the same colour. (Proposed by I. Tomescu, see *Amer. Math. Monthly*,
    95 (1988), 876-877.)

26. Consider the system of p equations in $q = 2p$ unknowns $x_1, x_2, \ldots, x_q$:

$$a_{11}x_1 + a_{12}x_2 + \cdots \quad + a_{1q}x_q = 0$$
$$a_{21}x_1 + a_{22}x_2 + \cdots \quad + a_{2q}x_q = 0$$
$$\cdots\cdots\cdots\cdots\cdots\cdots\cdots\cdots\cdots\cdots\cdots\cdots$$
$$a_{p1}x_1 + a_{p2}x_2 + \cdots \quad + a_{pq}x_q = 0$$

   with every coefficient a_{ij} a member of the set $\{-1, 0, 1\}$. Prove that the
   system has a solution $(x_1, x_2, \ldots, x_q)$ such that

   (a) all x_j $(j = 1, 2, \ldots, q)$ are integers,

   (b) there is at least one value of j for which $x_j \neq 0$,

   (c) $|x_j| \leq q$ $(j = 1, 2, \ldots, q)$.

   (IMO, 1976/5)

27. An international society has its members from six different countries.
    The list of members contains 1978 names, numbered $1, 2, \ldots, 1978$.
    Prove that there is at least one member whose number is the sum of the
    numbers of two members from his own country, or twice as large as the
    number of one member from his own country. (IMO, 1978/6)

28. Let $p, q \in \mathbf{N}$. Show that in any given sequence of $R(p,q)$ distinct integers, there is either an increasing subsequence of p terms or a decreasing subsequence of q terms.

29. Show that given any sequence of $pq + 1$ distinct real numbers, where p and q are nonnegative integers, there is either an increasing subsequence of $p + 1$ terms or a decreasing subsequence of $q + 1$ terms. (P. Erdös and G. Szekeres (1935))

30. Show that
    (a) $R(p,q) = R(q,p)$, for all $p, q \in \mathbf{N}$;
    (b) $R(2,q) = q$, for all $q \in \mathbf{N}$.

31. Let $p, p', q, q' \in \mathbf{N}$ with $p' \leq p$ and $q' \leq q$. Show that
    (i) $R(p', q') \leq R(p, q)$;
    (ii) $R(p - 1, q) \leq R(p, q) - 1$ for $p \geq 2$;
    (iii) $R(p', q') = R(p, q)$ iff $p' = p$ and $q' = q$.

32. For $p, q \in \mathbf{N}$, show that

$$R(p, q) \leq \binom{p + q - 2}{p - 1}.$$

33. Show that

$$R(3, q) \leq \frac{1}{2}(q^2 + 3)$$

    for $q \geq 1$.

34. Show that $R(3, 5) = 14$.

35. Show that
    (a) $R(4, 4) \leq 18$,
    (b) $R(3, 6) \leq 19$.

36. Show that
    (a) $R(p_1, p_2, \ldots, p_k) = 1$ if $p_i = 1$ for some $i \in \{1, 2, \ldots, k\}$;
    (b) $R(p, 2, 2, \ldots, 2) = p$ for $p \geq 2$.

37. Let $k, p_1, p_2, \ldots, p_k \in \mathbf{N}$ with $k \geq 2$. Show that

$$R(p_1, p_2, \ldots, p_k) = R(p_1, p_2, \ldots, p_k, 2).$$

38. Given any k integers $p_i \geq 2$, $i = 1, 2, \ldots, k$, where $k \geq 2$, show that

$$R(p_1, p_2, \ldots, p_k) \leq \sum_{i=1}^{k} R(p_1, \ldots, p_{i-1}, p_i - 1, p_{i+1}, \ldots, p_k) - (k - 2).$$

39. Let $k \in \mathbb{N}$, $p_1, p_2, \ldots, p_k \in \mathbb{N}^*$ and $p = \sum_{i=1}^{k} p_i$. Show by induction on p that

$$R(p_1 + 1, p_2 + 1, \ldots, p_k + 1) \leq \frac{p!}{p_1! p_2! \ldots p_k!}.$$

40. For $k \in \mathbb{N}$ with $k \geq 2$, let R_k denote $R(\underbrace{3, 3, \ldots, 3}_{k})$. Show that

(a) (i) $R_k \leq k(R_{k-1} - 1) + 2$ for $k \geq 3$;

(ii) $R_k \leq \lfloor k!e \rfloor + 1$;

(iii) $R_4 \leq 66$.

(R. E. Greenwood and A. M. Gleason, *Canad. J. Math.*, 7 (1955), 1-7.)

(b) $R_k \geq 2^k + 1$.

41. Let $k \in \mathbb{N}$ and let $\{S_1, S_2, \ldots, S_k\}$ be any partition of the set $\mathbb{N}_n = \{1, 2, \ldots, n\}$, where $n = R(\underbrace{3, 3, \ldots, 3}_{k})$. Show that there exist $i \in \{1, 2, \ldots, k\}$, and some integers a, b, c (not necessarily distinct) in S_i such that $a + b = c$.

42. Show that

(i) $R(3, 3, 2) = 6$,

(ii) $R(3, 3, 3) \leq 17$. (See also Example 3.4.1.)

43. A p-clique is *monochromatic* if all its edges are coloured by the same colour.

(a) Show that for any colouring of the edges of the 6-clique K_6 by 2 colours: blue or red, there are at least two monochromatic 3-cliques (not necessarily disjoint).

(b) Give a colouring of the edges of K_6 by 2 colours such that there are no three monochromatic 3-cliques.

44. The edges of the 7-clique K_7 are coloured by 2 colours: blue or red. Show that there are at least four monochromatic 3-cliques in the resulting configuration.

45. Given any colouring of the edges of an n-clique $K_n (n \in \mathbf{N}, n \geq 3)$ by 2 colours, let $T(n)$ denote the number of monochromatic 3-cliques in the resulting configuration. Show that

$$T(n) \geq \begin{cases} \frac{1}{3}k(k-1)(k-2) & \text{if } n = 2k, \\ \frac{2}{3}k(k-1)(4k+1) & \text{if } n = 4k+1, \\ \frac{2}{3}k(k+1)(4k-1) & \text{if } n = 4k+3. \end{cases}$$

(A.W. Goodman, *Amer. Math. Monthly*, **66** (1959), 778-783.)

46. Each of the 36 line segments joining 9 distinct points on a circle is coloured either red or blue. Suppose that each triangle determined by 3 of the 9 points contains at least one red side. Prove that there are four points such that the 6 segments connecting them are red. (Canadian MO, 1976)

References.

[CG] F.R.K. Chung and C.M. Grinstead, A survey of bounds for classical Ramsey numbers, *J. Graph Theory*, **7** (1983), 25-37.

[CL] V. Chokbowornpaishand and V. Longani, Lower bounds for some Ramsey numbers, *Southeast Asian Bulletin of Maths.*, **15** (1991), 105-107.

[E] P. Erdös, Some remarks on the theory of graphs, *Bull. Amer. Math. Soc.* **53** (1947), 292-294.

[ES] P. Erdös and G. Szekeres, A combinatorial problem in geometry, *Coposito Math..* **2** (1935), 464-470.

[G] M. Gardner, Mathematical Games, *Scientific American*, **237(5)** (November, 1977), 18-28.

[GR] C.M. Grinstead and S.M. Roberts, On the Ramsey numbers $R(3,8)$ and $R(3,9)$, *J. Combinatorial Theory Ser. B*, **33** (1982), 27-51.

[GRS] R.L. Graham, B.L. Rothschild and J.H. Spencer, *Ramsey theory*, Second Edition, John Wiley & Sons, Inc., 1990.

[GS] R.L. Graham and J.H. Spencer, Ramsey Theory, *Scientific American*, July (1990), 112 -117.

[GG] R.E. Greenwood and A.M. Gleason, Combinatorial relations and chromatic graphs, *Canad. J. Math.* **7** (1955), 1-7.

[MZ] B.D. McKay and K.M. Zhang, The value of the Ramsey number $R(3,8)$, *J. Graph Theory*, **16** (1992), 99-105.

[Ra] F.P. Ramsey, On a problem of formal logic, *Proc. London Math. Soc.* **30** (1930), 264-286.

[Re] K.R. Rebman, The Pigeonhole Principle, Mathematical Gems, *Two-Year College Mathematics Journal*, **10** (1979), 3-12.

[W] K. Walker, Dichromatic graphs and ramsey numbers, *J. Combinatorial Theory*, **5** (1968), 238-243.

Chapter 4

The Principle of Inclusion and Exclusion

4.1. Introduction

The addition principle (AP) was stated at the beginning of Chapter 1. Its simplest form may be addressed as follows:

> If A and B are finite sets such that $A \cap B = \emptyset$,
> then $|A \cup B| = |A| + |B|$.

What is the corresponding equality for $|A \cup B|$ if $A \cap B \neq \emptyset$? If $A \cap B \neq \emptyset$, then in the counting of $|A|$ and $|B|$, the elements in $A \cap B$ are counted exactly twice. Thus we have (see also Figure 4.1.1):

$$|A \cup B| = |A| + |B| - |A \cap B| \qquad (4.1.1)$$

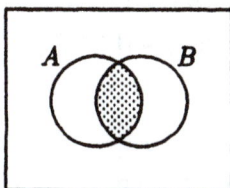

Figure 4.1.1.

As we have seen in the previous chapters, in solving certain more complicated counting problems, the sets whose elements are to be enumerated are usually divided into appropriate disjoint subsets so that (AP) can be directly applied. However, the task of dividing a set into such disjoint subsets may not be easy. Formula (4.1.1) provides us with a more flexible way:

145

Express the given set as $A \cup B$, where A and B need not be disjoint, and then count $|A|$, $|B|$ and $|A \cap B|$ independently. The 'inclusion' of $|A|$ and $|B|$ and the 'exclusion' of $|A \cap B|$ in Formula (4.1.1) will automatically give us the desired result for $|A \cup B|$.

Formula (4.1.1) is the simplest form of the so-called *Principle of Inclusion and Exclusion* (PIE), which we are going to study in the chapter. In Section 2 below, we shall extend formula (4.1.1) for 2 sets to a formula for n sets, $n \geq 2$. A much more general result which includes the latter as a special case will be established in Section 3. Applications of this general result to various classical enumeration problems will be discussed in the remaining sections.

4.2. The Principle

To begin with, let us see how we can apply (4.1.1) to get a corresponding formula for $|A \cup B \cup C|$, where A, B and C are three arbitrary finite sets.

Observe that

$$
\begin{aligned}
|A \cup B \cup C| &= |(A \cup B) \cup C| \quad \text{(associative law)} \\
&= |A \cup B| + |C| - |(A \cup B) \cap C| \quad \text{(by (4.1.1))} \\
&= |A \cup B| + |C| - |(A \cap C) \cup (B \cap C)| \quad \text{(distributive law)} \\
&= |A| + |B| - |A \cap B| + |C| \\
&\quad - (|A \cap C| + |B \cap C| - |(A \cap C) \cap (B \cap C)|) \quad \text{(by (4.1.1))} \\
&= (|A| + |B| + |C|) - (|A \cap B| + |A \cap C| + |B \cap C|) \\
&\quad + |A \cap B \cap C|.
\end{aligned}
$$

Thus we have:

$$|A \cup B \cup C| = (|A|+|B|+|C|)-(|A \cap B|+|A \cap C|+|B \cap C|)+|A \cap B \cap C|. \quad (4.2.1)$$

As a matter of fact, we have the following general result.

Theorem 4.2.1. (PIE) *For any q finite sets $A_1, A_2, ..., A_q$, $q \geq 2$,*

$$
\begin{aligned}
&|A_1 \cup A_2 \cup \cdots \cup A_q| \\
&= \sum_{i=1}^{q} |A_i| - \sum_{i<j} |A_i \cap A_j| + \sum_{i<j<k} |A_i \cap A_j \cap A_k| \quad (4.2.2) \\
&\quad - \cdots + (-1)^{q+1} |A_1 \cap A_2 \cap \cdots \cap A_q|. \quad \blacksquare
\end{aligned}
$$

Theorem 4.2.1 can be proved by induction on q. This proof is left to the reader (see Problem 4.7). Instead, we shall prove a more general result in Section 3 which includes Theorem 4.2.1 as a special case.

Example 4.2.1. Let $S = \{1, 2, ..., 500\}$. Find the number of integers in S which are divisible by 2, 3 or 5.

Before solving the problem, two observations are in order.

(1) For each $n \in \mathbf{N}$, the number of integers in S which are divisible by (or multiples of) n is given by $\lfloor \frac{500}{n} \rfloor$.

(2) For $a, b, c \in \mathbf{N}$, c is divisible by both a and b if and only if c is divisible by the LCM of a and b.

Bearing these in mind, you will find it easy to follow the solution given below.

Solution. For each $k \in \mathbf{N}$, let

$$B_k = \{x \in S \mid x \text{ is divisible by } k\}.$$

Thus, our aim is to find $|B_2 \cup B_3 \cup B_5|$.

To apply (PIE), we first need to perform the following computations.

By observation (1),

$$|B_2| = \left\lfloor \frac{500}{2} \right\rfloor = 250,$$

$$|B_3| = \left\lfloor \frac{500}{3} \right\rfloor = 166,$$

and

$$|B_5| = \left\lfloor \frac{500}{5} \right\rfloor = 100.$$

By observations (1) and (2),

$$|B_2 \cap B_3| = |B_6| = \left\lfloor \frac{500}{6} \right\rfloor = 83,$$

$$|B_2 \cap B_5| = |B_{10}| = \left\lfloor \frac{500}{10} \right\rfloor = 50,$$

$$|B_3 \cap B_5| = |B_{15}| = \left\lfloor \frac{500}{15} \right\rfloor = 33,$$

and $$|B_2 \cap B_3 \cap B_5| = |B_{30}| = \left\lfloor \frac{500}{30} \right\rfloor = 16.$$

Now, by (PIE),

$$\begin{aligned}
|B_2 \cup B_3 \cup B_5| &= (|B_2|+|B_3|+|B_5|)-(|B_2 \cap B_3|+|B_2 \cap B_5|+|B_3 \cap B_5|) \\
&\quad + |B_2 \cap B_3 \cap B_5| \\
&= (250 + 166 + 100) - (83 + 50 + 33) + 16 \\
&= 366. \quad \blacksquare
\end{aligned}$$

4.3. A Generalization

In Example 4.2.1, we have counted the number of integers in $S = \{1, 2, ..., 500\}$ which are divisible by at least one of the integers 2, 3, 5. We may ask further related questions. For instance, how many integers are there in S which are divisible by

        (1)   none of 2, 3, 5?

        (2)   exactly one of 2, 3, 5?

        (3)   exactly two of 2, 3, 5?

        (4)   all of 2, 3, 5?

For easy reference, we show in Figure 4.3.1 the desired sets corresponding to the above questions.

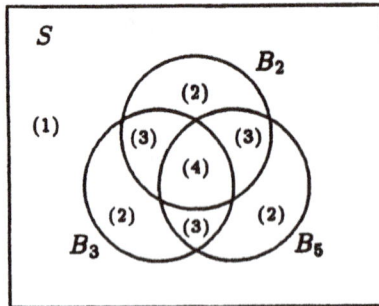

Figure 4.3.1.

The above questions cannot be solved directly by Theorem 4.2.1. In this section, we shall establish a general result which enables us to provide direct solutions to questions of this type.

Before proceeding any further, we first note the following. Let S be a given universal set. Then any subset A of S induces a *property* P such that, for any $x \in S$,

$$x \text{ possesses the property } P \quad \Leftrightarrow \quad x \in A.$$

For example, if $S = \{1, 2, ..., 10\}$ and $A = \{1, 2, 3, 4\}$, then $A = \{x \in S \mid x \text{ possesses } P\}$, where the property P may be taken to be "< 5". On the other hand, any property P of elements of S determines a *subset* A of S such that the elements of A are precisely those possessing P. For instance, if $S = \{1, 2, ..., 10\}$ and P is the property of being "divisible by 3", then P determines the subset $\{3, 6, 9\}$ of S. In view of this, it is reasonable for us to use the term "properties" to replace "subsets" in the following generalization. An advantage of this replacement is that the statements or formulae concerned can be substantially simplified.

In what follows, let S be an n-element universal set, and let $P_1, P_2, ..., P_q$ be q properties for the elements of S, where $q \geq 1$. It should be clear that a property may be possessed by none, some or all elements of S; and on the other hand, an element of S may have none, some or all of the properties.

For integer m with $0 \leq m \leq q$, let $E(m)$ denote the number of elements of S that possess *exactly* m of the q properties; and for $1 \leq m \leq q$, let $\omega(P_{i_1} P_{i_2} \cdots P_{i_m})$ denote the number of elements of S that possess the properties $P_{i_1}, P_{i_2}, \ldots, P_{i_m}$, and let

$$\omega(m) = \sum (\omega(P_{i_1} P_{i_2} \cdots P_{i_m})),$$

where the summation is taken over all m-combinations $\{i_1, i_2, \ldots, i_m\}$ of $\{1, 2, \ldots, q\}$.

We also define $\omega(0)$ to be $|S|$; i.e., $\omega(0) = |S| = n$. The result that we wish to establish is the following generalized principle of inclusion and exclusion (GPIE).

Theorem 4.3.1.   (GPIE)   *Let S be an n-element set and let $\{P_1, P_2, \ldots, P_q\}$ be a set of q properties for elements of S. Then for each $m = 0, 1, 2, \ldots, q$,*

$$E(m) = \omega(m) - \binom{m+1}{m}\omega(m+1) + \binom{m+2}{m}\omega(m+2)$$

$$- \cdots + (-1)^{q-m}\binom{q}{m}\omega(q)$$

$$= \sum_{k=m}^{q}(-1)^{k-m}\binom{k}{m}\omega(k). \tag{4.3.1}$$

We illustrate this result with the following example.

Example 4.3.1.   Let $S = \{1, 2, \ldots, 14\}$, and let P_1, P_2, P_3 and P_4 be 4 given properties. Assume that an element $j \in S$ possesses the property P_i if and only if the (i, j) entry in Table 4.3.1 is indicated by a tick "$\checkmark$".

S	1	2	3	4	5	6	7	8	9	10	11	12	13	14
P_1	$\checkmark$			$\checkmark$				$\checkmark$	$\checkmark$			$\checkmark$		
P_2	$\checkmark$	$\checkmark$	$\checkmark$	$\checkmark$		$\checkmark$		$\checkmark$		$\checkmark$	$\checkmark$		$\checkmark$	
P_3	$\checkmark$		$\checkmark$					$\checkmark$	$\checkmark$		$\checkmark$			$\checkmark$
P_4	$\checkmark$		$\checkmark$					$\checkmark$			$\checkmark$	$\checkmark$		$\checkmark$

Table 4.3.1.

Consider the property P_1. Since there are 5 elements of S (namely, 1, 4, 8, 9 and 12) having this property, we have $\omega(P_1) = 5$. Consider the properties P_2 and P_3. Since there are 4 elements of S (namely, 1, 3, 8 and 11) having both P_2 and P_3, we have $\omega(P_2P_3) = 4$. Checking through the table, we have the following data:

$$\omega(P_1) = 5, \qquad \omega(P_2) = 9, \qquad \omega(P_3) = 6, \qquad \omega(P_4) = 6;$$
$$\omega(P_1P_2) = 3, \qquad \omega(P_1P_3) = 3, \qquad \omega(P_1P_4) = 2,$$
$$\omega(P_2P_3) = 4, \qquad \omega(P_2P_4) = 5, \qquad \omega(P_3P_4) = 5;$$
$$\omega(P_1P_2P_3) = 2, \qquad \omega(P_1P_2P_4) = 2, \quad \omega(P_1P_3P_4) = 2, \quad \omega(P_2P_3P_4) = 4;$$
$$\omega(P_1P_2P_3P_4) = 2.$$

Thus, by definition,

$$\omega(0) = |S| = 14,$$

$$\omega(1) = \sum_{i=1}^{4} \omega(P_i) = 5 + 9 + 6 + 6 = 26,$$

$$\omega(2) = \sum_{i<j} \omega(P_i P_j) = 3 + 3 + 2 + 4 + 5 + 5 = 22,$$

$$\omega(3) = \sum_{i<j<k} \omega(P_i P_j P_k) = 2 + 2 + 2 + 4 = 10,$$

$$\omega(4) = \omega(P_1 P_2 P_3 P_4) = 2.$$

On the other hand, by scrutinizing the table again, we find

$E(0) = 2$ (elements 5 and 7), $E(1) = 4$ (elements 2, 6, 12, 13),
$E(2) = 4$ (elements 4, 9, 10, 14), $E(3) = 2$ (elements 3, 11),
$E(4) = 2$ (elements 1, 8).

Suppose $m = 0$. Observe that the RHS of identity (4.3.1) is

$$\omega(0) - \omega(1) + \omega(2) - \omega(3) + \omega(4)$$
$$= 14 - 26 + 22 - 10 + 2 = 2,$$

which agrees with $E(0)$.

We leave it to the reader to verify identity (4.3.1) for $m = 1, 2, 3$. ∎

We are now ready to prove Theorem 4.3.1.

Proof.   We shall show that each $x \in S$ contributes the same "count", either 0 or 1, to each side of the equality (4.3.1).

Let $x \in S$ be given. Assume that x possesses *exactly* t properties.

Case 1. $t < m$. Clearly, x contributes a count of 0 to both sides.

Case 2. $t = m$. In this case, x is counted once in $E(m)$. On the other hand, x contributes 1 to $\omega(m)$ but 0 to $\omega(r)$ for $r > m$. Thus x contributes a count of 1 to both sides.

Case 3. $t > m$. Now, x contributes a count of 0 to $E(m)$. On the other hand, x is counted

$$\binom{t}{m} \quad \text{times in} \quad \omega(m),$$

$$\binom{t}{m+1} \quad \text{times in} \quad \omega(m+1),$$

$$\vdots$$

$$\binom{t}{t} \quad \text{times in} \quad \omega(t);$$

but x contributes 0 to $\omega(r)$ for $r > t$.

Thus the count that x contributes to RHS is given by

$$\lambda = \binom{t}{m} - \binom{m+1}{m}\binom{t}{m+1} + \binom{m+2}{m}\binom{t}{m+2} - \cdots + (-1)^{t-m}\binom{t}{m}\binom{t}{t}.$$

It remains to show that the value of λ is equal to 0. Indeed, since

$$\binom{n}{k}\binom{k}{r} = \binom{n}{r}\binom{n-r}{k-r}$$

by identity (2.1.5), it follows that

$$\lambda = \binom{t}{m} - \binom{t}{m}\binom{t-m}{1} + \binom{t}{m}\binom{t-m}{2} - \cdots + (-1)^{t-m}\binom{t}{m}\binom{t-m}{t-m}$$

$$= \binom{t}{m}\left\{1 - \binom{t-m}{1} + \binom{t-m}{2} - \cdots + (-1)^{t-m}\binom{t-m}{t-m}\right\},$$

which is 0 by identity (2.3.2). The proof is thus complete. ∎

As we shall see later, Theorem 4.3.1 is particularly useful when $m = 0$.

Corollary 1. $E(0) = \omega(0) - \omega(1) + \omega(2) - \cdots + (-1)^q \omega(q)$ (4.3.2)

$$= \sum_{k=0}^{q}(-1)^k \omega(k). \quad \blacksquare$$

Corollary 2.   Let $A_1, A_2, ..., A_q$ be any q subsets of a finite set S. Then

$$|\bar{A}_1 \cap \bar{A}_2 \cap \cdots \cap \bar{A}_q|$$

$$= |S| - \sum_{i=1}^{q}|A_i| + \sum_{i<j}|A_i \cap A_j| - \sum_{i<j<k}|A_i \cap A_j \cap A_k| + \cdots$$

$$+ (-1)^q |A_1 \cap A_2 \cap \cdots \cap A_q|,$$

where $\bar{A}_i$ denotes the complement of A_i in S (i.e., $\bar{A}_i = S \backslash A_i$).

Proof.   For each $i = 1, 2, ..., q$, define a property P_i by saying that an element x of S possesses P_i if and only if $x \in A_i$. Then

$$\omega(0) = |S|, \qquad \omega(1) = \sum_{i=1}^{q} |A_i|,$$

$$\omega(2) = \sum_{i<j} |A_i \cap A_j|, \ldots, \omega(q) = \left| \bigcap_{i=1}^{q} A_i \right|,$$

and
$$E(0) = \left| \bigcap_{i=1}^{q} \bar{A}_i \right|.$$

With these, Corollary 2 now follows from Corollary 1.   ∎

We leave it to the reader to show that Theorem 4.2.1 now follows from Corollary 2. (see Problem 4.7).

In solving some complicated enumeration problems in which several properties are given, students may make mistakes by 'under-counting' or 'over-counting' in the problems. The significance of applying (PIE) or (GPIE) is this: We split such a problem into some simpler sub-problems, and the principle itself will automatically take care of the under-counting or over-counting. This point will be illustrated in many examples given in the remaining sections.

Historically, Theorem 4.2.1 was discovered by A. de Moivre in 1718 and its corresponding result in probability theory was found by H. Poincaré in 1896. The formulae given in Corollaries 1 and 2 to Theorem 4.3.1 were obtained independently by D.A. da Silva in 1854 and J.J. Sylvester in 1883. The probabilistic form of Theorem 4.3.1 was established by C. Jordan in 1927. For more details about the history and further generalizations of (PIE), the reader may refer to Takács [T].

4.4. Integer Solutions and Shortest Routes

In this section, we give two examples, one on integer solutions of linear equations and the other on shortest routes in rectangular grids, to illustrate how (GPIE) could be applied.

Example 4.4.1.   Find the number of nonnegative integer solutions to the equation

$$x_1 + x_2 + x_3 = 15 \tag{1}$$

where $x_1 \leq 5$, $x_2 \leq 6$ and $x_3 \leq 7$.

We learned in Chapter 1 that the number of nonnegative integer solutions to (1) (without any further condition) is given by

$$\binom{15 + 3 - 1}{15} = \binom{17}{2}.$$

The upper bounds "$x_1 \leq 5$, $x_2 \leq 6$, $x_3 \leq 7$" imposed in the problem make it not so straightforward. How can we cope with it? Notice that the problem of counting integer solutions of a linear equation is easy if the values of the variables are not bounded above. This then suggests that we may tackle the problem indirectly by considering the "complements" of the given upper bounds, which are "$x_1 \geq 6, x_2 \geq 7, x_3 \geq 8$". In the following solution, we shall see how this idea can be incorporated with (GPIE) to solve the problem.

Solution.   Let S be the set of nonnegative integer solutions of (1), namely $S = \{(a_1, a_2, a_3) \mid a_i \in \mathbf{N}^*, a_1 + a_2 + a_3 = 15\}$. We define 3 properties for elements of S. An element (a_1, a_2, a_3) in S is said to possess the property

$$P_1 \Leftrightarrow a_1 \geq 6,$$
$$P_2 \Leftrightarrow a_2 \geq 7,$$
and
$$P_3 \Leftrightarrow a_3 \geq 8.$$

Thus the number of integer solutions to (1) satisfying the requirement is the number of elements of S which possess none of the properties P_1, P_2 and P_3. This number is exactly $E(0)$ in (GPIE).

We now apply Corollary 1 to Theorem 4.3.1 to determine $E(0)$. First of all, we need to find $\omega(i)$, $i = 0, 1, 2, 3$. Observe that

$$\omega(0) = |S| = \binom{15 + 3 - 1}{15} = \binom{17}{2};$$
$$\omega(1) = \omega(P_1) + \omega(P_2) + \omega(P_3)$$

$$= \left(\binom{(15-6)+3-1}{2}\right) + \left(\binom{(15-7)+3-1}{2}\right)$$
$$+ \left(\binom{(15-8)+3-1}{2}\right)$$
$$= \binom{11}{2} + \binom{10}{2} + \binom{9}{2};$$
$$\omega(2) = \omega(P_1 P_2) + \omega(P_1 P_3) + \omega(P_2 P_3)$$
$$= \left(\binom{(15-6-7)+3-1}{2}\right) + \left(\binom{(15-6-8)+3-1}{2}\right)$$
$$+ \left(\binom{(15-7-8)+3-1}{2}\right)$$
$$= \binom{4}{2} + \binom{3}{2} + \binom{2}{2};$$

and $\omega(3) = \omega(P_1 P_2 P_3) = 0.$

Hence, $E(0) = \omega(0) - \omega(1) + \omega(2) - \omega(3) = \binom{17}{2} - \binom{11}{2} - \binom{10}{2} - \binom{9}{2} + \binom{4}{2} + \binom{3}{2} + \binom{2}{2}.$ ∎

Remarks. (1) To apply Theorem 4.3.1, we first have to know what the universal set S is in the problem, and then define "appropriate" properties for elements of S. In the above example, the properties we introduced are "complements" of the requirements: $x_1 \leq 5$, $x_2 \leq 6$, $x_3 \leq 7$ so that the desired integer solutions are the elements of S which possess "none" of the properties. Thus $E(0)$ is our required answer. The remaining task of computing $E(0)$ by formula is just a mechanical one.

(2) Using (GPIE) often enables us to obtain a more direct solution to a problem, as illustrated in the example above. However, this does not imply that the solution is always simple. For instance, we are able to provide a simpler solution to the problem in Example 4.4.1. We first introduce new variables t_1, t_2 and t_3 by putting

$$t_1 = 5 - x_1,$$
$$t_2 = 6 - x_2,$$
and
$$t_3 = 7 - x_3.$$

Then the equation $x_1 + x_2 + x_3 = 15$ becomes $t_1 + t_2 + t_3 = 3$ and the constraints $x_1 \leq 5$, $x_2 \leq 6$ and $x_3 \leq 7$ become $0 \leq t_1 \leq 5$, $0 \leq t_2 \leq 6$ and

$0 \leq t_3 \leq 7$, which are no constraints at all, since any nonnegative integers t_1, t_2 and t_3 satisfying the equation above do not exceed 3. So the required answer is $\binom{3+2}{2} = \binom{5}{2}$, which is the same as $E(0)$ in the above solution.

Example 4.4.2. Figure 4.4.1 shows a 11 by 6 rectangular grid with 4 specified segments AB, CD, EF and GH. Find the number of shortest routes from O to P in each of the following cases:

(i) All the 4 segments are deleted;

(ii) Each shortest route must pass through exactly 2 of the 4 segments.

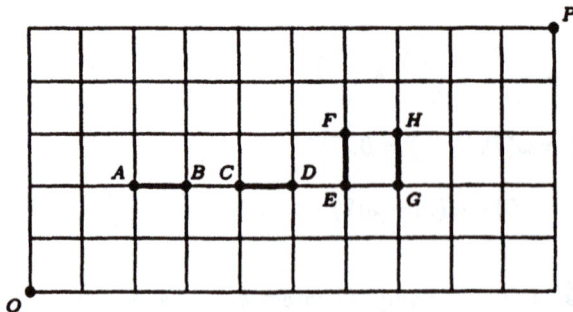

Figure 4.4.1.

We shall apply (GPIE) to solve this problem. First of all, we have to identify the universal set S. Since we are now dealing with shortest routes, it is natural that we take S to be the set of shortest routes from O to P (without any further condition). Note that from what we learned in Chapter 1, $|S| = \binom{10+5}{5} = \binom{15}{5}$. The next task is to define "appropriate" properties for elements of S. What properties should we introduce?

Solution. Let S be the set of shortest routes from O to P in the grid of Figure 4.4.1. We define 4 properties P_i $(i = 1, 2, 3, 4)$ as follows: A shortest route from O to P is said to possess the property

$$P_1 \Leftrightarrow \text{it passes through } AB;$$
$$P_2 \Leftrightarrow \text{it passes through } CD;$$
$$P_3 \Leftrightarrow \text{it passes through } EF;$$
$$P_4 \Leftrightarrow \text{it passes through } GH.$$

(i) *All the 4 segments are deleted.*

In this case, a desired shortest route is one that does not pass through any of the 4 segments; i.e., one that satisfies none of the 4 properties. Thus, the number of desired shortest routes is given by $E(0)$.

Observe that

$$\omega(0) = |S| = \binom{15}{5};$$

$$\omega(1) = \omega(P_1)+\omega(P_2)+\omega(P_3)+\omega(P_4)$$
$$= \binom{4}{2}\binom{10}{3}+\binom{6}{2}\binom{8}{3}+\binom{8}{2}\binom{6}{2}+\binom{9}{2}\binom{5}{2};$$

$$\omega(2) = \omega(P_1P_2)+\omega(P_1P_3)+\omega(P_1P_4)+\omega(P_2P_3)+\omega(P_2P_4)+\omega(P_3P_4)$$
$$= \binom{4}{2}\binom{8}{3}+\binom{4}{2}\binom{6}{2}+\binom{4}{2}\binom{5}{2}+\binom{6}{2}\binom{6}{2}+\binom{6}{2}\binom{5}{2}+0;$$

$$\omega(3) = \omega(P_1P_2P_3)+\omega(P_1P_2P_4)+\omega(P_1P_3P_4)+\omega(P_2P_3P_4)$$
$$= \binom{4}{2}\binom{6}{2}+\binom{4}{2}\binom{5}{2}+0+0;$$

and $\omega(4) = \omega(P_1P_2P_3P_4) = 0$.

Thus

$$E(0) = \omega(0) - \omega(1) + \omega(2) - \omega(3) + \omega(4)$$
$$= \binom{15}{5} - \binom{4}{2}\binom{10}{3} - \binom{6}{2}\binom{8}{3} - \binom{8}{2}\binom{6}{2} - \binom{9}{2}\binom{5}{2}$$
$$+ \binom{4}{2}\binom{8}{3} + \binom{4}{2}\binom{6}{2} + \binom{4}{2}\binom{5}{2} + \binom{6}{2}\binom{6}{2} + \binom{6}{2}\binom{5}{2}$$
$$- \binom{4}{2}\binom{6}{2} - \binom{4}{2}\binom{5}{2}.$$

(ii) *Each shortest route passes through exactly 2 of the 4 segments.*

The required number of shortest routes is $E(2)$, which is equal to

$$\omega(2)-\binom{3}{2}\omega(3)+\binom{4}{2}\omega(4)$$
$$= \binom{4}{2}\binom{8}{3}+\binom{4}{2}\binom{6}{2}+\binom{4}{2}\binom{5}{2}+\binom{6}{2}\binom{6}{2}+\binom{6}{2}\binom{5}{2}$$
$$- \binom{3}{2}\left\{\binom{4}{2}\binom{6}{2}+\binom{4}{2}\binom{5}{2}\right\}. \quad \blacksquare$$

4.5. Surjective Mappings and Stirling Numbers of the Second Kind

As shown in Section 2.6, the number of surjective (onto) mappings from $\mathbf{N}_n$ to $\mathbf{N}_m$ (where $n, m \in \mathbf{N}$) is given by $m!S(n, m)$, where $S(n, m)$, the Stirling number of the 2nd kind, is defined as the number of ways of distributing n distinct objects into m identical boxes so that no box is empty. In Section 1.7, we gave the values of $S(n, m)$ in some special cases. Now, we shall apply Corollary 1 to Theorem 4.3.1 to derive a general formula for the number of surjective mappings from $\mathbf{N}_n$ to $\mathbf{N}_m$ which, in turn, gives rise to a formula for $S(n, m)$.

Theorem 4.5.1.   *Let $F(n, m)$, $n, m \in \mathbf{N}$, denote the number of surjective mappings from $\mathbf{N}_n$ to $\mathbf{N}_m$. Then*

$$F(n, m) = \sum_{k=0}^{m} (-1)^k \binom{m}{k} (m - k)^n. \qquad (4.5.1)$$

Remark.   Evidently, $F(n, m)$ can also be regarded as the number of ways of distributing n distinct objects into m distinct boxes so that no box is empty.

Proof.   Let S be the set of mappings from $\mathbf{N}_n$ to $\mathbf{N}_m$. We define m properties P_i $(i = 1, 2, ..., m)$ for members of S as follows: For each $i = 1, 2, ..., m$, a mapping $f : \mathbf{N}_n \to \mathbf{N}_m$ is said to possess P_i if and only if $i \notin f(\mathbf{N}_n)$ (i.e., the element i of $\mathbf{N}_m$ is not contained in the image of $\mathbf{N}_n$ under f).

It then follows that a mapping $f : \mathbf{N}_n \to \mathbf{N}_m$ is surjective if and only if f possesses none of the properties P_i $(i = 1, 2, ..., m)$. We therefore have $F(n, m) = E(0)$.

Observe that

$$\omega(0) = |S| = m^n;$$

$$\omega(1) = \sum_{i=1}^{m} \omega(P_i) = \binom{m}{1}(m - 1)^n;$$

and in general, for each k with $0 \le k \le m$,

$$\omega(k) = \sum_{1 \le i_1 < i_2 < \cdots < i_k \le m} \omega(P_{i_1} P_{i_2} \cdots P_{i_k}) = \binom{m}{k}(m - k)^n.$$

Thus, by Corollary 1 to Theorem 4.3.1,

$$F(n,m) = E(0)$$
$$= \sum_{k=0}^{m}(-1)^k \omega(k)$$
$$= \sum_{k=0}^{m}(-1)^k \binom{m}{k}(m-k)^n,$$

as desired. ∎

Since $F(n,m) = m!S(n,m)$, we thus have:

Corollary 1. *For $n, m \in \mathbf{N}$,*

$$S(n,m) = \frac{1}{m!}\sum_{k=0}^{m}(-1)^k \binom{m}{k}(m-k)^n. \quad ∎$$

The following results about the Stirling numbers of the 2nd kind were stated in Section 1.7: For $n, m \in \mathbf{N}$,

(1) $S(n,m) = 0$ if $n < m$;

(2) $S(n,n) = 1$;

(3) $S(n,n-1) = \binom{n}{2}$; and

(4) $S(n,n-2) = \binom{n}{3} + 3\binom{n}{4}$.

Combining these with Corollary 1 to Theorem 4.5.1, we obtain some nontrivial identities involving alternating sums.

Corollary 2. *For $n, m \in \mathbf{N}$,*

(1) $\sum_{k=0}^{m}(-1)^k \binom{m}{k}(m-k)^n = 0$ if $n < m$;   (4.5.2)

(2) $\sum_{k=0}^{n}(-1)^k \binom{n}{k}(n-k)^n = n!$;   (4.5.3)

(3) $\sum_{k=0}^{n-1}(-1)^k \binom{n-1}{k}(n-1-k)^n = (n-1)!\binom{n}{2}$;   (4.5.4)

(4) $\sum_{k=0}^{n-2}(-1)^k \binom{n-2}{k}(n-2-k)^n = (n-2)!\left\{\binom{n}{3} + 3\binom{n}{4}\right\}$.   (4.5.5)

Remark. The identities (4.5.2) and (4.5.3) are usually referred to as Euler's formula. For their applications and relations to other combinatorial notions, the reader may read the interesting article [G] by H.W. Gould.

4.6. Derangements and A Generalization

In 1708, the Frenchman Pierre Rémond de Montmort (1678-1719) posed the following problem. Suppose two decks, A, and B, of cards are given. The cards of A are first laid out in a row, and those of B are then placed at random, one at the top on each card of A such that 52 pairs of cards are formed. Find the probability that no 2 cards are the same in each pair. This problem is known as "le problème des rencontres" (in French, 'rencontres' means 'match').

The essential part of the above problem is to find, given the layout of cards of A, the number of ways of placing the cards of B such that no 'match' can occur. This can naturally be generalized as follows: Find the number of permutations $a_1 a_2 \cdots a_n$ of N_n such that $a_i \neq i$ for each $i = 1, 2, ..., n$. We call such a permutation a *derangement* (nothing is in its right place) of N_n, and we denote by D_n the number of derangements of N_n. Thus "le problème des rencontres" is essentially the problem of enumerating D_n for $n = 52$. The general problem for arbitrary n was later solved by N. Bernoulli and P.R. Montmort in 1713.

In 1983, Hanson, Seyffarth and Weston [HSW] introduced the following notion, which is a generalization of derangements. For $1 \leq r \leq n$, recall that an r-permutation of N_n is an arrangement $a_1 a_2 \cdots a_r$ of r elements of N_n in a row. An r-permutation $a_1 a_2 \cdots a_r$ of N_n is said to have a *fixed point* at i ($i = 1, 2, ..., r$) if $a_i = i$. For $0 \leq k \leq r$, let $D(n, r, k)$ denote the number of r-permutations of N_n that have exactly k fixed points. Thus, $D_n = D(n, n, 0)$. Our aim here is to find a formula for $D(n, r, k)$ by (GPIE).

Example 4.6.1. The 24 ($= P_3^4$) 3-permutations of N_4 are classified into 4 groups according to the number of fixed points as shown in Table 4.6.1.

Theorem 4.6.1. [HSW] *For integers n, r, k such that $n \geq r \geq k \geq 0$ and $r \geq 1$,*

$$D(n, r, k) \doteq \frac{\binom{r}{k}}{(n-r)!} \sum_{i=0}^{r-k} (-1)^i \binom{r-k}{i} (n-k-i)! . \qquad (4.6.1)$$

Number of Fixed Points	3-permutations of $\mathbf{N_4}$	$D(4,3,k)$
$k = 0$	231, 312, 214, 241, 412, 314, 341, 431, 234, 342, 432	11
1	132, 213, 321, 142, 421, 134, 413, 243, 324	9
2	124, 143, 423	3
3	123	1

Table 4.6.1

Proof. Let S be the set of r-permutations of $\mathbf{N}_n$. We define r properties for elements of S as follows:

An element $a_1 a_2 \cdots a_r$ in S is said to possess the property P_i if and only if $a_i = i$, where $i = 1, 2, ..., r$.

It thus follows by definition that

$$D(n, r, k) = E(k).$$

Observe that for $0 \le t \le r$,

$$\omega(P_1 P_2 \cdots P_t) = \binom{n-t}{r-t} \cdot (r-t)! = \frac{(n-t)!}{(n-r)!}.$$

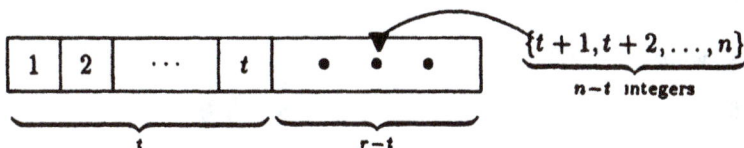

Likewise, $\omega(P_{i_1} P_{i_2} \cdots P_{i_t}) = \omega(P_1 P_2 \cdots P_t) = \frac{(n-t)!}{(n-r)!}$, for any t-element subset $\{i_1, i_2, ..., i_t\}$ of $\{1, 2, ..., r\}$. Thus,

$$\omega(t) = \sum_{1 \le i_1 < i_2 < \cdots < i_t \le r} \omega(P_{i_1} P_{i_2} \cdots P_{i_t}) = \binom{r}{t} \frac{(n-t)!}{(n-r)!}.$$

By (GPIE),

$$D(n,r,k) = E(k) = \sum_{i=0}^{r-k}(-1)^i\binom{k+i}{k}\omega(k+i)$$

$$= \sum_{i=0}^{r-k}(-1)^i\binom{k+i}{k}\binom{r}{k+i}\frac{(n-k-i)!}{(n-r)!}$$

$$= \frac{1}{(n-r)!}\sum_{i=0}^{r-k}(-1)^i\binom{r}{k}\binom{r-k}{k+i-k}(n-k-i)!$$

$$= \frac{\binom{r}{k}}{(n-r)!}\sum_{i=0}^{r-k}(-1)^i\binom{r-k}{i}(n-k-i)!,$$

as desired. ∎

Some interesting identities involving the $D(n,r,k)$'s, that can be found in [HSW], are listed below.

(1) $D(n,r,k) = \binom{r}{k}D(n-k,r-k,0)$;   (4.6.2)

(2) $D(n,r,k) = D(n-1,r-1,k-1) + (n-1)D(n-1,r-1,k)$

$$+(r-1)\{D(n-2,r-2,k) - D(n-2,r-2,k-1)\},$$

where $D(n,r,-1)$ is defined to be 0;   (4.6.3)

(3) $D(n,n,k) = nD(n-1,n-1,k) + (-1)^{n-k}\binom{n}{k}$;   (4.6.4)

(4) $\binom{k}{t}D(n,r,k) = \binom{r}{t}D(n-t,r-t,k-t)$, $t \geq 0$;   (4.6.5)

(5) $D(n,r,k) = rD(n-1,r-1,k) + D(n-1,r,k)$,

where $r < n$;   (4.6.6)

(6) $r!D(n,n-r,0) = \sum_{i=0}^{r}\binom{r}{i}D(n-i,n-i,0)$.   (4.6.7)

Since $D_n = D(n,n,0)$, by Theorem 4.6.1, we have

$$D_n = \binom{n}{0}\sum_{i=0}^{n}(-1)^i\binom{n}{i}(n-i)!$$

$$= \sum_{i=0}^{n}(-1)^i\frac{n!}{i!(n-i)!}(n-i)! = n!\sum_{i=0}^{n}\frac{(-1)^i}{i!}.$$

Corollary. *For any $n \in \mathbf{N}$,*

(i) $D_n = n! \left(1 - \frac{1}{1!} + \frac{1}{2!} - \frac{1}{3!} + \cdots + (-1)^n \frac{1}{n!}\right);$ (4.6.8)

(ii) $\lim\limits_{n \to \infty} \frac{D_n}{n!} = e^{-1} \simeq 0.367.$ ∎ (4.6.9)

We state below two useful identities involving D_n that are, respectively, special cases of identities (4.6.3) and (4.6.4).

(7) $D_n = (n-1)(D_{n-1} + D_{n-2});$ (4.6.10)

(8) $D_n = nD_{n-1} + (-1)^n;$ (4.6.11)

The reader may refer to the article by Karl [Kr] for different types of generalization of derangements.

For reference, the first 10 values of D_n are given in Table 4.6.2.

n	1	2	3	4	5	6	7	8	9	10
D_n	0	1	2	9	44	265	1854	14833	133496	1334961

Table 4.6.2.

4.7. The Sieve of Eratosthenes and Euler φ-function

In this section, we present two classical problems in number theory that can be solved by (GPIE).

A number $n \geq 2$ is said to be *composite* if n is not a prime. The number "1" is neither a prime nor a composite number. Just like "bricks" which can be combined together to build a "wall", primes can be combined to form any natural number greater than 1 by multiplication. This can be seen in the following result which is so important to the study of integers that it is called the *Fundamental Theorem of Arithmetic*:

For every $n \in \mathbf{N}$, $n > 1$, there exist primes

$$p_1 < p_2 < \cdots < p_k$$

and positive integers $m_1, m_2, ..., m_k$ such that

$$n = p_1^{m_1} p_2^{m_2} \cdots p_k^{m_k} = \prod_{i=1}^{k} p_i^{m_i};$$

and such a factorization is unique if we disregard the order of primes.

The first example that we shall discuss here is concerned with the counting of primes. Given $n \in \mathbf{N}$, $n \geq 2$, how many primes are there between 2 and n inclusive? We shall solve this problem by applying Corollary 1 to Theorem 4.3.1. But first of all, we need to introduce a special device for distinguishing primes from composite numbers. This device, which was discovered by the Greek mathematician Eratosthenes (276-194 B.C.) who lived in Alexandra around 2000 years ago, is known as the *Sieve of Eratosthenes*.

The Sieve of Eratosthenes

Write down the numbers $2, 3, ..., n$ in order. Keep the first prime "2" and cross off all other multiples of 2. Keep the first of the remaining integers greater than "2" (i.e., the prime "3") and cross off all other multiples of "3" that remain. Keep the first of the remaining integers greater than "3" (i.e., the prime "5") and cross off all other multiples of "5" that remain. This procedure is repeated until the first of the currently remaining integers is greater than $\sqrt{n}$. The numbers on the list that are not crossed off are the primes between 1 and n.

2̶ 3̶ 4̶ 5̶ 6̶ 7̶ 8̶ 9̶ 1̶0̶ 11 1̶2̶ 13

1̶4̶ 1̶5̶ 1̶6̶ 17 1̶8̶ 19 2̶0̶ 2̶1̶ 2̶2̶ 23 2̶4̶ 2̶5̶

2̶6̶ 2̶7̶ 2̶8̶ 29 3̶0̶ 31 3̶2̶ 3̶3̶ 3̶4̶ 3̶5̶ 3̶6̶ 37

3̶8̶ 3̶9̶ 4̶0̶ 41 4̶2̶ 43 4̶4̶ 4̶5̶ 4̶6̶ 47 4̶8̶

Example 4.7.1. To find the primes between 2 and 48 inclusive by the Sieve of Eratosthenes, we first write down the number 2, 3, ..., 48 in order:

We then keep 2 and cross off all multiples of 2 (i.e., 4, 6, 8, ..., 48). The first of the remaining integers (i.e., "3") is kept and all multiples of 3 that remain (i.e., 9, 15, 21, 27, 33, 39, 45) are crossed off. We then keep "5", the first remaining integer and cross off the multiples of 5 that remain (i.e., 25, 35). The procedure terminates now, since the first remaining integer is "7", which is greater than $\sqrt{48}$. The numbers that are not crossed off are:

$$2, 3, 5, 7, 11, 13, 17, 19, 23, 29, 31, 37, 41, 43, 47$$

which are the required primes. Note that there are 15 primes altogether. ∎

Remark. In the above procedure, we actually cross off the multiples of the primes not exceeding $\sqrt{n}$ (i.e., 2, 3, 5,) except the primes themselves. The reason we do not have to proceed beyond $\sqrt{n}$ is this: If a number, say k, $2 \leq k \leq n$, is a multiple of a prime p, where $p > \sqrt{n}$, then k must be a multiple of a smaller prime p', where $p' \leq \sqrt{n}$, and so k has already been crossed off.

Using the idea behind the above procedure, we now illustrate by an example how (GPIE) can be used to compute the number of primes from 1 to n, for a given $n \in \mathbf{N}$.

Example 4.7.2. Find the number of primes between 1 and 48 inclusive.

Solution. Let $S = \{1, 2, ..., 48\}$. There are 3 primes not exceeding $\sqrt{48}$, namely, 2, 3 and 5. We define 3 corresponding properties P_1, P_2, P_3 as follows: A number $x \in S$ is said to possess property

$$P_1 \Leftrightarrow 2|x;$$
$$P_2 \Leftrightarrow 3|x;$$
$$P_3 \Leftrightarrow 5|x.$$

It follows from the sieve that the desired number of primes is equal to

$$E(0) + 3 - 1,$$

because the 3 primes "2, 3, 5" not counted in $E(0)$ must be included, whereas, the number "1" counted in $E(0)$ must be excluded. Observe that

$$\omega(0) = |S| = 48;$$
$$\omega(1) = \omega(P_1) + \omega(P_2) + \omega(P_3)$$
$$= \left\lfloor \frac{48}{2} \right\rfloor + \left\lfloor \frac{48}{3} \right\rfloor + \left\lfloor \frac{48}{5} \right\rfloor = 24 + 16 + 9 = 49;$$
$$\omega(2) = \omega(P_1 P_2) + \omega(P_1 P_3) + \omega(P_2 P_3)$$
$$= \left\lfloor \frac{48}{6} \right\rfloor + \left\lfloor \frac{48}{10} \right\rfloor + \left\lfloor \frac{48}{15} \right\rfloor = 8 + 4 + 3 = 15;$$

and
$$\omega(3) = \omega(P_1 P_2 P_3) = \left\lfloor \frac{48}{30} \right\rfloor = 1.$$

Thus $E(0) = \omega(0) - \omega(1) + \omega(2) - \omega(3) = 48 - 49 + 15 - 1 = 13$ and the desired number of primes is $E(0) + 3 - 1 = 15.$ ∎

We shall now discuss our second example. For $a, b \in \mathbf{N}$, let (a, b) denote the HCF of a and b. Thus $(8, 15) = 1$ while $(9, 15) = 3$. We say that a is *coprime* to b (and vice versa) if $(a, b) = 1$. Around 1760, in his attempt to generalize a result of Fermat's in number theory, the Swiss mathematician Leonard Euler (1707-1783) introduced the following notion. For $n \in \mathbf{N}$, let $\varphi(n)$ denote the number of integers between 1 and n which are coprime to n. Table 4.7.1 shows those integers x, $1 \leq x \leq n$, which are coprime to n, and the values of $\varphi(n)$ for $n \leq 15$. The function $\varphi(n)$, now known as the *Euler φ-function*, plays a significant role in many enumeration problems in number theory and modern algebra. As seen in Table 4.7.1, the values of $\varphi(n)$ are rather irregularly distributed except when n is a prime. Mathematicians had been interested in finding a general formula of $\varphi(n)$, and it really took some time before the following result was established.

n	integers x such that $1 \le x \le n$ and $(x,n)=1$	$\varphi(n)$
1	1	1
2	1	1
3	1,2	2
4	1,3	2
5	1,2,3,4	4
6	1,5	2
7	1,2,3,4,5,6	6
8	1,3,5,7	4
9	1,2,4,5,7,8	6
10	1,3,7,9	4
11	1,2,3,4,5,6,7,8,9,10	10
12	1,5,7,11	4
13	1,2,3,4,5,6,7,8,9,10,11,12	12
14	1,3,5,9,11,13	6
15	1,2,4,7,8,11,13,14	8

Table 4.7.1.

Example 4.7.3. Let $n \in \mathbb{N}$, and let

$$n = p_1^{m_1} p_2^{m_2} \cdots p_k^{m_k}$$

be its prime factorization as stated in the fundamental theorem of arithmetic. Show that

$$\varphi(n) = n \left(1 - \frac{1}{p_1}\right)\left(1 - \frac{1}{p_2}\right) \cdots \left(1 - \frac{1}{p_k}\right) = n \prod_{i=1}^{k} \left(1 - \frac{1}{p_i}\right). \quad (4.7.1)$$

The following two observations are useful in the proof below.

(i) Let $x \in \mathbb{N}$ such that $x \le n$, where n is given in Example 4.7.3. Then $(x,n)=1$ if and only if $p_i \nmid x$ for all $i = 1, 2, ..., k$.

(ii) For real numbers $r_1, r_2, ..., r_k$,

$$(1-r_1)(1-r_2)\cdots(1-r_k) = 1 - \sum_{i=1}^{k} r_i + \sum_{i<j} r_i r_j - \sum_{i<j<\ell} r_i r_j r_\ell$$
$$+ \cdots + (-1)^k r_1 r_2 \cdots r_k.$$

Proof of (4.7.1). Let $S = \{1, 2, ..., n\}$. Corresponding to the k primes $p_1, p_2, ..., p_k$ in the factorization of n, we define k properties $P_1, P_2, ..., P_k$ as follows: An element $x \in S$ is said to possess

$$P_i \iff p_i | x, \quad \text{where } i = 1, 2, ..., k.$$

It follows from the observation (i) above that $x \in S$ is coprime to n if and only if x possesses none of the properties $P_1, P_2, ..., P_k$. Consequently, we have

$$\varphi(n) = E(0).$$

Observe that $\omega(0) = |S| = n$; and for $1 \leq t \leq k - 1$,

$$\omega(t) = \sum_{i_1 < i_2 < \cdots < i_t} \omega(P_{i_1} P_{i_2} \cdots P_{i_t}) = \sum_{i_1 < i_2 < \cdots < i_t} \left\lfloor \frac{n}{p_{i_1} p_{i_2} \cdots p_{i_t}} \right\rfloor$$

$$= \sum_{i_1 < i_2 < \cdots < i_t} \frac{n}{p_{i_1} p_{i_2} \cdots p_{i_t}}$$

and $\quad \omega(k) = \left\lfloor \frac{n}{p_1 p_2 \cdots p_k} \right\rfloor = \frac{n}{p_1 p_2 \cdots p_k}.$

Hence

$$\varphi(n) = E(0)$$

$$= n - \sum_{i=1}^{k} \frac{n}{p_i} + \sum_{i<j} \frac{n}{p_i p_j} - \sum_{i<j<l} \frac{n}{p_i p_j p_l} + \cdots + (-1)^k \frac{n}{p_1 p_2 \cdots p_k}$$

$$= n \left(1 - \sum \frac{1}{p_i} + \sum \frac{1}{p_i p_j} - \sum \frac{1}{p_i p_j p_l} + \cdots + (-1)^k \frac{1}{p_1 p_2 \cdots p_k} \right)$$

$$= n \left(1 - \frac{1}{p_1} \right) \left(1 - \frac{1}{p_2} \right) \cdots \left(1 - \frac{1}{p_k} \right) \quad \text{(by observation (ii))}$$

$$= n \prod_{i=1}^{k} \left(1 - \frac{1}{p_i} \right). \quad \blacksquare$$

It is noted that from expression (4.7.1), $\varphi(n)/n$ is independent of the powers m_i's of the primes in the factorization of n. For some interesting properties and generalizations of $\varphi(n)$, and historical remarks on the above result, the reader may read [D, p113-158]. To end this section, we state the following beautiful identity involving Euler φ-function, due to Smith (1875):

$$\begin{vmatrix} (1,1) & (1,2) & \cdots & (1,n) \\ (2,1) & (2,2) & \cdots & (2,n) \\ \vdots & \vdots & \ddots & \vdots \\ (n,1) & (n,2) & \cdots & (n,n) \end{vmatrix} = \varphi(1)\varphi(2)\cdots\varphi(n),$$

where (a,b) is the HCF of a and b.

4.8. The 'Probléme des Ménages'

At the end of Section 1.3, we stated the following problem, known as the probléme des ménages (in French, 'ménages' means 'married couples'):

> How many ways are there to seat n married couples, $n \geq 3$, around a table such that men and women alternate and each woman is not adjacent to her husband?

This famous problem was raised and popularized by E. Lucas in his book [L] published in 1891. In fact, an equivalent problem was first posed by P.G. Tait much earlier in 1876 and was settled by A. Cayley and T. Muir independently in 1877.

In this section, we shall apply Theorem 4.3.1 to solve the above problem in a more general way. Before doing this, let us first study a problem due to I. Kaplansky [Kp].

Example 4.8.1. Suppose that the numbers $1, 2, ..., m$ ($m \geq 3$) are placed in order around a circle as shown below. For $0 \leq k \leq \lfloor \frac{m}{2} \rfloor$, let $\alpha(k)$ denote the number of k-element subsets of $\mathbf{N}_m$ in which no two elements are adjacent around the table. Show that

$$\alpha(k) = \frac{m}{k}\binom{m-k-1}{k-1}. \tag{4.8.1}$$

For instance, if $m = 10$ and $k = 4$, then $\{1,3,6,9\}$ and $\{3,5,8,10\}$ are such subsets while $\{1,6,8,10\}$ and $\{2,6,7,9\}$ are not. Note that if $\lfloor \frac{m}{2} \rfloor < k \leq m$, no such k-element subsets can exist. When $k = 3$, Example 4.8.1 is the same as Problem 1.34. If the term "circle" is replaced by "row" in Example 4.8.1, the problem is identical to that in Example 1.5.3.

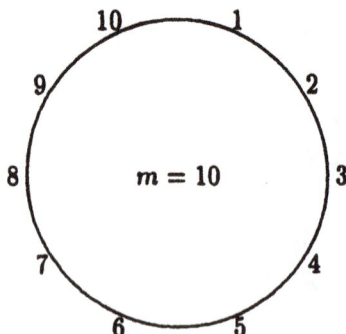

Proof. For each $i = 1, 2, ..., m$, let α_i denote the number of such k-element subsets of $\mathbf{N}_m$ which contain "i". By symmetry, $\alpha_1 = \alpha_2 = \cdots = \alpha_m$. We now count α_1.

If B is such a k-element subset of $\mathbf{N}_m$ containing "1", then by the hypothesis, $2, m \notin B$, and thus the remaining $k - 1$ elements of B must be chosen from $\{3, 4, ..., m - 1\}$ such that no two are adjacent (in a row). Hence, by the result of Example 1.5.3,

$$\alpha_1 = \binom{(m-3)-(k-1)+1}{k-1} = \binom{m-k-1}{k-1}$$

and so $\sum_{i=1}^m \alpha_i = m\binom{m-k-1}{k-1}$.

Since $\sum_{i=1}^m \alpha_i = k \cdot \alpha(k)$ (why?), it follows that

$$\alpha(k) = \frac{1}{k}\sum_{i=1}^m \alpha_i = \frac{m}{k}\binom{m-k-1}{k-1}. \quad \blacksquare$$

We are now in a position to establish the following result.

Example 4.8.2. There are n married couples ($n \geq 3$) to be seated in the $2n$ chairs around a table. Suppose that the n wives have already been seated such that there is one and only one empty chair between two adjacent wives as shown below. Let $M(n, r)$, $0 \leq r \leq n$, denote the number of ways to seat the n husbands in the remaining chairs such that exactly r husbands are adjacent to their own wives. Show that

$$M(n, r) = \sum_{k=r}^n (-1)^{k-r} \binom{k}{r} \frac{2n}{2n-k}\binom{2n-k}{k}(n-k)! \tag{4.8.2}$$

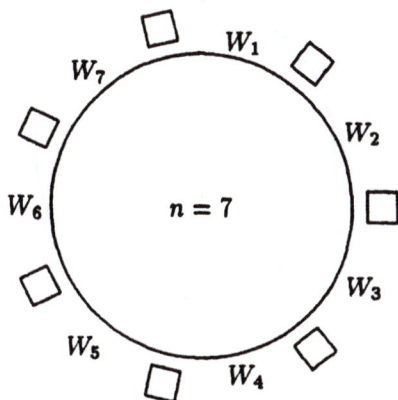

Proof. Let S be the set of all arrangements of the n husbands $H_1, H_2, ..., H_n$. We define $2n$ properties $P_1, P_2, ..., P_{2n}$ as follows: An arrangement in S is said to possess the property:

$$
\begin{array}{lll}
P_1 & \Leftrightarrow & H_1 \text{ sits to the right of his wife } W_1; \\
P_2 & \Leftrightarrow & H_1 \text{ sits to the left of his wife } W_1; \\
P_3 & \Leftrightarrow & H_2 \text{ sits to the right of his wife } W_2; \\
P_4 & \Leftrightarrow & H_2 \text{ sits to the left of his wife } W_2; \\
& \vdots & \\
P_{2n-1} & \Leftrightarrow & H_n \text{ sits to the right of his wife } W_n; \\
P_{2n} & \Leftrightarrow & H_n \text{ sits to the left of his wife } W_n.
\end{array}
$$

It is important to note that P_i and P_{i+1} cannot hold at the same time, for each $i = 1, 2, ..., 2n$, where P_{2n+1} is defined as P_1. Thus

$$\omega(P_i P_{i+1}) = 0 \quad \text{for each } i = 1, 2, .., 2n. \tag{1}$$

If we arrange the $2n$ properties in order around a circle as shown below, then by (1)

$$\omega(P_{i_1} P_{i_2} \cdots P_{i_k}) = 0,$$

if the k-element subset $\{P_{i_1}, P_{i_2}, \ldots, P_{i_k}\}$ contains 2 adjacent members around the circle.

This implies, in particular, that

(i) For $n < k \leq 2n$, $\omega(P_{i_1} P_{i_2} \cdots P_{i_k}) = 0$ (and so $\omega(k) = 0$); $\tag{2}$

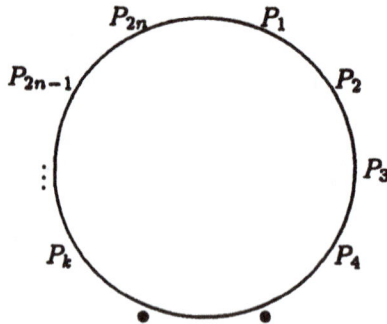

(ii) For $1 \leq k \leq n$,

$$\omega(k) = \sum_{1 \leq i_1 < i_2 < \cdots < i_k \leq 2n} \omega(P_{i_1} P_{i_2} \cdots P_{i_k})$$

$$= \underbrace{\frac{2n}{k} \binom{2n-k-1}{k-1}}_{\uparrow} \bullet \underbrace{(n-k)!}_{\uparrow} \qquad (3)$$

$$\boxed{\text{By (4.8.1)}} \qquad \boxed{\begin{array}{l} \text{number of ways to} \\ \text{seat the remaining} \\ n - k \text{ husbands} \end{array}}$$

Finally, we have
$$M(n, r) = E(r)$$

$$= \sum_{k=r}^{2n} (-1)^{k-r} \binom{k}{r} \omega(k) \quad \text{(by GPIE)}$$

$$= \sum_{k=r}^{n} (-1)^{k-r} \binom{k}{r} \frac{2n}{k} \binom{2n-k-1}{k-1} (n-k)! \quad \text{(by (2) and (3))}$$

$$= \sum_{k=r}^{n} (-1)^{k-r} \binom{k}{r} \frac{2n}{2n-k} \binom{2n-k}{k} (n-k)!,$$

as required. ∎

The case when $r = 0$ gives the solution to the 'problème des ménages'. The formula for this special case, i.e.,

$$M(n, 0) = \sum_{k=0}^{n} (-1)^k \frac{2n}{2n-k} \binom{2n-k}{k} (n-k)! \qquad (4.8.3)$$

was discovered by J. Touchard in 1934. The idea used in the above proof is due to I. Kaplansky [Kp]. For a different proof of formula (4.8.3) (but still based on (PIE)), the reader may refer to Bogart and Doyle [BD].

For simplicity, let $M_n = M(n,0)$. Two interesting identities involving M_n's are given below:

$$(n - 2)M_n = n(n - 2)M_{n-1} + nM_{n-2} + 4(-1)^{n+1} \qquad (4.8.4)$$

$$\sum_{k=0}^{n} \binom{2n}{k} M_{n-k} = n!, \quad \text{where } M_0 = 1 \text{ and } M_1 = -1. \qquad (4.8.5)$$

As pointed out in [Kp], the following limit follows from identity (4.8.3):

$$\lim_{n \to \infty} \frac{M_n}{n!} = e^{-2}. \qquad (4.8.6)$$

To end this chapter, we give in Table 4.8.1 the values of M_n for $2 \leq n \leq 10$.

n	2	3	4	5	6	7	8	9	10
M_n	0	1	2	13	80	579	4738	43387	439792

Table 4.8.1

Exercise 4

1. A group of 102 students took examinations in Chinese, English and Mathematics. Among them, 92 passed Chinese, 75 English and 63 Mathematics; at most 65 passed Chinese and English, at most 54 Chinese and Mathematics, and at most 48 English and Mathematics. Find the largest possible number of the students that could have passed all the three subjects.

2. (a) Let A, B and C be finite sets. Show that
   (i) $|\bar{A} \cap B| = |B| - |A \cap B|$;
   (ii) $|\bar{A} \cap \bar{B} \cap C| = |C| - |A \cap C| - |B \cap C| + |A \cap B \cap C|$.
   (b) Find the number of integers in the set $\{1, 2, \ldots, 10^3\}$ which are not divisible by 5 nor by 7 but are divisible by 3.

3. Find the number of integers in the set $\{1, 2, \ldots, 120\}$ which are divisible by exactly 'm' of the integers: 2, 3, 5, 7, where $m = 0, 1, 2, 3, 4$. Find also the number of primes which do not exceed 120.

4. How many positive integers n are there such that n is a divisor of at least one of the numbers 10^{40}, 20^{30}? (Putnum 1983)

5. Find the number of positive divisors of at least one of the numbers: 10^{60}, 20^{50}, 30^{40}.

6. Find the number of integers in each of the following sets which are not of the form n^2 or n^3, where $n \in \mathbf{N}$:

   (i) $\{1, 2, \ldots, 10^4\}$,

   (ii) $\{10^3, 10^3 + 1, \ldots, 10^4\}$.

7. Prove Theorem 4.2.1 by

   (a) induction on q;

   (b) Corollary 2 to Theorem 4.3.1.

8. A year is a *leap* year if it is either (i) a multiple of 4 but not a multiple of 100, or (ii) a multiple of 400. For example, 1600 and 1924 were leap years while 2200 will not be. Find the number of leap years between 1000 and 3000 inclusive.

9. Each of n boys attends a school gathering with both of his parents. In how many ways can the $3n$ people be divided into groups of three such that each group contains a boy, a male parent and a female parent, and no boy is with both of his parents in his group?

10. A man has 6 friends. At dinner in a certain restaurant, he has met each of them 12 times, every two of them 6 times, every three of them 4 times, every four of them 3 times, every five twice and all six only once. He has dined out 8 times without meeting any of them. How many times has he dined out altogether?

11. Three identical black balls, four identical red balls and five identical white balls are to be arranged in a row. Find the number of ways that this can be done if all the balls with the same colour do not form a single block.

12. How many arrangements of $a, a, a, b, b, b, c, c, c$ are there such that

    (i) no three consecutive letters are the same?

    (ii) no two consecutive letters are the same?

13. Find the number of shortest routes from corner X to corner Y in the following rectangular grid if the segments AB, BC and BD are all deleted.

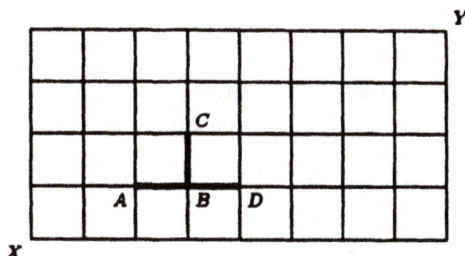

14. Find the number of integer solutions to the equation

$$x_1 + x_2 + x_3 = 28$$

where $3 \le x_1 \le 9, 0 \le x_2 \le 8$ and $7 \le x_3 \le 17$.

15. Find the number of integer solutions to the equation

$$x_1 + x_2 + x_3 = 40$$

where $6 \le x_1 \le 15, 5 \le x_2 \le 20$ and $10 \le x_3 \le 25$.

16. Find the number of integer solutions to the equation

$$x_1 + x_2 + x_3 + x_4 = 20$$

where $1 \le x_1 \le 5, 0 \le x_2 \le 7, 4 \le x_3 \le 8$ and $2 \le x_4 \le 6$.

17. Let $k, n, r \in \mathbf{N}$. Show that the number of integer solutions to the equation

$$x_1 + x_2 + \cdots + x_n = r$$

such that $0 \le x_i \le k$ for each $i = 1, 2, \ldots, n$ is given by

$$\sum_{i=0}^{n} (-1)^i \binom{n}{i} \binom{r - (k+1)i + n - 1}{n-1}.$$

18. Let $k, n, r \in \mathbf{N}$. Show that the number of integer solutions to the equation

$$x_1 + x_2 + \cdots + x_n = r$$

such that $1 \leq x_i \leq k$ for each $i = 1, 2, \ldots, n$ is given by

$$\sum_{i=0}^{n} (-1)^i \binom{n}{i} \binom{r - ki - 1}{n - 1}.$$

19. Find the number of ways of arranging n couples $\{H_i, W_i\}, i = 1, 2, \ldots, n$, in a row such that H_i is not adjacent to W_i for each $i = 1, 2, \ldots, n$.

20. Let $p, q \in \mathbb{N}$ with p odd. There are pq beads of q different colours: $1, 2, \ldots, q$ with exactly p beads in each colour. Assuming that beads of the same colour are identical, in how many ways can these beads be put in a string in such a way that

   (i) beads of the same colour must be in a single block?

   (ii) beads of the same colour must be in two separated blocks?

   (iii) beads of the same colour must be in at most two blocks?

   (iv) beads of the same colour must be in at most two blocks and the size of each block must be at least 2?

21. (a) Find the number of ways of distributing r identical objects into n distinct boxes such that no box is empty, where $r \geq n$.

   (b) Show that

$$\sum_{i=0}^{n-1} (-1)^i \binom{n}{i} \binom{r + n - i - 1}{r} = \binom{r-1}{n-1},$$

where $r, n \in \mathbb{N}$ with $r \geq n$.

22. (a) Let B be a subset of A with $|A| = n$ and $|B| = m$. Find the number of r-element subsets of A which contain B as a subset, where $m \leq r \leq n$.

   (b) Show that for $m, r, n \in \mathbb{N}$ with $m \leq r \leq n$,

$$\binom{n-m}{n-r} = \sum_{i=0}^{m} (-1)^i \binom{m}{i} \binom{n-i}{r}.$$

23. (a) For $n \in \mathbb{N}$, find the number of binary sequences of length n which do not contain '01' as a block.

   (b) Show that

$$n + 1 = \sum_{i=0}^{\lfloor \frac{n}{2} \rfloor} (-1)^i \binom{n-i}{i} 2^{n-2i}.$$

24. In each of the following configurations, each vertex is to be coloured by one of the λ different colours. It how many ways can this be done if any two vertices which are joined by a line segment must be coloured by different colours?

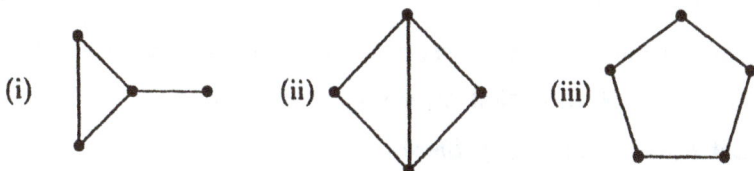

(i)   (ii)   (iii)

25. n persons are to be allocated to q distinct rooms. Find the number of ways that this can be done if only m of the q rooms have exactly k persons each, where $1 \le m \le q$ and $qk \le n$.

26. Suppose that $A = \{k \cdot x_1, k \cdot x_2, \ldots, k \cdot x_n\}$ is a multiset, where $k, n \in \mathbf{N}$. For $m \in \mathbf{N}^*$ with $m \le n$, let $\alpha(m)$ denote the number of ways to arrange the members of A in a row such that the number of blocks containing all the k elements of the same type in the arrangement is exactly m. Show that

$$\alpha(m) = \frac{(-1)^m}{(k!)^n} \binom{n}{m} \sum_{i=m}^{n} (-1)^i \binom{n-m}{i-m} (k!)^i \cdot \{kn - i(k-1)\}!$$

27. Prove identities (4.6.2)–(4.6.7).

    ([HSW]; for (4.6.7), see E. T. H. Wang, E2947, *Amer. Math. Monthly*, 89 (1982), 334.)

28. For $n \in \mathbf{N}$, let C_n denote the number of permutations of the set $\{1, 2, \ldots, n\}$ in which k is never followed immediately by $k + 1$ for each $k = 1, 2, \ldots, n - 1$.

    (i) Find C_n;

    (ii) Show that $C_n = D_n + D_{n-1}$ for each $n \in \mathbf{N}$.

29. Let $m, n \in \mathbf{N}$ with $m < n$. Find, in terms of D_k's, the number of derangements $a_1 a_2 \ldots a_n$ of $\mathbf{N}_n$ such that

$$\{a_1, a_2, \ldots, a_m\} = \{1, 2, \ldots, m\}.$$

30. Let $m, n \in \mathbf{N}$ with $n \ge 2m$. Find the number of derangements $a_1 a_2 \ldots a_n$ of $\mathbf{N}_n$ such that

$$\{a_1, a_2, \ldots, a_m\} = \{m + 1, m + 2, \ldots, 2m\}$$

in each of the following cases:

(i) $n = 2m$;

(ii) $n = 2m + 1$;

(iii) $n = 2m + r, r \geq 2$.

31. Apply identity (4.6.8) to prove identities (4.6.10) and (4.6.11).

32. Given $n \in \mathbf{N}$, show that D_n is even iff n is odd.

33. Let $D_n(k) = D(n, n, k)$. Show that

(i) $D_n(k) = \binom{n}{k} D_{n-k}$;

(ii) $\binom{n}{0} D_0 + \binom{n}{1} D_1 + \cdots + \binom{n}{n} D_n = n!$, where $D_0 = 1$;

(iii) $(k + 1) D_{n+1}(k + 1) = (n + 1) D_n(k)$.

34. Let $D_n(k)$ be the number of permutations of the set $\{1, 2, \ldots, n\}, n \geq 1$, which have exactly k fixed points (i.e., $D_n(k) = D(n, n, k)$). Prove that

$$\sum_{k=0}^{n} k \cdot D_n(k) = n! \ .$$

(IMO, 1987/1)

35. Let $D_n(k)$ denote $D(n, n, k)$. Show that

$$D_n(0) - D_n(1) = (-1)^n$$

for each $n \in \mathbf{N}$.

36. Let $D_n(k)$ denote $D(n, n, k)$. Prove that

$$\sum_{k=0}^{n} (k - 1)^2 D_n(k) = n!.$$

(West Germany MO, 1987)

37. Let $D_n(k)$ denote $D(n, n, k)$. Prove that

$$\sum_{k=r}^{n} k(k - 1) \cdots (k - r + 1) D_n(k) = n!,$$

where $r, n \in \mathbf{N}^*$ with $r \leq n$. (D. Hanson, *Cruz Mathematicorum*, 15(5) (1989), 139.)

38. (a) Without using equality (4.7.1), show that
    (i) the Euler φ-function is a multiplicative function; that is, $\varphi(mn) = \varphi(m)\varphi(n)$ whenever $m, n \in \mathbf{N}$ with $(m, n) = 1$.
    (ii) for a prime p and an integer $i \geq 1$,

    $$\varphi(p^i) = p^i - p^{i-1}.$$

    (b) Derive equality (4.7.1) from (i) and (ii).

39. (i) Compute $\varphi(100)$ and $\varphi(300)$.
    (ii) Show that $\varphi(m)\big|\varphi(n)$ whenever $m\big|n$.

40. Show that for $n \in \mathbf{N}$,

    $$\sum(\varphi(d) \mid d \in \mathbf{N}, d|n) = n.$$

41. Let $m, n \in \mathbf{N}$ with $(m, n) = h$. Show by using equality (4.7.1) that

    $$\varphi(mn) \cdot \varphi(h) = \varphi(m) \cdot \varphi(n) \cdot h.$$

42. Show that for $n \in \mathbf{N}$ with $n \geq 3$, $\varphi(n)$ is always even.

43. Let $n \in \mathbf{N}$ with $n \geq 2$. Show that if n has exactly k distinct prime factors, then

    $$\varphi(n) \geq n \cdot 2^{-k}.$$

44. Let $n \in \mathbf{N}$ with $n \geq 2$. Show that if n has exactly k distinct odd prime factors, then

    $$2^k\big|\varphi(n).$$

45. Does there exist an $n \in \mathbf{N}$ such that $\varphi(n) = 14$? Justify your answer.

46. For $n \in \mathbf{N}$, show that

    $$\varphi(2n) = \begin{cases} \varphi(n) & \text{if } n \text{ is odd} \\ 2\varphi(n) & \text{if } n \text{ is even.} \end{cases}$$

47. For $m, r, q \in \mathbf{N}$ with $m \leq r \leq q$, let

    $$A(m, r) = \sum_{k=m}^{r} (-1)^{k-m} \binom{k}{m} \omega(k).$$

Thus Theorem 4.3.1 says that $E(m) = A(m, q)$. Prove that

(i) if m and r have the same parity (i.e., $m \equiv r \pmod 2$), then

$$E(m) \leq A(m, r);$$

(ii) if m and r have different parities, then

$$E(m) \geq A(m, r);$$

(iii) strict inequality in (i) (resp., (ii)) holds iff $\omega(t) > 0$ for some t with $r < t \leq q$.

(See K. M. Koh, Inequalities associated with the principle of inclusion and exclusion, *Mathematical Medley*, Singapore Math. Soc. **19** (1991), 43-52.)

48. Prove the following Bonferroni inequality:

$$\sum_{k=j}^{q} (-1)^{k-j} \omega(k) \geq 0$$

for each $j = 0, 1, \ldots, q$.

49. (i) Let $A_1, A_2, \ldots, A_n$ be n finite sets. Show that

$$\left| \bigcup_{k=1}^{n} A_k \right| \geq \sum_{k=1}^{n} |A_k| - \sum_{1 \leq i < j \leq n} |A_i \cap A_j|.$$

(ii) Apply (i) to prove the following (see Example 1.5.4): A permutation of n couples $\{H_1, W_1, H_2, W_2, \ldots, H_n, W_n\}$ ($n \geq 1$) in a row is said to have property P if at least one couple H_i and $W_i (i = 1, 2, \ldots, n)$ are adjacent in the row. Show that for each n there are more permutations with property P than without.

50. Let $B_0 = 1$ and for $r \in \mathbb{N}$, let $B_r = \sum_{k=1}^{r} S(r, k)$. The number B_r is called the rth *Bell* number (see Section 1.7). Show that

(i) Corollary 1 to Theorem 4.5.1 can be written as

$$S(r, k) = \frac{1}{k!} \sum_{j=0}^{k} (-1)^{k-j} \binom{k}{j} j^r,$$

where $r, k \in \mathbb{N}$;

(ii) $B_r = e^{-1} \sum_{j=0}^{\infty} \frac{j^r}{j!}$.

51. For $n \in \mathbb{N}^*$ and $r \in \mathbb{N}$, let

$$a_n = \sum_{i=0}^{n} (-1)^i \frac{r}{i+r} \binom{n}{i}.$$

Show that

$$a_n = \frac{n}{n+r} a_{n-1}.$$

Deduce that

$$a_n = \frac{1}{\binom{n+r}{r}}.$$

52. We follow the terminology given in Theorem 4.3.1. For $1 \le m \le q$, let $L(m)$ denote the number of elements of S that possess *at least* m of the q properties. Show that

$$L(m) = \sum_{k=m}^{q} (-1)^{k-m} \binom{k-1}{m-1} \omega(k).$$

Note. One possible proof is to follow the argument given in the proof of Theorem 4.3.1 and to apply the identity given in the preceding problem.

53. For $k = 1, 2, \ldots, 1992$, let A_k be a set such that $|A_k| = 44$. Assume that $|A_i \cap A_j| = 1$ for all $i, j \in \{1, 2, \ldots, 1992\}$ with $i \ne j$. Evaluate $\left| \bigcup_{k=1}^{1992} A_k \right|$.

54. Twenty-eight random draws are made from the set

$$\{1, 2, 3, 4, 5, 6, 7, 8, 9, A, B, C, D, J, K, L, U, X, Y, Z\}$$

containing 20 elements. What is the probability that the sequence

$$CUBAJULY\,1987$$

occurs in that order in the chosen sequence? (Belgium, 1987)

55. A sequence of 35 random draws, one at a time with replacement, is made from the set of the English alphabet:

$$\{A, B, C, \ldots, X, Y, Z\}.$$

What is the probability that the string

$$MERRYCHRISTMAS$$

occurs as a block in the sequence?

56. In a group of 1990 people, each person has at least 1327 friends. Show that there are 4 people in the group such that every two of them are friends (assuming that friendship is a mutual relationship). (Proposed by France at the 31st IMO.)

57. Let C be the set of complex numbers, and let $S = \{z \in C \mid |z| = 1\}$. For each mapping $f : S \to S$ and $k \in N$, define the mapping $f^k : S \to S$ by $f^k(z) = \underbrace{f(f(\cdots(f(z))\cdots))}_{k}$. An element $w \in S$ is called an *n-periodic point* $(n \in N)$ of f if

$$f^i(w) \neq w \text{ for all } i = 1, 2, \ldots, n-1, \text{ but } f^n(w) = w.$$

Suppose $f : S \to S$ is a mapping defined by

$$f(z) = z^m \quad (m \in N).$$

Find the number of 1989-periodic points of f. (Chinese Math. Competition, 1989)

58. For $m, n \in N$, let $\mathcal{M}$ be the set of all $m \times n$ $(0,1)$-matrices. Let

$$\mathcal{M}_r = \{M \in \mathcal{M} \mid M \text{ has at least one zero row}\}$$

and

$$\mathcal{M}_c = \{M \in \mathcal{M} \mid M \text{ has at least one zero column}\}.$$

Show that the number of matrices in $(\mathcal{M} \backslash \mathcal{M}_r) \cap \mathcal{M}_c$ is given by

$$\sum_{i=1}^{n} (-1)^{i-1} \binom{n}{i} (2^{n-i} - 1)^m.$$

(C. J. Everett and P. R. Stein, *Discrete Math.* **6** (1973), 29.)

59. For $n, m \in N$ with $m \leq n$, let $P_n(m)$ denote the number of permutations of $\{1, 2, \ldots, n\}$ for which m is the first number whose position is left unchanged. Thus $P_n(1) = (n-1)!$ and $P_n(2) = (n-1)! - (n-2)!$. Show that
   (i) $P_n(m) = \sum_{i=0}^{m-1} (-1)^i \binom{m-1}{i}(n-1-i)!$;
   (ii) $P_n(m+1) = P_n(m) - P_{n-1}(m)$ for each $m = 1, 2, \ldots, n-1$.
   (see Problem 979, *Maths. Magazine*, **50** (1977), 269-270)

60. Let P be a nonempty, finite set with p members, and Q be a finite set with q members. Let $N_k(p,q)$ be the number of binary relations of cardinality k with domain P and range Q. (Equivalently, $N_k(p,q)$ is the number of $p \times q$ matrices of 0's and 1's with exactly k entries equal to 1 and no row or column identically 0.) Compute $\sum_{k=1}^{pq}(-1)^{k-1}N_k(p,q)$. (Proposed by S. Leader, see *Amer. Math. Monthly*, **80** (1973), 84)

61. Let D_n and M_n denote the derangement number and the ménage number respectively. Prove or disprove that the sequence $\{M_n/D_n\}, n = 4,5,6,\ldots$ is monotonically increasing and $\lim_{n\to\infty}(M_n/D_n) = 1/e$. (Proposed by E. T. H. Wang, see *Amer. Math. Monthly*, **87** (1980), 829-830.)

62. Show that for $n \in \mathbf{N}$ and $r \in \mathbf{N}^*$,

$$\sum_{k=0}^{n} k^r \binom{n}{k} D_{n-k} = n! \sum_{m=0}^{\min\{r,n\}} S(r,m).$$

Deduce that for $n \geq r$,

$$\sum_{k=0}^{n} k^r \binom{n}{k} D_{n-k} = B_r \cdot n!,$$

where B_r is the rth Bell number. (See *Amer. Math. Monthly*, **94** (1987), 187-189)

63. Let $S = \{1,2,3,\ldots,280\}$. Find the smallest integer n such that each n-element subset of S contains at least 5 numbers which are pairwise relatively prime. (IMO, 1991/3)

References.

[B] K. Bogart and P.G. Doyle, Non-sexist solution of the ménage problem, *Amer. Math. Monthly,* **93** (1986), 514-518.

[D] L.E. Dickson, *History of the Theory of Numbers,* Vol. I, Carnegie Institution of Washington, 1919. Reprinted by Chelsea, New York, 1952.

[G]   H.W. Gould, Euler's formula for nth differences of powers, *Amer.*
      Math. Monthly, **85** (1978), 450-467.

[HSW] D. Hanson, K. Seyffarth and J.H. Weston, Matchings, Derange-
      ments, Rencontres, *Math. Magazine,* **56(4)** (1983), 224-229.

[Kp] I. Kaplansky, Solution of the "problème des ménages", *Bull.*
      Amer. Math. Soc., **49** (1943), 784-785.

[Kr] D. Karl, Rencontres reencountered, *The College Maths. J.,*
      19(2) (1988), 139-148.

[L]   E. Lucas, *Théorié de nombres,* Paris 1891. Reprinted by   Blan-
      chard, 1961.

[T]   L. Takács, On the method of inclusion and exclusion, *J. Amer.*
      Statist. Ass., **62** (1967), 102-113.

Chapter 5

Generating Functions

5.1. Ordinary Generating Functions

As seen in the previous chapters, one of the main tasks in combinatorics is to develop tools for counting. Perhaps, one of the most powerful tools frequently used in counting is the notion of generating functions. This notion has its roots in the work of de Moivre around 1720 and was developed by Euler in 1748 in connection with his study on the partitions of integers. It was later on extensively and systematically treated by Laplace in the late 18th century. In fact, the name "generating functions" owes its origin to Laplace in his great work "Théorie Analytique des Probabilities" (Paris, 1812).

Let $(a_r) = (a_0, a_1, ..., a_r, ...)$ be a sequence of numbers. The (ordinary) *generating function* for the sequence (a_r) is defined to be the power series

$$A(x) = \sum_{r=0}^{\infty} a_r x^r = a_0 + a_1 x + a_2 x^2 + \cdots.$$

Two generating functions $A(x)$ and $B(x)$ for the sequences (a_r) and (b_r), respectively are considered *equal* (written $A(x) = B(x)$) if and only if $a_i = b_i$ for each $i \in \mathbf{N^*}$.

In considering the summation in a generating function, we may assume that x has been chosen such that the series converges. In fact, we do not have to concern ourselves so much with questions of convergence of the series, since we are only interested in the coefficients. Ivan Niven [N] gave an excellent account of the theory of formal power series, that allows us to ignore questions of convergence, so that we can add and multiply formal power series term by term like polynomials, as given below:

Let $A(x)$ and $B(x)$ be, respectively, the generating functions for the sequences (a_r) and (b_r). That is,

$$A(x) = a_0 + a_1 x + a_2 x^2 + \cdots,$$
$$B(x) = b_0 + b_1 x + b_2 x^2 + \cdots.$$

The *sum* $A(x) + B(x)$ and the *product* $A(x)B(x)$ of $A(x)$ and $B(x)$ are defined by:

$$A(x) + B(x) = c_0 + c_1 x + c_2 x^2 + \cdots,$$

and
$$A(x)B(x) = d_0 + d_1 x + d_2 x^2 + \cdots,$$

where

$c_r = a_r + b_r, \quad$ for $r = 0, 1, 2, ...,$ and
$d_r = a_0 b_r + a_1 b_{r-1} + a_2 b_{r-2} + \cdots + a_{r-1} b_1 + a_r b_0, \quad$ for $r = 0, 1, 2, ...$

Writing explicitly, we have:

$$A(x) + B(x) = (a_0 + b_0) + (a_1 + b_1)x + (a_2 + b_2)x^2 + \cdots,$$
and
$$A(x)B(x) = (a_0 b_0) + (a_0 b_1 + a_1 b_0)x + (a_0 b_2 + a_1 b_1 + a_2 b_0)x^2 + \cdots.$$

Also, for each constant α, we put

$$\alpha A(x) = (\alpha a_0) + (\alpha a_1)x + (\alpha a_2)x^2 + \cdots.$$

Remark. The sequence (c_r) above is defined "componentwise", whereas, the sequence (d_r) is called the *Cauchy product* or the *convolution* of the sequences (a_r) and (b_r). When the sequences are finite, both operations are exactly the same as those for polynomials. In this chapter, we shall see how combinatorial considerations can be converted into algebraic manipulations using generating functions. This, in fact, is the main advantage of the theory of generating functions.

Now, for each $\alpha \in \mathbf{R}$ and each $r \in \mathbf{N}$, we introduce the "generalized binomial coefficient" $\binom{\alpha}{r}$ by putting:

$$\binom{\alpha}{r} = \frac{P_r^\alpha}{r!},$$

where $P_r^{\alpha} = \alpha(\alpha-1)(\alpha-2)\cdots(\alpha-r+1)$. We further set $\binom{\alpha}{0} = 1$ for each $\alpha \in \mathbf{R}$.

We now state the following generalized binomial expansion due to Newton: For every $\alpha \in \mathbf{R}$,

$$
\begin{aligned}
(1 \pm x)^{\alpha} &= \sum_{r=0}^{\infty} \binom{\alpha}{r}(\pm x)^r \\
&= 1 \pm \alpha x + \frac{\alpha(\alpha-1)}{2!}x^2 \pm \frac{\alpha(\alpha-1)(\alpha-2)}{3!}x^3 + \cdots \\
&\quad + (-1)^r \frac{\alpha(\alpha-1)\cdots(\alpha-r+1)}{r!}x^r + \cdots
\end{aligned}
\tag{5.1.1}
$$

The proof of this expansion can be found in many books on advanced calculus. Note that the series in (5.1.1) is infinite if α is not a positive integer. The generalized notion $\binom{\alpha}{r}$ has some properties similar to those of the usual binomial coefficients. For instance, we have:

$$
\binom{\alpha}{r-1} + \binom{\alpha}{r} = \binom{\alpha+1}{r},
$$

for each $\alpha \in \mathbf{R}$ and $r \in \mathbf{N}$.

By (5.1.1), we have

$$
\frac{1}{1-x} = (1-x)^{-1} = 1 + x + x^2 + x^3 + \cdots,
$$

and

$$
\frac{1}{(1-x)^2} = (1-x)^{-2} = 1 + 2x + 3x^2 + 4x^3 + \cdots.
$$

In general,

$$
\begin{aligned}
\frac{1}{(1-x)^n} = (1-x)^{-n} &= 1 + nx + \frac{n(n+1)}{2!}x^2 + \frac{n(n+1)(n+2)}{3!}x^3 + \cdots \\
&= 1 + \binom{1+n-1}{1}x + \binom{2+n-1}{2}x^2 + \cdots + \binom{r+n-1}{r}x^r + \cdots,
\end{aligned}
$$

for each $n \in \mathbf{N}$.

Example 5.1.1. (a)   For each $n \in \mathbb{N}^*$, let (a_r) be the sequence where

$$a_r = \begin{cases} 1 & \text{if } r = n, \\ 0 & \text{otherwise.} \end{cases}$$

That is,

$$(a_r) = (\underset{\underset{0}{\uparrow}}{0}, \underset{\underset{1}{\uparrow}}{0}, \dots, 0, \underset{\underset{n}{\uparrow}}{1}, 0, 0, \dots).$$

Then the generating function for (a_r) is x^n.

(b)   The generating function for the sequence $\left(\binom{n}{0}, \binom{n}{1}, \dots, \binom{n}{n}, 0, 0, \dots\right)$ is

$$\sum_{r=0}^{n} \binom{n}{r} x^r = (1+x)^n. \tag{5.1.2}$$

(c)   The generating function for the sequence $(1, 1, 1, \dots)$ is

$$1 + x + x^2 + \dots = \frac{1}{1-x}. \tag{5.1.3}$$

More generally, the generating function for the sequence $(1, k, k^2, \dots)$, where k is an arbitrary constant, is

$$1 + kx + k^2 x^2 + k^3 x^3 + \dots = \frac{1}{1-kx}. \tag{5.1.4}$$

(d)   The generating function for the sequence $(1, 2, 3, \dots)$ is

$$1 + 2x + 3x^2 + \dots = \frac{1}{(1-x)^2}. \tag{5.1.5}$$

(e)   The generating function for the sequence

$$\left(\binom{n-1}{0}, \binom{1+n-1}{1}, \dots, \binom{r+n-1}{r}, \dots\right)$$

is

$$\sum_{r=0}^{\infty} \binom{r+n-1}{r} x^r = \frac{1}{(1-x)^n}. \quad \blacksquare \tag{5.1.6}$$

Formulae (5.1.2) – (5.1.6) are very useful in finding the coefficients of generating functions, as illustrated in the following example.

Example 5.1.2. Find the coefficient of x^k, $k \geq 18$, in the expansion
of

$$(x^3 + x^4 + x^5 + \cdots)^6.$$

Solution. Observe that

$$
\begin{aligned}
&(x^3 + x^4 + x^5 + \cdots)^6 \\
&= \{x^3(1 + x + x^2 + \cdots)\}^6 \\
&= x^{18}(1 + x + x^2 + \cdots)^6 \\
&= x^{18}\left(\frac{1}{1-x}\right)^6 \quad \text{(by (5.1.3))} \\
&= x^{18}\sum_{r=0}^{\infty}\binom{r+6-1}{r}x^r \quad \text{(by (5.1.6))} \\
&= x^{18}\sum_{r=0}^{\infty}\binom{r+5}{5}x^r.
\end{aligned}
$$

Thus the coefficient of x^k, $k \geq 18$, in the expansion of $(x^3 + x^4 + x^5 + \cdots)^6$ is the coefficient of x^{k-18} in $\sum \binom{r+5}{5}x^r$, which is $\binom{k-18+5}{5} = \binom{k-13}{5}$.

In particular, the coefficient of x^{30} in $(x^3 + x^4 + x^5 + \cdots)^6$ is $\binom{17}{5}$. ∎

To facilitate algebraic manipulations of generating functions, we have the following results.

Theorem 5.1.1. (**Operations on Generating Functions**) *Let $A(x)$ and $B(x)$ be, respectively, the generating functions for the sequences (a_r) and (b_r). Then*

(i) *for any numbers α and β, $\alpha A(x) + \beta B(x)$ is the generating function for the sequence (c_r), where*

$$c_r = \alpha a_r + \beta b_r, \quad \text{for all } r;$$

(ii) *$A(x)B(x)$ is the generating function for the sequence (c_r), where*

$$c_r = a_0 b_r + a_1 b_{r-1} + a_2 b_{r-2} + \cdots + a_{r-1}b_1 + a_r b_0, \quad \text{for all } r;$$

(iii) *$A^2(x)$ is the generating function for the sequence (c_r), where*

$$c_r = a_0 a_r + a_1 a_{r-1} + a_2 a_{r-2} + \cdots + a_{r-1}a_1 + a_r a_0, \quad \text{for all } r;$$

(iv) $x^m A(x)$, $m \in \mathbf{N}$, *is the generating function for the sequence* (c_r), *where*

$$c_r = \begin{cases} 0 & \text{if } 0 \le r \le m-1 \\ a_{r-m} & \text{if } r \ge m; \end{cases}$$

(v) $A(kx)$, *where k is a constant, is the generating function for the sequence* (c_r), *where*

$$c_r = k^r a_r, \quad \text{for all } r;$$

(vi) $(1-x)A(x)$ *is the generating function for the sequence* (c_r), *where*

$$c_0 = a_0 \quad \text{and} \quad c_r = a_r - a_{r-1}, \quad \text{for all } r \ge 1;$$

i.e., $\qquad (c_r) = (a_0, a_1 - a_0, a_2 - a_1, \ldots);$

(vii) $\frac{A(x)}{1-x}$ *is the generating function for the sequence* (c_r), *where*

$$c_r = a_0 + a_1 + \cdots + a_r, \quad \text{for all } r;$$

i.e., $\qquad (c_r) = (a_0, a_0 + a_1, a_0 + a_1 + a_2, \ldots);$

(viii) $A'(x)$ *is the generating function for the sequence* (c_r), *where*

$$c_r = (r+1)a_{r+1}, \quad \text{for all } r;$$

i.e., $\qquad (c_r) = (a_1, 2a_2, 3a_3, \ldots);$

(ix) $xA'(x)$ *is the generating function for the sequence* (c_r), *where*

$$c_r = ra_r, \quad \text{for all } r;$$

i.e., $\qquad (c_r) = (0, a_1, 2a_2, 3a_3, \ldots);$

(x) $\int_0^x A(t)dt$ *is the generating function for the sequence* (c_r), *where*

$$c_0 = 0 \quad \text{and} \quad c_r = \frac{a_{r-1}}{r}, \quad \text{for all } r \ge 1;$$

i.e., $\qquad (c_r) = (0, a_0, \frac{a_1}{2}, \frac{a_2}{3}, \ldots).$

Proof. (i), (ii) and (v) follow directly from the definition, whereas (iii), (iv) and (vi) are special cases of (ii). Also, (viii), (ix) and (x) are straightfoward. We shall prove (vii) only.

(vii) By (5.1.3), $\frac{1}{1-x} = 1 + x + x^2 + \cdots$. Thus

$$\frac{A(x)}{1-x} = (a_0 + a_1 x + a_2 x^2 + \cdots)(1 + x + x^2 + \cdots)$$
$$= a_0 + (a_0 + a_1)x + (a_0 + a_1 + a_2)x^2 + \cdots.$$

Hence $\frac{A(x)}{1-x}$ is the generating function for the sequence (c_r), where $c_r = a_0 + a_1 + \cdots + a_r$. ∎

We see from Theorem 5.1.1 that operations on the terms of sequences correspond to simpler operations on their generating functions. Thus the generating function becomes a useful tool in the algebraic manipulations of sequences.

Example 5.1.3. Express the generating function for each of the following sequences (c_r) in closed form (i.e., a form not involving any series):

(i) $c_r = 3r + 5$ for each $r \in \mathbf{N}^*$;

(ii) $c_r = r^2$ for each $r \in \mathbf{N}^*$.

Solution. (i) Let $a_r = r$ and $b_r = 1$ for all r. The generating function for the sequence (a_r) is $\frac{x}{(1-x)^2}$, by (5.1.5) and Theorem 5.1.1(iv); while the generating function for (b_r) is $\frac{1}{1-x}$, by (5.1.3). Thus, by Theorem 5.1.1(i), the generating function for the sequence (c_r), where $c_r = 3r + 5 = 3a_r + 5b_r$, is given by $\frac{3x}{(1-x)^2} + \frac{5}{1-x}$.

(ii) Let $a_r = r$ for all r. As in (i), the generating function for the sequence (a_r) is $A(x) = \frac{x}{(1-x)^2}$. Since $c_r = r^2 = ra_r$, by Theorem 5.1.1(ix), the generating function for the sequence (c_r) is

$$xA'(x) = x \cdot \frac{(1-x)^2 + x \cdot 2(1-x)}{(1-x)^4} = \frac{x(1+x)}{(1-x)^3}. \quad \blacksquare$$

5.2. Some Modelling Problems

In this section, we shall discuss how the notion of generating functions, as introduced in the preceding section, can be used to solve some combinatorial problems. Through the examples provided, the reader will be able to see the applicability of the technique studied here.

To begin with, let $S = \{a, b, c\}$. Consider the various ways of selecting objects from S.

To select one object from S, we have:

$$\{a\} \text{ or } \{b\} \text{ or } \{c\} \text{ (denoted by } a + b + c).$$

To select two objects from S, we have:

$$\{a, b\} \text{ or } \{b, c\} \text{ or } \{c, a\} \text{ (denoted by } ab + bc + ca).$$

To select three objects from S, we have:

$$\{a, b, c\} \text{ (denoted by } abc).$$

These symbols can be found in the following expression:

$$(1 + ax)(1 + bx)(1 + cx)$$
$$= 1x^0 + (a + b + c)x^1 + (ab + bc + ca)x^2 + (abc)x^3. \qquad (*)$$

We may write $1 + ax = x^0 + ax^1$, which may be interpreted as "a is not selected or a is selected once" (see the figure below).

Similarly, $1 + bx$ and $1 + cx$ may be interpreted likewise. Now, expanding the product on the LHS of the equality $(*)$, we obtain the expression on the RHS, from which we see that the exponent of x in a term indicates the number of objects in a selection and the corresponding coefficient shows all the possible ways of selections.

Since we are only interested in the number of ways of selection, we may simply let $a = b = c = 1$ and obtain the following:

$$(1 + x)(1 + x)(1 + x) = 1 + 3x + 3x^2 + 1x^3,$$

which is the generating function for the sequence $(1, 3, 3, 1, 0, 0, \ldots)$ (or simply $(1, 3, 3, 1)$ after truncating the 0's at the end of the sequence). Hence the generating function for the number of ways to select r objects from 3 distinct objects is $(1 + x)^3$.

Example 5.2.1. Let $S = \{s_1, s_2, \ldots, s_n\}$, and let a_r denote the number of ways of selecting r elements from S. Then the generating function for the sequence (a_r) is given by

$$\underset{(s_1)}{(1+x)} \underset{(s_2)}{(1+x)} \cdots \underset{(s_n)}{(1+x)} = (1+x)^n = \sum_{r=0}^{n} \binom{n}{r} x^r.$$

Thus $\sum_{r=0}^{\infty} a_r x^r = \sum_{r=0}^{n} \binom{n}{r} x^r$, which implies that

$$a_r = \begin{cases} \binom{n}{r} & \text{if } 0 \leq r \leq n, \\ 0 & \text{if } r \geq n+1. \end{cases} \blacksquare$$

Now, let S be the multi-set $\{2 \cdot a, 1 \cdot b\}$. Consider the various ways of selecting objects from S.

To select one object from S, we have:

$$\{a\} \text{ or } \{b\} \text{ (denoted by } a + b\text{)}.$$

To select two objects from S, we have:

$$\{a, a\} \text{ or } \{a, b\} \text{ (denoted by } a^2 + ab\text{)}.$$

To select three objects from S, we have:

$$\{a, a, b\} \text{ (denoted by } a^2 b\text{)}.$$

These symbols can be found in the following expression:

$$(1 + ax + a^2 x^2)(1 + bx) = 1x^0 + (a+b)x^1 + (a^2 + ab)x^2 + (a^2 b)x^3.$$

As before, the exponent of x in the equality indicates the number of objects in a selection and the corresponding coefficients show all the possible ways of selections.

Again, since we are only interested in the number of ways of selection, we may simply let $a = b = 1$ and obtain the following

$$(1 + x + x^2)(1 + x) = 1 + 2x + 2x^2 + 1x^3,$$

which is the generating function for the sequence $(1, 2, 2, 1, 0, 0, \ldots)$ (or simpy $(1, 2, 2, 1)$). Hence the generating function for the number of ways to select r objects from the multi-set $\{2 \cdot a, 1 \cdot b\}$ is $(1 + x + x^2)(1 + x)$.

Example 5.2.2.   Find the number of ways to select 4 members from the multi-set $M = \{2 \cdot b, 1 \cdot c, 2 \cdot d, 1 \cdot e\}$.

Solution.   Let a_r be the number of ways of selecting r members from M. Then the generating function for the sequence (a_r) is given by

$$\underset{(b)}{(1 + x + x^2)} \underset{(c)}{(1 + x)} \underset{(d)}{(1 + x + x^2)} \underset{(e)}{(1 + x)}$$

$$= (1 + 2x + 2x^2 + x^3)(1 + 2x + 2x^2 + x^3).$$

The required answer is a_4, which is the coefficient of x^4. Thus $a_4 = 2 + 4 + 2 = 8$. ∎

More generally, we have:

Let a_r be the number of ways of selecting r members from the multi-set $M = \{n_1 \cdot b_1, n_2 \cdot b_2, \ldots, n_k \cdot b_k\}$. Then the generating function for the sequence (a_r) is given by

$$\underset{(b_1)}{(1 + x + \cdots + x^{n_1})} \underset{(b_2)}{(1 + x + \cdots + x^{n_2})} \cdots \underset{(b_k)}{(1 + x + \cdots + x^{n_k})}.$$

That is, a_r is the coefficient of x^r in the expansion of the above product.

Example 5.2.3.   Let a_r be the number of ways of selecting r members from the multi-set $M = \{\infty \cdot b_1, \infty \cdot b_2, \cdots, \infty \cdot b_k\}$. Then the generating function for the sequence (a_r) is given by

$$\underset{(b_1)}{(1 + x + x^2 + \cdots)} \underset{(b_2)}{(1 + x + x^2 + \cdots)} \cdots \underset{(b_k)}{(1 + x + x^2 + \cdots)}$$

$$= \left(\frac{1}{1-x}\right)^k = \sum_{r=0}^{\infty} \binom{r+k-1}{r} x^r.$$

Thus $a_r = \binom{r+k-1}{r}$. ∎

Remark. The answer a_r in Example 5.2.3 can also be obtained by enumerating the coefficient of x^r in the expansion of the following generating function:

$$(1 + x + x^2 + \cdots + x^r)^k.$$

Though now the number of terms in each factor is finite, it actually does not simplify the computation, as

$$(1 + x + \cdots + x^r)^k = \left(\frac{1 - x^{r+1}}{1 - x}\right)^k,$$

which leads to a more complicated expansion than the one given in the example above.

Example 5.2.4. Let a_r be the number of ways of distributing r identical objects into n distinct boxes. Then the generating function for (a_r) is:

$$\underbrace{(1 + x + x^2 + \cdots)}_{\text{(box 1)}}\underbrace{(1 + x + x^2 + \cdots)}_{\text{(box 2)}}\cdots\underbrace{(1 + x + x^2 + \cdots)}_{\text{(box n)}}$$

$$= \left(\frac{1}{1 - x}\right)^n = \sum_{r=0}^{\infty}\binom{r + n - 1}{r}x^r.$$

Thus $a_r = \binom{r+n-1}{r}$. ∎

Example 5.2.5. Let a_r be the number of ways of distributing r identical objects into n distinct boxes such that no box is empty. Since a box must hold at least one object, the corresponding generating function for each box is $(x + x^2 + x^3 + \cdots)$. Hence, the generating function for (a_r) is

$$(x + x^2 + \cdots)^n = x^n(1 + x + x^2 + \cdots)^n$$

$$= x^n\left(\frac{1}{1 - x}\right)^n = x^n\sum_{i=0}^{\infty}\binom{i + n - 1}{i}x^i.$$

Thus

$$a_r = \begin{cases} 0 & \text{if } r < n, \\ \binom{r-n+n-1}{n-1} = \binom{r-1}{n-1} & \text{if } r \geq n. \end{cases} \quad ∎$$

Example 5.2.6.   Each of the 3 boys tosses a die once. Find the number of ways for them to get a total of 14.

Solution.   Let a_r be the number of ways to get a total of r. Since the outcomes of tossing a die are $1, 2, 3, 4, 5$ and 6, the generating function for (a_r) is

$$(x + x^2 + \cdots + x^6)^3$$

$$= x^3(1 + x + \cdots + x^5)^3 = x^3 \left(\frac{1 - x^6}{1 - x}\right)^3$$

$$= x^3(1 - 3x^6 + 3x^{12} - x^{18}) \sum_{i=0}^{\infty} \binom{i + 2}{2} x^i.$$

The required answer is a_{14}, which is the coefficient of x^{14}. Thus

$$a_{14} = \binom{11 + 2}{2} - 3\binom{5 + 2}{2} = \binom{13}{2} - 3\binom{7}{2}. \quad \blacksquare$$

5.3. Partitions of Integers

A *partition* of a positive integer n is a collection of positive integers whose sum is n (or a way of expressing n as a sum of positive integers, ordering not taken into account). Since the ordering is immaterial, we may regard a partition of n as a finite nonincreasing sequence $n_1 \geq n_2 \geq \cdots \geq n_k$ of positive integers such that $\sum_{i=1}^{k} n_i = n$. The number of different partitions of n is denoted by $p(n)$.

Example 5.3.1.   The following table shows the partitions of 1, 2, 3, 4 and 5.

n	partitions of n	$p(n)$
1	1	1
2	$2 = 1 + 1$	2
3	$3 = 2 + 1 = 1 + 1 + 1$	3
4	$4 = 3 + 1 = 2 + 2 = 2 + 1 + 1 = 1 + 1 + 1 + 1$	5
5	$5 = 4 + 1 = 3 + 2 = 3 + 1 + 1 = 2 + 2 + 1$	
	$= 2 + 1 + 1 + 1 = 1 + 1 + 1 + 1 + 1$	7

Notes. (1) If $n = n_1 + n_2 + \cdots n_k$ is a partition of n, we say that n is partitioned into k parts of sizes $n_1, n_2, \ldots, n_k$ respectively. Thus, in the partition $9 = 3 + 3 + 2 + 1$, there are 4 parts of sizes 3, 3, 2 and 1 respectively.

(2) A partition of n is equivalent to a way of distributing n identical objects into n identical boxes (with empty boxes allowed), as illustrated below:

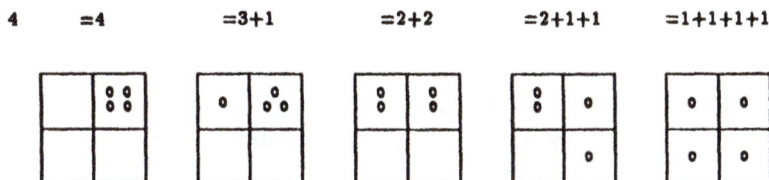

Example 5.3.2. Let a_r be the number of partitions of an integer r into parts of sizes 1, 2 or 3. The generating function for (a_r) is

$$\underset{\text{(size 1)}}{(1 + x + x^2 + \cdots)} \underset{\text{(size 2)}}{(1 + x^2 + x^4 + \cdots)} \underset{\text{(size 3)}}{(1 + x^3 + x^6 + \cdots)}$$

$$= \frac{1}{(1-x)(1-x^2)(1-x^3)}.$$

Note that the three factors in the above generating function are of the form

$$(x^k)^0 + (x^k)^1 + (x^k)^2 + \cdots,$$

where $k = 1, 2, 3$ and a term $(x^k)^j$ indicates that, in the partition, there are j parts of size k.

Now, consider the term containing x^3 and its coefficient. We see that the coefficient of x^3 is 3 since there are 3 ways of getting x^3 (namely, $x^3 = (x^1)^0 (x^2)^0 (x^3)^1 = (x^1)^1 (x^2)^1 (x^3)^0 = (x^1)^3 (x^2)^0 (x^3)^0$) in the above generating function, as illustrated in the following table.

	Size 1	Size 2	Size 3	
	x^0	x^0	x^3	$3 = 3$
$3x^3$ $\{$	x^1	x^2	x^0	$3 = 1 + 2$
	x^3	x^0	x^0	$3 = 1 + 1 + 1$

Similarly, consider the term containing x^4 and its coefficient. We see that the coefficient of x^4 is 4 since there are 4 ways of getting x^4 in the above generating function, as illustrated in the following table.

	Size 1	Size 2	Size 3	
	x^0	x^4	x^0	$4 = 2 + 2$
$4x^4$	x^1	x^0	x^3	$4 = 1 + 3$
	x^2	x^2	x^0	$4 = 1 + 1 + 2$
	x^4	x^0	x^0	$4 = 1 + 1 + 1 + 1.$

Example 5.3.3. Let a_r be the number of partitions of r into *distinct* parts of sizes 1, 2, 3 or 4. The generating function for (a_r) is

$$(1 + x)(1 + x^2)(1 + x^3)(1 + x^4).$$

We note that, in this partition, no repetition is allowed. So a part of size k is used at most once and thus the corresponding generating function is $(x^k)^0 + (x^k)^1 = 1 + x^k$. There are two ways to form x^6, namely:

$$x^6 = 1 \cdot x^2 \cdot 1 \cdot x^4 \quad \leftrightarrow \quad 6 = 2 + 4$$
$$x^6 = x \cdot x^2 \cdot x^3 \cdot 1 \quad \leftrightarrow \quad 6 = 1 + 2 + 3.$$

Thus $a_6 = 2$. ∎

Example 5.3.4. Let a_r denote the number of partitions of r into *distinct* parts (of arbitrary sizes). For instance,

$$6 = 5 + 1 = 4 + 2 = 3 + 2 + 1;$$
$$7 = 6 + 1 = 5 + 2 = 4 + 3 = 4 + 2 + 1;$$
$$8 = 7 + 1 = 6 + 2 = 5 + 3 = 5 + 2 + 1 = 4 + 3 + 1.$$

Thus, $a_6 = 4$, $a_7 = 5$ and $a_8 = 6$.

It is easy to see that the generating function for (a_r) is

$$\underset{(1)}{(1 + x)} \underset{(2)}{(1 + x^2)} \underset{(3)}{(1 + x^3)} \cdots = \prod_{i=1}^{\infty} (1 + x^i).$$

We note that, since the size of each part is arbitrary, the number of terms on the LHS is infinite.

For example, in the above product, there are 4 ways to form x^6, namely:

$$x^6 = x^6 \qquad \leftrightarrow \qquad 6 = 6$$
$$x^6 = x^1 x^5 \qquad \leftrightarrow \qquad 6 = 5 + 1.$$
$$x^6 = x^2 x^4 \qquad \leftrightarrow \qquad 6 = 4 + 2.$$
$$x^6 = x^1 x^2 x^3 \qquad \leftrightarrow \qquad 6 = 3 + 2 + 1.$$

Thus $a_6 = 4$. ∎

Example 5.3.5. A part in a partition is said to be *odd* if its size is odd. Let b_r denote the number of partitions of r into odd parts. For instance,

$$6 = 5 + 1 = 3 + 3 = 3 + 1 + 1 + 1 = 1 + 1 + 1 + 1 + 1 + 1;$$
$$7 = 7 = 5 + 1 + 1 = 3 + 3 + 1 = 3 + 1 + 1 + 1 + 1$$
$$= 1 + 1 + 1 + 1 + 1 + 1 + 1;$$
$$8 = 7 + 1 = 5 + 3 = 5 + 1 + 1 + 1 = 3 + 3 + 1 + 1$$
$$= 3 + 1 + 1 + 1 + 1 + 1 = 1 + 1 + 1 + 1 + 1 + 1 + 1 + 1.$$

Thus, $b_6 = 4$, $b_7 = 5$ and $b_8 = 6$.

The generating function for (b_r) is

$$\underbrace{(1 + x + x^2 + \cdots)}_{(1)} \underbrace{(1 + x^3 + x^6 + \cdots)}_{(3)} \underbrace{(1 + x^5 + x^{10} + \cdots)}_{(5)} \cdots$$
$$= \frac{1}{(1 - x)(1 - x^3)(1 - x^5) \cdots}.$$

For example, in the above product, there are 4 ways to form x^6, namely:

$$(x^1)^6, \qquad (x^1)^3 x^3, \qquad x^1 x^5, \qquad (x^3)^2.$$
$$\downarrow \qquad\qquad \downarrow \qquad\qquad \downarrow \qquad \downarrow$$
$$1+1+1+1+1+1 \quad 1+1+1+3 \quad 1+5 \quad 3+3$$

Thus $b_6 = 4$. ∎

From the two examples above, we notice that $a_6 = 4 = b_6$, $a_7 = 5 = b_7$ and $a_8 = 6 = b_8$. This is by no means a coincidence. In fact, these equalities are just special cases of the following result due to Euler, who laid the foundation of the theory of partitions, around 1748, by proving many beautiful theorems about partitions.

Theorem 5.3.1. (Euler) *The number of partitions of r into distinct parts is equal to the number of partitions of r into odd parts.*

Proof. Let a_r (resp., b_r) denote the number of partitions of r into distinct (resp., odd) parts. Then the generating function for (a_r) is

$$(1+x)(1+x^2)(1+x^3)(1+x^4)\cdots$$
$$=\frac{1-x^2}{1-x}\frac{1-x^4}{1-x^2}\frac{1-x^6}{1-x^3}\frac{1-x^8}{1-x^4}\cdots$$
$$=\frac{1}{(1-x)(1-x^3)(1-x^5)\cdots},$$

which is exactly equal to the generating function for (b_r). Hence $a_r = b_r$ for each $r = 1, 2, \ldots$. ∎

The technique used in the proof of Theorem 5.3.1 can be utilized to prove many other results of the "Euler type". For instance, we have:

Theorem 5.3.2. *For each $n \in \mathbb{N}$, the number of partitions of n into parts each of which appears at most twice, is equal to the number of partitions of n into parts the sizes of which are not divisible by 3.*

Before proving the result, let us examine it by taking $n = 6$. We see that there are 7 ways of partitioning 6 into parts, each of which appears at most twice, as shown below:

$$6 = 5 + 1 = 4 + 2 = 4 + 1 + 1 = 3 + 3$$
$$= 3 + 2 + 1 = 2 + 2 + 1 + 1.$$

There are also 7 ways of partitioning 6 into parts, the sizes of which are not divisible by 3, namely:

$$5 + 1 = 4 + 2 = 4 + 1 + 1 = 2 + 2 + 2 = 2 + 2 + 1 + 1$$
$$= 2 + 1 + 1 + 1 + 1 = 1 + 1 + 1 + 1 + 1 + 1.$$

Proof of Theorem 5.3.2. The generating function for the number of partitions of n into parts, each of which appears at most twice, is

$$(1 + x + x^2)(1 + x^2 + x^4)(1 + x^3 + x^6)(1 + x^4 + x^8) \cdots .$$

However, we have

$$(1 + x + x^2)(1 + x^2 + x^4)(1 + x^3 + x^6)(1 + x^4 + x^8) \cdots$$

$$= \frac{(1-x)(1+x+x^2)}{(1-x)} \frac{(1-x^2)(1+x^2+x^4)}{(1-x^2)} \frac{(1-x^3)(1+x^3+x^6)}{(1-x^3)}$$

$$\cdot \frac{(1-x^4)(1+x^4+x^8)}{(1-x^4)} \cdots$$

$$= \frac{1-x^3}{1-x} \frac{1-x^6}{1-x^2} \frac{1-x^9}{1-x^3} \frac{1-x^{12}}{1-x^4} \cdots$$

$$= \frac{1}{1-x} \frac{1}{1-x^2} \frac{1}{1-x^4} \frac{1}{1-x^5} \frac{1}{1-x^7} \cdots$$

$$= \prod \left(\frac{1}{1-x^k} \,\middle|\, k \in \mathbf{N}, 3 \nmid k \right),$$

which is exactly the generating function for the number of partitions of n into parts the sizes of which are not divisible by 3. ∎

Theorem 5.3.2 has the following generalization that was discovered by J.W.L. Glaisher in 1883.

Theorem 5.3.3. [G] *For any $n, k \in \mathbf{N}$, the number of partitions of n into parts, each of which appears at most k times, is equal to the number of partitions of n into parts the sizes of which are not divisible by $k+1$.* ∎

We leave the proofs of this and the following result as exercises for the reader (see Problems 5.59).

Theorem 5.3.4. *For any $n \in \mathbf{N}$, the number of partitions of n into parts each of which appears at least twice is equal to the number of partitions of n into parts the sizes of which are not congruent to 1 or -1 (mod 6).* ∎

Theorem 5.3.4 first appeared in the literature as an exercise in the book [An1] by Andrew. Interested readers may read the paper by H.L. Alder [Al] which gives a very comprehensive account of results and problems of the Euler type.

Ferrers Diagram

A convenient tool, in the form of a diagram, to study partitions of integers is due to Norman M. Ferrers (1829-1903). The *Ferrers diagram* for a partition $n = n_1 + n_2 + \cdots + n_k$ of a positive integer n ($n_1 \geq n_2 \geq \cdots \geq n_k$) is an array of asterisks in left-justified rows with n_i asterisks in the ith row. For each partition P of an integer, we shall denote by $\mathcal{F}(P)$ the Ferrers diagram for P.

Example 5.3.6. Let P be the partition of the number 15 as shown below:

$$P : 15 = 6 + 3 + 3 + 2 + 1.$$

Then, the Ferrers diagram $\mathcal{F}(P)$ of P is:

$$\mathcal{F}(P) : \quad \begin{cases} * \quad * \quad * \quad * \quad * \quad * \\ * \quad * \quad * \\ * \quad * \quad * \\ * \quad * \\ * \end{cases}$$

The transpose $\mathcal{F}^t$ of a Ferrers diagram is the Ferrers diagram whose rows are the columns of $\mathcal{F}$. Thus the transpose of the Ferrers diagram above is:

$$\mathcal{F}(P)^t : \quad \begin{cases} * \quad * \quad * \quad * \quad * \\ * \quad * \quad * \quad * \\ * \quad * \quad * \\ * \\ * \\ * \end{cases}$$

which gives another partition of 15:

$$Q : 15 = 5 + 4 + 3 + 1 + 1 + 1. \quad \blacksquare$$

Two partitions of n whose Ferrers diagrams are transpose of each other are called *conjugate partitions*. Thus, P and Q in the above example are conjugate partitions. It follows readily from the definition that the number of parts in P (which is 5, the number of rows in $\mathcal{F}(P)$) is equal to the largest size in Q (which is the number of columns in $\mathcal{F}(P)^t$). This observation enables us to have the following simple proof of another result, also due to Euler.

Theorem 5.3.5. (Euler) *Let $k, n \in \mathbb{N}$ with $k \leq n$. Then the number of partitions of n into k parts is equal to the number of partitions of n into parts the largest size of which is k.*

Proof. Let $\mathcal{P}$ be the family of all partitions of n into k parts and $\mathcal{Q}$ be the family of all partitions of n into parts the largest size of which is k. Define a mapping $f : \mathcal{P} \rightarrow \mathcal{Q}$ as follows: For each $P \in \mathcal{P}$, we put $f(P)$ to be the partition of n whose Ferrers diagram is $\mathcal{F}(P)^t$ (i.e., $f(P)$ is just the conjugate of P). It is easy to see that f establishes a bijection between $\mathcal{P}$ and $\mathcal{Q}$. Thus $|\mathcal{P}| = |\mathcal{Q}|$, by (BP). ∎

We illustrate the above proof for $n = 8$ and $k = 3$ by the following table:

partitions of 8 into 3 parts	partitions of 8 into parts the largest size of which is 3
P	$f(P)$
$6 + 1 + 1$	$\longleftrightarrow$ $\quad 3 + 1 + 1 + 1 + 1 + 1$
$5 + 2 + 1$	$\longleftrightarrow$ $\quad 3 + 2 + 1 + 1 + 1$
$4 + 3 + 1$	$\longleftrightarrow$ $\quad 3 + 2 + 2 + 1$
$4 + 2 + 2$	$\longleftrightarrow$ $\quad 3 + 3 + 1 + 1$
$3 + 3 + 2$	$\longleftrightarrow$ $\quad 3 + 3 + 2$

An application of Theorem 5.3.5 is given in the following example.

Example 5.3.7. Let a_r denote the number of ways of distributing r identical objects into 3 identical boxes such that no box is empty. Find the generating function for (a_r).

Solution. First, note that a_r is equal to the number of partition of r into 3 parts. Thus by Theorem 5.3.5, a_r is equal to the number of partitions of r into parts the largest size of which is 3. With this observation, we can now obtain the generating function for (a_r), as shown below:

$$(1 + x + x^2 + \cdots)(1 + x^2 + x^4 + \cdots)(x^3 + x^6 + \cdots)$$
$$\text{(size 1)} \qquad\qquad \text{(size 2)} \qquad\qquad \text{(size 3)}$$

$$= \frac{x^3}{(1 - x)(1 - x^2)(1 - x^3)}. \quad\blacksquare$$

Remark. The reader should notice that the third factor on the LHS of the above equality is $(x^3+x^6+\cdots)$ rather than $(1+x^3+x^6+\cdots)$ (why?).

As an immediate consequence of Theorem 5.3.5, we have:

Corollary. *Let $m, n \in \mathbf{N}$ with $m \leq n$. Then the number of partitions of n into at most m parts is equal to the number of partitions of n into parts with sizes not exceeding m.* ∎

For a detailed and advanced treatment of the theory of partitions of numbers, we refer the reader to the book [An2] by Andrew.

5.4. Exponential Generating Functions

From the problems as discussed in the previous two sections, we see that (ordinary) generating functions are applicable in distribution problems or arrangement problems, in which the ordering of the objects involved is immaterial. In this section, we shall study the so-called "exponential generating functions" that will be useful in the counting of arrangements of objects where the ordering is taken into consideration.

The *exponential generating function* for the sequence of numbers (a_r) is defined to be the power series

$$a_0 + a_1\frac{x}{1!} + a_2\frac{x^2}{2!} + a_3\frac{x^3}{3!} + \cdots + a_r\frac{x^r}{r!} + \cdots = \sum_{r=0}^{\infty} a_r\frac{x^r}{r!}.$$

Example 5.4.1. (1) The exponential generating function for $(1, 1, ..., 1, ...)$ is

$$\sum_{r=0}^{\infty} \frac{x^r}{r!} = e^x.$$

(This explains why the name "exponential generating function" is used, as it includes the exponential function e^x as a special case.)

(2) The exponential generating function for $(0!, 1!, 2!, ..., r!, ...)$ is

$$\sum_{r=0}^{\infty} r!\frac{x^r}{r!} = 1 + x + x^2 + \cdots = \frac{1}{1-x}.$$

(3) The exponential generating function for $(1, k, k^2, ..., k^r, ...)$, where k is a nonzero constant, is

$$1 + \frac{kx}{1!} + \frac{k^2 x^2}{2!} + \cdots = \sum_{r=0}^{\infty} \frac{(kx)^r}{r!} = e^{kx}. \quad \blacksquare$$

Example 5.4.2. Show that the exponential generating function for the sequence

$$(1, \ 1\cdot 3, \ 1\cdot 3\cdot 5, \ 1\cdot 3\cdot 5\cdot 7, \ ...)$$

is $(1 - 2x)^{-\frac{3}{2}}$.

Proof. It suffices to show that the coefficient of x^r in $(1 - 2x)^{-\frac{3}{2}}$ is $\dfrac{1\cdot 3\cdot 5\cdots(2r+1)}{r!}$.

Indeed, the coefficient of x^r in $(1 - 2x)^{-\frac{3}{2}} = \sum_{i=0}^{\infty} \binom{-\frac{3}{2}}{i}(-2x)^i$ is

$$(-2)^r \binom{-\frac{3}{2}}{r} = (-2)^r \frac{(-\frac{3}{2})(-\frac{3}{2} - 1)\cdots(-\frac{3}{2} - r + 1)}{r!}$$

$$= (-2)^r (-\frac{1}{2})^r \frac{3\cdot 5\cdot 7\cdots(2r+1)}{r!} = \frac{1\cdot 3\cdot 5\cdots(2r+1)}{r!},$$

as required. $\blacksquare$

Exponential generating functions for permutations

Recall that P_r^n denotes the number of r-permutations of n distinct objects, and

$$P_r^n = \binom{n}{r} \cdot r! \ .$$

Then

$$\sum_{r=0}^{n} P_r^n \frac{x^r}{r!} = \sum_{r=0}^{n} \binom{n}{r} x^r = (1 + x)^n.$$

Thus, by definition, the exponential generating function for the sequence $(P_r^n)_{r=0,1,2,...}$ is $(1 + x)^n$.

Note that

$$(1 + x)^n = \underset{(1)}{(1 + \frac{x^1}{1!})} \underset{(2)}{(1 + \frac{x^1}{1!})} \cdots \underset{(n)}{(1 + \frac{x^1}{1!})},$$

where, as before, each bracket on the RHS corresponds to a distinct object in the arrangement.

Example 5.4.3.   Let a_r denote the number of r-permutations of p identical objects. The exponential generating function for (a_r) is

$$1 + \frac{x}{1!} + \frac{x^2}{2!} + \cdots + \frac{x^p}{p!},$$

since $a_r = 1$ for each $r = 0, 1, 2, \ldots, p$ and $a_r = 0$ for each $r > p$. ∎

Example 5.4.4.   Let a_r denote the number of r-permutations of p identical blue balls and q identical red balls. The exponential generating function for (a_r) is

$$\underbrace{(1 + \frac{x}{1!} + \frac{x^2}{2!} + \cdots + \frac{x^p}{p!})}_{(B)} \underbrace{(1 + \frac{x}{1!} + \frac{x^2}{2!} + \cdots + \frac{x^q}{q!})}_{(R)}. \text{∎}$$

In general, we have

Let a_r denote the number of r-permutations of the multi-set

$$\{n_1 \cdot b_1, n_2 \cdot b_2, \ldots, n_k \cdot b_k\}.$$

Then the exponential generating function for (a_r) is

$$\underbrace{(1 + \frac{x}{1!} + \cdots + \frac{x^{n_1}}{n_1!})}_{(b_1)} \underbrace{(1 + \frac{x}{1!} + \cdots + \frac{x^{n_2}}{n_2!})}_{(b_2)} \cdots \underbrace{(1 + \frac{x}{1!} + \cdots + \frac{x^{n_k}}{n_k!})}_{(b_k)},$$

and a_r is the coefficient of $\frac{x^r}{r!}$ in the expansion of the above product.

Example 5.4.5.   In how many ways can 4 of the letters from PAPAYA be arranged?

Solution.   Let a_r be the number of r-permutations of the multi-set

$$\{3 \cdot A, 2 \cdot P, 1 \cdot Y\}$$

formed by all the letters from PAPAYA. Then the exponential generating function for (a_r) is

$$\underbrace{(1 + \frac{x^1}{1!} + \frac{x^2}{2!} + \frac{x^3}{3!})}_{(A)} \underbrace{(1 + \frac{x^1}{1!} + \frac{x^2}{2!})}_{(P)} \underbrace{(1 + \frac{x^1}{1!})}_{(Y)}.$$

Grouping the like terms x^4 in the product, we have

$$x \cdot \frac{x^2}{2!} \cdot x + \frac{x^2}{2!} \cdot x \cdot x + \frac{x^2}{2!} \cdot \frac{x^2}{2!} \cdot 1 + \frac{x^3}{3!} \cdot x \cdot 1 + \frac{x^3}{3!} \cdot 1 \cdot x$$

$$= a_4 \frac{x^4}{4!},$$

where

$$a_4 = \underset{\{A,2\cdot P,Y\}}{\frac{4!}{2!}} + \underset{\{2\cdot A,P,Y\}}{\frac{4!}{2!}} + \underset{\{2\cdot A,2\cdot P\}}{\frac{4!}{2!2!}} + \underset{\{3\cdot A,P\}}{\frac{4!}{3!}} + \underset{\{3\cdot A,Y\}}{\frac{4!}{3!}},$$

which is the required answer. ∎

Example 5.4.6. Let (a_r) denote the number of r-permutations of the multi-set $\{\infty \cdot b_1, \infty \cdot b_2, \ldots, \infty \cdot b_k\}$. Then the exponential generating function for (a_r) is

$$(1 + x + \frac{x^2}{2!} + \frac{x^3}{3!} + \cdots)^k = (e^x)^k = e^{kx} = \sum_{r=0}^{\infty} \frac{(kx)^r}{r!} = \sum_{r=0}^{\infty} k^r \frac{x^r}{r!}.$$

Thus, $a_r = k^r$ for each $r \in \mathbf{N}^*$. ∎

Example 5.4.7. For each $r \in \mathbf{N}^*$, let a_r denote the number of r-digit quaternary sequences (whose digits are 0, 1, 2, 3) in which each of the digits 2 and 3 appears at least once. Find a_r.

Solution. The exponential generating function for (a_r) is

$$\underset{(0)\ (1)}{(1 + x + \frac{x^2}{2!} + \cdots)^2} \underset{(2)\ (3)}{(x + \frac{x^2}{2!} + \cdots)^2} = (e^x)^2 (e^x - 1)^2$$

$$= e^{2x}(e^{2x} - 2e^x + 1)$$

$$= e^{4x} - 2e^{3x} + e^{2x}$$

$$= \sum_{r=0}^{\infty}(4^r - 2 \cdot 3^r + 2^r)\frac{x^r}{r!}.$$

Thus, $a_r = 4^r - 2 \cdot 3^r + 2^r$ for each $r \in \mathbf{N}^*$. ∎

Remark.   Since

$$e^x = 1 + x + \frac{x^2}{2!} + \frac{x^3}{3!} + \cdots + \frac{x^n}{n!} + \cdots$$

and

$$e^{-x} = 1 - x + \frac{x^2}{2!} - \frac{x^3}{3!} + \cdots + (-1)^n \frac{x^n}{n!} + \cdots,$$

we have:

$$
\begin{aligned}
\frac{e^x + e^{-x}}{2} &= 1 + \frac{x^2}{2!} + \frac{x^4}{4!} + \cdots, \\
\frac{e^x - e^{-x}}{2} &= x + \frac{x^3}{3!} + \frac{x^5}{5!} + \cdots.
\end{aligned}
$$

We note that, in the above expansions, $\frac{e^x + e^{-x}}{2}$ involves only even powers of x whereas, $\frac{e^x - e^{-x}}{2}$ involves only odd powers of x. This observation is useful in solving the following problem.

Example 5.4.8.   For each $r \in \mathbf{N}^*$, let a_r denote the number of r-digit ternary sequences that contain an odd number of 0's and an even number of 1's. Find a_r.

Solution.   The exponential generating function for (a_r) is

$$\underset{(0)}{\left(\frac{e^x - e^{-x}}{2}\right)} \underset{(1)}{\left(\frac{e^x + e^{-x}}{2}\right)} \underset{(2)}{e^x}$$

$$= \frac{1}{4} e^x (e^{2x} - e^{-2x})$$

$$= \frac{1}{4} (e^{3x} - e^{-x})$$

$$= \frac{1}{4} \sum_{r=0}^{\infty} \{3^r - (-1)^r\} \frac{x^r}{r!}.$$

Thus, $a_r = \frac{1}{4}\{3^r - (-1)^r\}$.   ∎

Distribution Problems

We have seen in Sections 2 and 3 that the notion of (ordinary) generating functions can be used to tackle distribution problems where the objects to be distributed are *identical*. On the other hand, if we are to distribute *distinct* objects into *distinct* boxes, then the notion of exponential generating functions turns out to be very helpful, as seen in the following two examples.

Example 5.4.9. For each $r \in \mathbb{N}^*$, find a_r, the number of ways of distributing r distinct objects into 4 distinct boxes such that boxes 1 and 2 must hold an even number of objects and box 3 must hold an odd number of objects.

Before giving the solution, we shall see how the given distribution problem can be transformed into the problem of finding the number of certain r-digit quaternary sequences. Assume here that the 4 digits used are $1, 2, 3$ and 4. Then a_r is the number of r-digit quaternary sequences that contain an even number of 1's, an even number of 2's and an odd number of 3's. For instance, when $r = 7$, the correspondence between such distributions and quaternary sequences is illustrated in the following figure.

$\leftrightarrow$ 2312144

$\leftrightarrow$ 3442323

Note that a ball labelled i is placed in a box labelled j if and only if j occurs in the ith position in the corresponding quaternary sequence. For instance, in the sequence 3442323, there are two 4's in the 2nd and 3rd positions; and thus, in this distribution, balls labelled 2 and 3 are placed in box 4.

In view of the correspondence mentioned above, we can now used the notion of exponential generating function to solve the given distribution problem.

Solution. The exponential generating function for (a_r) is

$$\left(\frac{e^x + e^{-x}}{2}\right)^2 \left(\frac{e^x - e^{-x}}{2}\right) e^x$$

$$\text{(1)(2)} \qquad\qquad \text{(3)} \qquad \text{(4)}$$

$$= \frac{1}{8}(e^{2x} - e^{-2x})(e^{2x} + 1)$$

$$= \frac{1}{8}(e^{4x} - 1 + e^{2x} - e^{-2x})$$

$$= \frac{1}{8}\left\{-1 + \sum_{r=0}^{\infty}(4^r + 2^r - (-2)^r)\frac{x^r}{r!}\right\}.$$

Thus, $a_r = \frac{1}{8}\{4^r + 2^r - (-2)^r\}$, for each $r \in \mathbf{N}$. ∎

Example 5.4.10. For each $r \in \mathbf{N}^*$, find a_r, the number of ways of distributing r distinct objects into n distinct boxes such that no box is empty.

Solution. The exponential generating function for (a_r) is

$$\left(x + \frac{x^2}{2!} + \frac{x^3}{3!} + \cdots\right)^n$$

$$= (e^x - 1)^n$$

$$= \sum_{i=0}^{n}\binom{n}{i}(e^x)^{n-i}(-1)^i$$

$$= \sum_{i=0}^{n}\binom{n}{i}\left(\sum_{r=0}^{\infty}\frac{(n-i)^r x^r}{r!}\right)(-1)^i$$

$$= \sum_{r=0}^{\infty}\left(\sum_{i=0}^{n}(-1)^i\binom{n}{i}(n-i)^r\right)\frac{x^r}{r!}.$$

Thus, $a_r = \sum_{i=0}^{n}(-1)^i\binom{n}{i}(n-i)^r$, which is the number $F(r,n)$ of surjective mappings from $\mathbf{N}_r$ to $\mathbf{N}_n$, as shown in Theorem 4.5.1. ∎

Generally speaking, distribution problems can be classified into 4 types, according to whether the objects to be distributed are identical or distinct and the boxes containing these objects are identical or distinct. We end this chapter by summarizing the results for these 4 types of problems that we have obtained so far in the following table, where # denotes the number of ways to distibute r objects into n boxes subject to the conditions in columns 2 and 3 of the table.

Type	r objects	n boxes	#
I	distinct	distinct	n^r
II	identical	distinct	$\binom{r+n-1}{r}$
III	distinct	identical	$\sum_{i=1}^{n} S(r, i)$
IV	identical	identical	number of partitions of r into n or fewer parts

In this chapter, we have seen how generating functions can be used to solve distribution problems of Types I, II and IV. Briefly speaking, in a distribution problem, when identical objects are distributed to distinct boxes (cf., Examples 5.2.4 and 5.2.5), the corresponding generating function for each box is just an ordinary generating function. When distinct objects are distributed to distinct boxes (cf., Examples 5.4.9 and 5.4.10), we introduce an exponential generating function for each box. The case when identical objects are distributed to identical boxes (cf., Example 5.3.7) is just a partition problem and we introduce an ordinary generating function for the size of each part in the partition.

Exercise 5

1. Find the coefficient of x^{20} in the expansion of $(x^3 + x^4 + x^5 + \cdots)^3$.

2. Find the coefficients of x^9 and x^{14} in the expansion of $(1 + x + x^2 + \cdots + x^5)^4$.

3. Prove Theorem 5.1.1 (iv), (vi), (viii), (ix) and (x).

4. Find the generating function for the sequence (c_r), where $c_0 = 0$ and $c_r = \sum_{i=1}^{r} i^2$ for $r \in \mathbb{N}$. Hence show that

$$\sum_{i=1}^{r} i^2 = \binom{r+1}{3} + \binom{r+2}{3}.$$

5. Find the generating function for the sequence (c_r), where $c_r = \sum_{i=0}^{r} i2^i$ with $r \in \mathbf{N}^*$. Hence show that

$$\sum_{i=0}^{r} i2^i = 2 + (r-1)2^{r+1}.$$

6. (i) For $r \in \mathbf{N}^*$, let $a_r = \frac{1}{4^r}\binom{2r}{r}$. Show that the generating function for the sequence (a_r) is given by $(1-x)^{-\frac{1}{2}}$.

   (ii) Using the identity

$$(1-x)^{-1} = (1-x)^{-\frac{1}{2}}(1-x)^{-\frac{1}{2}},$$

   show that

$$\sum_{k=0}^{n} \binom{2k}{k}\binom{2(n-k)}{n-k} = 4^n$$

   for each $n \in \mathbf{N}^*$.

7. Show that

$$\sum_{r=1}^{n} r\binom{n}{r}\binom{m}{r} = n\binom{n+m-1}{n}.$$

8. Find the number of ways to distribute 10 identical pieces of candy to 3 children so that no child gets more than 4 pieces.

9. Find the number of ways to distribute 40 identical balls to 7 distinct boxes if box 1 must hold at least 3, and at most 10, of the balls.

10. Find the number of ways to select $2n$ balls from n identical blue balls, n identical red balls and n identical white balls, where $n \in \mathbf{N}$.

11. In how many ways can 100 identical chairs be divided among 4 different rooms so that each room will have 10, 20, 30, 40 or 50 chairs?

12. Let a_r be the number of ways of distributing r identical objects into 5 distinct boxes so that boxes 1, 3 and 5 are not empty. Let b_r be the number of ways of distributing r identical objects into 5 distinct boxes so that each of the boxes 2 and 4 contains at least two objects.

    (i) Find the generating function for the sequence (a_r).

    (ii) Find the generating function for the sequence (b_r).

    (iii) Show that $a_r = b_{r+1}$ for each $r = 1, 2, \ldots$.

13. For $r \in \mathbf{N}^*$, let a_r denote the number of integer solutions to the equation

$$x_1 + x_2 + x_3 = r$$

where $3 \leq x_1 \leq 9$, $0 \leq x_2 \leq 8$ and $7 \leq x_3 \leq 17$. Find the generating function for (a_r), and determine the value of a_{28}.

14. In how many ways can 3000 identical pencils be divided up, in packages of 25, among four student groups so that each group gets at least 150, but not more than 1000, of the pencils?

15. Find the number of selections of 10 letters from "F, U, N, C, T, I, O" that contain at most three U's and at least one O.

16. Find the generating function for the sequence (a_r) in each of the following cases: a_r is

    (i) the number of selections of r letters (not necessarily distinct) from the set $\{D, R, A, S, T, I, C\}$ that contain at most 3 D's and at least 2 T's;

    (ii) the number of partitions of r into parts of sizes 1, 2, 3, 5, and 8;

    (iii) the number of partitions of r into distinct parts of sizes 5, 10, and 15;

    (iv) the number of partitions of r into distinct odd parts;

    (v) the number of partitions of r into distinct even parts;

    (vi) the number of integer solutions to the inequality

$$x_1 + x_2 + x_3 + x_4 + x_5 \leq r$$

    with $1 \leq x_i \leq 6$ for each $i = 1, 2, \ldots, 5$.

17. Find the number of $4n$-element multi-subsets of the multi-set

$$\{(3n) \cdot x, (3n) \cdot y, (3n) \cdot z\},$$

    where $n \in \mathbf{N}$.

18. Find the number of $3n$-element multi-subsets of the multi-set

$$M = \{n \cdot z_1, n \cdot z_2, \ldots, n \cdot z_m\},$$

    where $n, m \in \mathbf{N}$ and $n, m \geq 3$.

19. What is the probability that a roll of 5 distinct dice yields a sum of 17?

20. Find the generating function for the sequence (a_r), where a_r is the number of ways to obtain a sum of r by a roll of *any* number of distinct dice.

21. For $k, m \in \mathbb{N}$ and $r \in \mathbb{N}^*$, let a_r denote the number of ways of distributing r identical objects into $2k+1$ distinct boxes such that the first $k+1$ boxes are non-empty, and b_r denote the number of ways of distributing r identical objects into $2k + 1$ distinct boxes such that each of the last k boxes contains at least m objects.

    (i) Find the generating function for the sequence (a_r);

    (ii) Find the generating function for the sequence (b_r);

    (iii) Show that $a_r = b_{r+(m-1)k-1}$.

22. Find the generating function for the sequence (a_r), where a_r is the number of integer solutions to the equation

$$x_1 + 2x_2 + 3x_3 + 4x_4 = r$$

with $x_i \geq 0$ for each $i = 1, 2, 3, 4$.

23. For $r \in \mathbb{N}^*$, let a_r denote the number of ways of selecting 4 distinct integers from $\{1, 2, \ldots, r\}$ such that no two are consecutive. Find the generating function for (a_r) and deduce that $a_r = \binom{r-3}{4}$.

24. For $r \in \mathbb{N}^*$, and $m, t \in \mathbb{N}$, let a_r denote the number of m-element subsets $\{n_1, n_2, \ldots, n_m\}$ of the set $\{1, 2, \ldots, r\}$, where $n_1 < n_2 < \cdots < n_m$ and $n_{i+1} - n_i \geq t$ for each $i = 1, 2, \ldots, m - 1$. Find the generating function for (a_r) and deduce that

$$a_r = \binom{r - (m-1)(t-1)}{m}.$$

(See Problem 1.91.)

25. For $r \in \mathbb{N}^*$, let a_r be the number of integer solutions to the inequality

$$x_1 + x_2 + x_3 + x_4 \leq r,$$

where $3 \leq x_1 \leq 9$, $1 \leq x_2 \leq 10$, $x_3 \geq 2$ and $x_4 \geq 0$. Find the generating function for the sequence (a_r) and the value of a_{20}.

26. Prove that if $-1 < \alpha < 0$ and $n \in \mathbf{N}^*$, then

$$\binom{2\alpha}{2n} \geq (2n+1)\binom{\alpha}{n}^2;$$

while if $\alpha < -1$, the inequality is reversed. (Proposed by S. I. Rosen-crans, see *Amer. Math. Monthly*, **79** (1972), 1136.)

27. For $n \in \mathbf{N}$, let

$$a_{n-1} = \sum_{k=0}^{n-1} \left\{ \binom{n}{0} + \binom{n}{1} + \cdots + \binom{n}{k} \right\} \cdot$$
$$\left\{ \binom{n}{k+1} + \binom{n}{k+2} + \cdots + \binom{n}{n} \right\}.$$

Let $B(x)$ be the generating function for the sequence (b_k), where $b_k = \binom{n}{0} + \binom{n}{1} + \cdots + \binom{n}{k}$.

(i) Show that

$$B(x) = \frac{(1+x)^n}{1-x}.$$

(ii) Show that

$$a_{n-1} = \sum_{r=0}^{n-1} \binom{2n}{r}(n-r).$$

(iii) Show that

$$a_{n-1} = \frac{n}{2}\binom{2n}{n}.$$

(G. Chang and Z. Shan, 1984.)

28. For $m, n \in \mathbf{N}$ and $r \in \mathbf{N}^*$, a generalized quantity $\binom{n}{r}_m$ of binomial coefficients is defined as follows:

$$\binom{1}{r}_m = \begin{cases} 1 & \text{if } 0 \leq r \leq m-1 \\ 0 & \text{otherwise,} \end{cases}$$

and

$$\binom{n}{r}_m = \sum_{i=0}^{m-1} \binom{n-1}{r-i}_m \quad \text{for } n \geq 2.$$

Note that $\binom{n}{r}_2 = \binom{n}{r}$. Show that

(i) $\binom{n}{r}_m$ is the number of integer solutions to the equation

$$x_1 + x_2 + \cdots + x_n = r$$

with $0 \le x_i \le m - 1$ for each $i = 1, 2, \ldots, n$;

(ii) $\binom{n}{0}_m = 1$;

(iii) $\binom{n}{1}_m = n$, where $m \ge 2$;

(iv) $\binom{n}{r}_m = \binom{n}{s}_m$, where $r + s = n(m - 1)$;

(v) $\sum_{r=0}^{n(m-1)} \binom{n}{r}_m = m^n$;

(vi) the generating function for $\left(\binom{n}{r}_m\right)_{r=0,1,2,\ldots}$ is $(1 + x + \cdots + x^{m-1})^n$;

(vii) $\sum_{r=0}^{n(m-1)}(-1)^r \binom{n}{r}_m = \begin{cases} 0 & \text{if } m \text{ is even} \\ 1 & \text{if } m \text{ is odd} \end{cases}$

(viii) $\sum_{r=1}^{n(m-1)} r\binom{n}{r}_m = \frac{n(m-1)m^n}{2}$;

(ix) $\sum_{r=1}^{n(m-1)}(-1)^{r-1} r\binom{n}{r}_m = \begin{cases} 0 & \text{if } m \text{ is even} \\ \frac{n(1-m)}{2} & \text{if } m \text{ is odd} \end{cases}$

(x) $\sum_{i=0}^{r} \binom{p}{i}_m \binom{q}{r-i}_m = \binom{p+q}{r}_m$, where $p, q \in \mathbf{N}$;

(xi) $\binom{n}{r}_m = \sum_{i=0}^{n}(-1)^i \binom{n}{i}\binom{n-1+r-mi}{n-1}$.

(See C. Cooper and R. E. Kennedy, A dice-tossing problem, *Crux Mathematicorum*, **10** (1984), 134-138.)

29. Given $n \in \mathbf{N}$, evaluate the sum

$$S_n = \sum_{r=0}^{n} 2^{r-2n}\binom{2n-r}{n}.$$

(Proposed by the Israeli Team at the 31st IMO.)

30. For each $r \in \mathbf{N}^*$, let

$$a_r = 1 \cdot 4 \cdot 7 \cdots (3r + 1).$$

Show that the exponential generating function for the sequence (a_r) is given by $(1 - 3x)^{-\frac{4}{3}}$.

31. For $n \in \mathbf{N}$, find the number of ways to colour the n squares of a $1 \times n$ chessboard using the colours: blue, red and white, if each square is coloured by a colour and an even number of squares are to be coloured red.

32. Find the number of n-digit quaternary sequences that contain an odd number of 0's, an even number of 1's and at least one 3.

33. For $n \in \mathbf{N}$, find the number of words of length n formed by the symbols: $\alpha, \beta, \gamma, \delta, \epsilon, \lambda$ in which the total number of α's and β's is (i) even, (ii) odd.

34. For $r \in \mathbf{N}^*$, find the number of ways of distributing r distinct objects into 5 distinct boxes such that each of the boxes 1, 3, and 5 must hold an odd number of objects while each of the remaining boxes must hold an even number of objects.

35. Prove the following summations for all real z :

   (i) $\sum_{k=0}^{n} \binom{z}{2k} \binom{z-2k}{n-k} 2^{2k} = \binom{2z}{2n}$,

   (ii) $\sum_{k=0}^{n} \binom{z+1}{2k+1} \binom{z-2k}{n-k} 2^{2k+1} = \binom{2z+2}{2n+1}$.

   (Proposed by M. Machover and H. W. Gould, see *Amer. Math. Monthly*, **75** (1968), 682.)

36. Prove that

$$\sum_{r=1}^{n} \sum_{k=0}^{r} (-1)^{k+1} \frac{k}{r} \binom{r}{k} k^{n-1} = 0,$$

   where $n = 2, 3, 4, \ldots$. (Proposed by G. M. Lee, see *Amer. Math. Monthly*, **77** (1970), 308-309.)

37. Prove that

$$\sum \frac{1}{k_1! k_2! \cdots k_n!} = \frac{1}{r!} \binom{n-1}{r-1},$$

   where the sum is taken over all $k_1, k_2, \ldots, k_n \in \mathbf{N}^*$ with $\sum_{i=1}^{n} k_i = r$ and $\sum_{i=1}^{n} i k_i = n$.

   (Proposed by D. Ž. Djoković, see *Amer. Math. Monthly*, **77** (1970), 659.)

38. Ten female workers and eight male workers are to be assigned to work in one of four different departments of a company. In how many ways can this be done if

(i) each department gets at least one worker?

(ii) each department gets at least one female worker?

(iii) each department gets at least one female worker and at least one male worker?

39. For $r \in \mathbf{N}^*$, find the number of r-permutations of the multi-set

$$\{\infty \cdot \alpha, \ \infty \cdot \beta, \ \infty \cdot \gamma, \ \infty \cdot \lambda\}$$

in which the number of α's is odd while the number of λ's is even.

40. For $r \in \mathbf{N}^*$ and $n \in \mathbf{N}$, let $a_r = F(r, n)$, which is the number of ways to distribute r distinct objects into n distinct boxes so that no box is empty (see Theorem 4.5.1). Thus $a_r = n!S(r, n)$, where $S(r, n)$ is a Stirling number of the second kind. Find the exponential generating function for the sequence (a_r), and show that for $r \geq 2$,

$$\sum_{m=0}^{\infty} (-1)^m m! S(r, m + 1) = 0.$$

41. For $n \in \mathbf{N}$, let $A_n(x)$ be the exponential generating function for the sequence $(S(0, n), \ S(1, n), \ldots, \ S(r, n), \ldots)$. Find $A_n(x)$ and show that

$$\frac{d}{dx} A_n(x) = n A_n(x) + A_{n-1}(x),$$

where $n \geq 2$.

42. Let $B_0 = 1$ and for $r \in \mathbf{N}$, let $B_r = \sum_{k=1}^{r} S(r, k)$. The numbers B_r's are called the Bell numbers (see Section 1.7). Show that the exponential generating function for the sequence (B_r) is given by $e^{e^x - 1}$.

43. Let $n \in \mathbf{N}$ and $r \in \mathbf{N}^*$.

(a) Find the number of ways of distributing r distinct objects into n distinct boxes such that the objects in each box are ordered.

(b) Let a_r denote the number of ways to select at most r objects from r distinct objects and to distribute them into n distinct boxes such that the objects in each box are ordered. Show that

(i) $a_r = \sum_{i=0}^{r} \binom{r}{i} n^{(i)}$, where $n^{(i)} = n(n+1)\cdots(n+i-1)$ with $n^{(0)} = 1$;

(ii) the exponential generating function for the sequence (a_r) is given by

$$e^x(1-x)^{-n}.$$

44. Find the generating function for the sequence (a_r) in each of the following cases: a_r is the number of ways of distributing r identical objects into

(i) 4 distinct boxes;

(ii) 4 distinct boxes so that no box is empty;

(iii) 4 identical boxes so that no box is empty;

(iv) 4 identical boxes.

45. For $n \in N$, show that the number of partitions of n into parts where no even part occurs more than once is equal to the number of partitions of n in which parts of each size occur at most three times.

46. For $r \in N^*$ and $n \in N$, let a_r be the number of integer solutions to the equation

$$x_1 + x_2 + \cdots + x_n = r,$$

where $x_1 \geq x_2 \geq \cdots \geq x_n \geq 1$. Find the generating function for the sequence (a_r).

47. For $r \in N^*$ and $n \in N$, let b_r be the number of integer solutions to the equation

$$x_1 + x_2 + \cdot \cdot + x_n = r,$$

where $x_1 \geq x_2 \geq \cdots \geq x_n \geq 0$. Find the generating function for the sequence (b_r).

48. For $r \in N^*$ and $n \in N$, let a_r denote the number of ways to distribute r identical objects into n identical boxes, and b_r denote the number of integer solutions to the equation

$$\sum_{k=1}^{n} k x_k = r$$

with $x_k \geq 0$ for each $k = 1, 2, \ldots, n$. Show that $a_r = b_r$ for each $r \in N^*$.

49. For $r \in \mathbb{N}^*$, let a_r denote the number of partitions of r into distinct powers of 2.
    (i) Find the generating function for (a_r);
    (ii) Show that $a_r = 1$ for all $r \geq 1$;
    (iii) Give an interpretation of the result in (ii).

50. Show that for $n \in \mathbb{N}$, the number of partitions of $2n$ into *distinct even* parts is equal to the number of partitions of n into *odd* parts.

51. Let $k, n \in \mathbb{N}$. Show that the number of partitions of n into odd parts is equal to the number of partitions of kn into distinct parts whose sizes are multiples of k.

52. Let $p(n)$ be the number of partitions of n. Show that

$$p(n) \leq \frac{1}{2}(p(n+1) + p(n-1)),$$

where $n \in \mathbb{N}$ with $n \geq 2$.

53. For $n, k \in \mathbb{N}$ with $k \leq n$, let $p(n, k)$ denote the number of partitions of n into exactly k parts.
    (i) Determine the values of $p(5, 1)$, $p(5, 2)$, $p(5, 3)$ and $p(8, 3)$.
    (ii) Show that

$$\sum_{k=1}^{m} p(n, k) = p(n + m, m),$$

where $m \in \mathbb{N}$ and $m \leq n$.

54. (i) With $p(n, k)$ as defined in the preceding problem, determine the values of $p(5, 3)$, $p(7, 2)$ and $p(8, 3)$.
    (ii) Show that

$$p(n - 1, k - 1) + p(n - k, k) = p(n, k).$$

55. Given $n, k \in \mathbb{N}$ with $n \leq k$, show that

$$p(n + k, k) = p(2n, n) = p(n).$$

56. For $n, k \in \mathbb{N}$ with $k \leq n$, show that

$$p(n, k) \geq \frac{1}{k!}\binom{n-1}{k-1}.$$

57. Given $n, k \in \mathbb{N}$, show that the number of partitions of n into k *distinct* parts is equal to $p\left(n - \binom{k}{2}, k\right)$.

58. Prove the corollary to Theorem 5.3.5.

59. (i) Prove Theorem 5.3.3

    (ii) Prove Theorem 5.3.4.

60. For positive integers n, let $C(n)$ be the number of representations of n as a sum of nonincreasing powers of 2, where no power can be used more than three times. For example, $C(8) = 5$ since the representations for 8 are:

$$8, \ 4+4, \ 4+2+2, \ 4+2+1+1, \ \text{and } 2+2+2+1+1.$$

Prove or disprove that there is a polynoimal $Q(x)$ such that $C(n) = \lfloor Q(n) \rfloor$ for all positive integers n.

(Putnam, 1983.)

61. For $n \in \mathbf{N}$, let $C(n)$ be the number defined in the preceding problem. Show that the generating function for the sequence $(C(n))$ is given by

$$\frac{1}{(1+x)(1-x)^2}.$$

Deduce that $C(n) = \lfloor \frac{n+2}{2} \rfloor$ for each $n \in \mathbf{N}$.

62. (a) (i) List all partitions of 8 into 3 parts.

    (ii) List all noncongruent triangles whose sides are of integer length a, b, c such that $a + b + c = 16$.

    (iii) Is the number of partitions obtained in (i) equal to the number of noncongruent triangles obtained in (ii)?

    (b) For $r \in \mathbf{N}^*$, let a_r denote the number of noncongruent triangles whose sides are of integer length a, b, c such that $a + b + c = 2r$, and let b_r denote the number of partitions of r into 3 parts.

    (i) Show by (BP) that $a_r = b_r$ for each $r \in \mathbf{N}^*$.

    (ii) Find the generating function for (a_r).

63. A partition P of a positive integer n is said to be *self-conjugate* if P and its conjugate have the same Ferrers diagram.

    (i) Find all the self-conjugate partitions of 15.

    (ii) Find all the partitions of 15 into distinct odd parts.

    (iii) Show that the number of the self-conjugate partitions of n is equal to the number of partitions of n into distinct odd parts.

64. Show that the number of self-conjugate partitions of n with largest size equal to m is equal to the number of self-conjugate partitions of $n - 2m + 1$ with largest size not exceeding $m - 1$.

65. (i) The largest square of asterisks in the upper left-hand corner of the Ferrers diagram is called the *Durfee* square of the diagram. Find the generating function for the number of self-conjugate partitions of r whose Durfee square is an $m \times m$ square, where $m \in \mathbf{N}$.

    (ii) Deduce that

    $$\prod_{k=0}^{\infty}(1 + x^{2k+1}) = 1 + \sum_{m=1}^{\infty} \frac{x^{m^2}}{\prod_{k=1}^{m}(1 - x^{2k})}.$$

66. Let $A(x)$ be the generating function for the sequence $(p(r))$ where $p(r)$ is the number of partitions of r.

    (i) Find $A(x)$;

    (ii) Use the notion of Durfee square to prove that

    $$\left[\prod_{k=1}^{\infty}(1 - x^k)\right]^{-1} = 1 + \sum_{m=1}^{\infty} \frac{x^{m^2}}{\prod_{k=1}^{m}(1 - x^k)^2}.$$

67. By considering isosceles right triangles of asterisks in the upper left-hand corner of a Ferrers diagram, show that

    $$\prod_{k=1}^{\infty}(1 + x^{2k}) = 1 + \sum_{m=1}^{\infty} \frac{x^{m(m+1)}}{\prod_{k=1}^{m}(1 - x^{2k})}.$$

68. Let $p, q, r \in \mathbf{N}$ with $p < r$ and $q < r$. Show that the number of partitions of $r - p$ into $q - 1$ parts with sizes not exceeding p, is equal to the number of partitions of $r - q$ into $p - 1$ parts with sizes not exceeding q.

69. For $n \in \mathbf{N}$, let $p_e(n)$ (resp., $p_o(n)$) denote the number of partitions of n into an even (resp., odd) number of *distinct* parts. Show that

    $$p_e(n) - p_o(n) = \begin{cases} (-1)^k & \text{if } n = \frac{k(3k\pm1)}{2} \\ 0 & \text{otherwise.} \end{cases}$$

70. Prove the following Euler's pentagonal number theorem:

    $$\prod_{k=1}^{\infty}(1 - x^k) = \sum_{m=-\infty}^{\infty} (-1)^m x^{\frac{1}{2}m(3m-1)}.$$

71. For $n \in \mathbb{N}$, show that

$$p(n) - p(n-1) - p(n-2) + p(n-5) + p(n-7)$$
$$+ \cdots + (-1)^m p(n - \frac{1}{2}m(3m-1)) + \cdots$$
$$+ (-1)^m p(n - \frac{1}{2}m(3m+1)) + \cdots = 0.$$

72. For $j \in \mathbb{N}^*$, let $\beta(j) = \frac{3j^2+j}{2}$. Prove the following Euler identity:

$$\sum_{j \text{ even}} p(n - \beta(j)) = \sum_{j \text{ odd}} p(n - \beta(j))$$

by (BP), where $n \in \mathbb{N}$.

(See D. M. Bressoud and D. Zeilberger, Bijecting Euler's partitions-recurrence, *Amer. Math. Monthly*, **92** (1985), 54-55.)

73. For $r, n \in \mathbb{N}$, let $f(r, n)$ denote the number of partitions of n of the form

$$n = n_1 + n_2 + \cdots + n_s,$$

where, for $i = 1, 2, \ldots, s-1$, $n_i \geq rn_{i+1}$, and let $g(r, n)$ denote the number of partitions of n, where each part is of the form $1 + r + r^2 + \cdots + r^k$ for some $k \in \mathbb{N}^*$. Show that

$$f(r, n) = g(r, n).$$

(See D. R. Hickerson, A partition identity of the Euler type, *Amer. Math. Monthly*, **81** (1974), 627-629.)

References.

[Al] H.L. Alder, The Use of Generating Functions to Discover and Prove Partition Identities, *Two-Year College Mathematics Journal*, **10** (1979), 318-329.

[An1] G.E. Andrew, *Number Theory*, Saunders, Philadelphia, PA., 1971.

[An2] G.E. Andrew, *The Theory of Partitions*, Encyclopedia of Mathematics and Its Applications, Vol. 2, Addison-Wesley, Reading, 1976.

[G] J.W.L. Glaisher, *Messenger of Mathematics*, **12** (1883), 158-170.

[N] I. Niven, Formal Power Series, *Amer. Math. Monthly*, **76** (1969), 871-889.

Chapter 6

Recurrence Relations

6.1. Introduction

Let us begin our discussion with the following counting problem. Figure 6.1.1 shows a $1 \times n$ rectangle $ABCD$, that is to be fully paved by two types of tiles of different sizes: 1×1 and 1×2. What is the number of ways that this can be done?

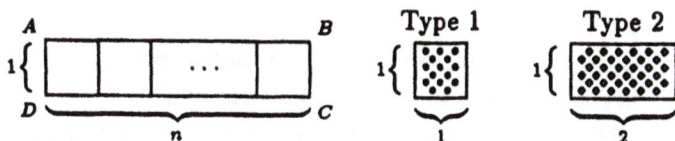

Figure 6.1.1.

Well, after some thought, we may find that it is not so easy to get a direct answer to the problem. Also, it seems that the methods we learnt in the previous chapters are not of much help. Let us therefore use a different approach. First of all, we consider some very special cases. When $n = 1$, it is clear that there is one and only one way to pave the 1×1 rectangle:

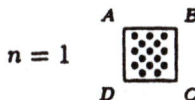

When $n = 2$, it is also easy to see that there are exactly 2 ways to pave the 1×2 rectangle:

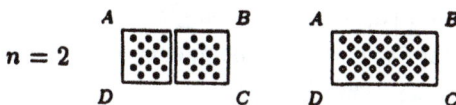

When $n = 3$, there are 3 different ways as shown below:

$n = 3$

For convenience, let a_n denote the required number of ways to pave the $1 \times n$ rectangle $ABCD$. As shown above, we have

$$a_1 = 1, \ a_2 = 2, \ a_3 = 3.$$

If you proceed as before, you will find that

$$a_4 = 5, \ a_5 = 8, \text{ etc.}$$

However, up to this stage, we do not see any direct way of solving the problem. Let us go back to analyze the case when $n = 3$. Paving the rectangle $ABCD$ from left to right, there are 2 possibilities for the first step:

(i) a tile of type 1 is used;

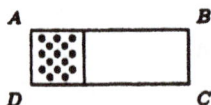

or (ii) a tile of type 2 is used.

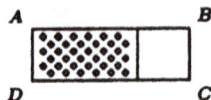

We now have a crucial observation. In case (i), a 1×2 rectangle is left behind, while in case (ii), a 1×1 rectangle is left behind. As noted earlier, there are $a_2 = 2$ ways to complete the paving in the former case, and $a_1 = 1$ way in the latter case. Thus by (AP),

$$a_3 = a_2 + a_1.$$

Can this relation for a_3 be extended to an arbitrary term a_n, $n \geq 3$? To see this, we follow the same argument as we did before and obtain two cases for the first step:

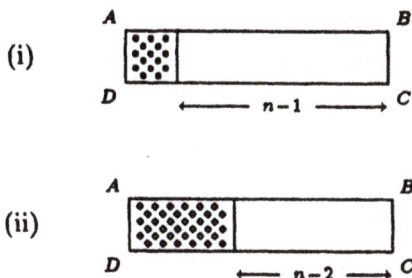

(i)

(ii)

In case (i), there are by definition a_{n-1} ways to complete the paving and in case (ii), there are a_{n-2} ways to do so. Thus by (AP),

$$a_n = a_{n-1} + a_{n-2}, \quad \text{for } n \geq 3. \tag{6.1.1}$$

Although, up till now, we have not been able to find a formula $f(n)$ for a_n, we should be content with the relation (6.1.1), which at least enables us to compute a_n indirectly from the preceding numbers a_{n-2} and a_{n-1} (thus $a_4 = a_2 + a_3 = 2 + 3 = 5$, $a_5 = a_3 + a_4 = 3 + 5 = 8$, and so on).

The relation (6.1.1) governing the sequence (a_n) is called a *recurrence relation* for the sequence (a_n). In general, given a sequence $(a_n) = (a_0, a_1, a_2, ...)$ of numbers, a *recurrence relation* for (a_n) is an equation which relates the nth term a_n to some of its predecessors in the sequence. Thus the following are some more examples of recurrence relations:

$$a_n = a_{n-1} + 1$$
$$a_n - 5a_{n-1} + 6a_{n-2} = 0$$
$$a_n + 7a_{n-1} + 12a_{n-2} = 2^n$$
$$n(n-1)a_n = (n-1)(n-2)a_{n-1} - (n-3)a_{n-2}$$
$$a_n = \frac{a_{n-1}}{(2n-1)a_{n-1} + 1}$$

To initiate the computation for the terms of a recurrence relation, we need to know the values of some terms of the sequence (a_n). They are called *initial conditions* of the recurrence relation. For instance, to compute a_n

in the recurrence relation (6.1.1), we need to find out a_1 and a_2 before we can proceed. The values $a_1 = 1$ and $a_2 = 2$ in this example are the initial conditions.

The *solution* of a recurrence relation is an expression $a_n = g(n)$, where $g(n)$ is a function of n, which satisfies the recurrence relation. For instance, the expression

$$a_n = n$$

is the solution of the recurrence relation $a_n = a_{n-1}+1$ with initial condition $a_1 = 1$, since "$a_n = n$" satisfies the recurrence relation $(a_n = n = (n-1)+ 1 = a_{n-1} + 1)$.

In combinatorics there are many problems that, like the above paving problem, may not be easily or directly enumerated, but could be well handled using the notion of recurrence relations. For each of these problems, deriving a recurrence relation is the first important step towards its solution. In this chapter, we shall gain, through various examples, some experience of deriving recurrence relations. We shall also learn some standard methods of solving (i.e., finding solutions of) certain families of "well-behaved" recurrence relations.

6.2. Two Examples

In this section, we introduce two counting problems that can be solved with the help of recurrence relations. We begin with a famous problem, known as the *Tower of Hanoi*, that was first formulated and studied by the French mathematician Edouard Lucas (1842-1891) in 1883.

Example 6.2.1.   A tower of n circular discs of different sizes is stacked on one of the 3 given pegs in decreasing size from the bottom, as shown in Figure 6.2.1. The task is to transfer the entire tower to another peg by a sequence of moves under the following conditions:

(i) each move carries exactly one disc,   and

(ii) no disc can be placed on top of a smaller one.

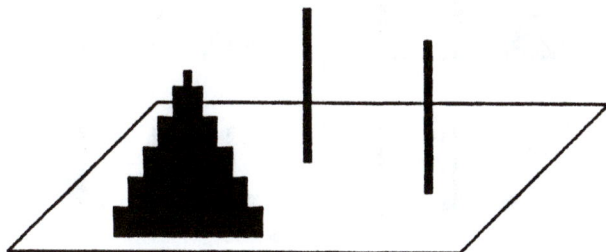

Figure 6.2.1.

For $n \geq 1$, let a_n denote the *minimum* number of moves needed to accomplish the task with n discs. Show that

$$a_1 = 1, \ a_2 = 3, \ a_3 = 7$$

and
$$a_n = 2a_{n-1} + 1 \qquad (6.2.1)$$

for $n \geq 2$. Solve also the recurrence relation (6.2.1).

Solution. Obviously, $a_1 = 1$. For $n = 2$, the 3 moves shown in Figure 6.2.2 accomplish the task. It is clear that any two moves are not enough to do so. Thus $a_2 = 3$.

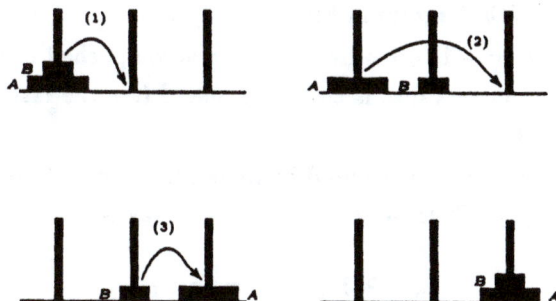

Figure 6.2.2.

For $n = 3$, the 7 moves shown in Figure 6.2.3 do the job. Any 6 moves are not sufficient to do so (why?). Thus $a_3 = 7$.

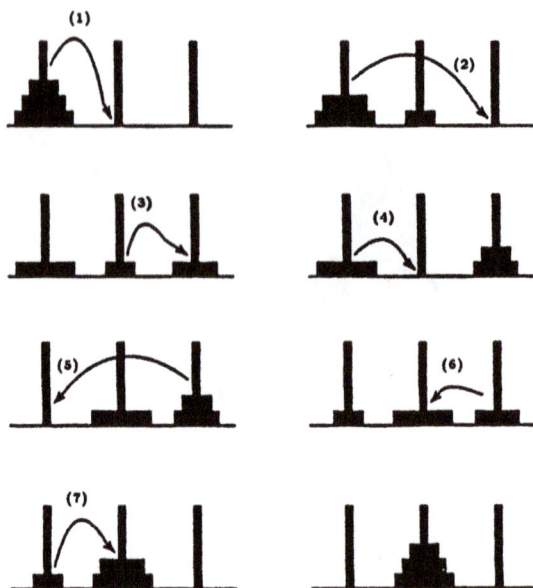

Figure 6.2.3.

We shall now consider the general term a_n, $n \geq 2$. The given task with n discs can be accomplished via the following main steps:

1° Transfer the top $(n - 1)$ discs from the original peg to a different peg (see the first 3 diagrams in Figure 6.2.3);

2° Move the largest disc from the original peg to the only empty peg (see the 4th and 5th diagram in Figure 6.2.3); and

3° Transfer the $(n - 1)$ discs from the peg accomplished in step 1° to the peg that the largest disc is currently placed (see the last 4 diagrams in Figure 6.2.3).

The number of moves required in steps 1°, 2° and 3° are, respectively, a_{n-1}, 1, and a_{n-1}. Thus, we have provided a way with

$$a_{n-1} + 1 + a_{n-1} = 2a_{n-1} + 1$$

moves to transfer the tower with n discs from one peg to another. By the definition of a_n, we have

$$a_n \leq 2a_{n-1} + 1. \tag{1}$$

On the other hand, we notice that for any way of transfering the tower with n discs, the largest disc at the bottom has to be moved to an empty peg at some point, and this is possible only when step 1° has been performed. To complete the task, step 3° has to be done somehow. Thus, any way of transfering requires at least $2a_{n-1} + 1$ moves; i.e.,

$$a_n \geq 2a_{n-1} + 1. \tag{2}$$

Combining (1) and (2), we obtain

$$a_n = 2a_{n-1} + 1,$$

as required.

Finally, we shall solve the recurrence relation (6.2.1) with the initial condition $a_1 = 1$ as follows: for $n \geq 2$,

$$
\begin{aligned}
a_n &= 2a_{n-1} + 1 \\
&= 2(2a_{n-2} + 1) + 1 \\
&= 2^2 a_{n-2} + 2 + 1 \\
&= 2^2 (2a_{n-3} + 1) + 2 + 1 \\
&= 2^3 a_{n-3} + 2^2 + 2 + 1 \\
&\ \ \vdots \\
&= 2^{n-1} a_1 + 2^{n-2} + 2^{n-3} + \cdots + 2 + 1 \\
&= 2^{n-1} + 2^{n-2} + \cdots + 2 + 1 \\
&= \frac{1(2^n - 1)}{2 - 1} \\
&= 2^n - 1.
\end{aligned}
$$

Thus, $a_n = 2^n - 1$ is the required solution. ∎

Remarks. (1) The above method of obtaining a solution is often referred to as the *backward substitution*.

(2)   The recurrence relation (6.2.1) is a special example of the following recurrence relation:

$$a_n = pa_{n-1} + q \quad \text{with } a_0 = r \tag{6.2.2}$$

where p, q and r are arbitrary constants. It can be proved (see Problem 6.12) that the solution of (6.2.2) is given by

$$a_n = \begin{cases} r + qn & \text{if } p = 1, \\ rp^n + \frac{(p^n - 1)q}{p-1} & \text{if } p \neq 1. \end{cases}$$

Recall that in Example 2.5.3, we evaluated the number $g(n)$ of parallelograms contained in the nth subdivision of an equilateral triangle, and found that $g(n) = 3\binom{n+3}{4}$. In what follows, we shall give another proof of this result by the method of recurrence relation.

Example 6.2.2.   Let a_n denote the number of parallelograms contained in the nth subdivision of an equilateral triangle. Find a recurrence relation for a_n and solve the recurrence relation.

Solution.   Let ABC of Figure 6.2.4 be a given equilateral triangle. For convenience, call a point of intersection of any 2 line segments in the nth subdivision of $\triangle ABC$ a *node*. Thus there are altogether

$$1 + 2 + 3 + \cdots + (n + 2) = \frac{1}{2}(n + 2)(n + 3)$$

nodes in the nth subdivision of $\triangle ABC$.

Clearly, $a_1 = 3$. For $n \geq 2$, observe that every parallelogram of the nth subdivision of $\triangle ABC$ contains *either* no node on BC as a vertex *or* at least one node on BC as a vertex. Thus, if we let X be the set of parallelograms of the latter case, then we have

$$a_n = a_{n-1} + |X| . \tag{1}$$

We shall now count $|X|$ indirectly. Let Y be the set of pairs $\{u, v\}$ of nodes such that u is on BC, v is not on BC, and u, v are both not contained on a common line segment. Define a correspondence from X to Y as follows: given a parallelogram in X, let u and v be the opposite vertices of the

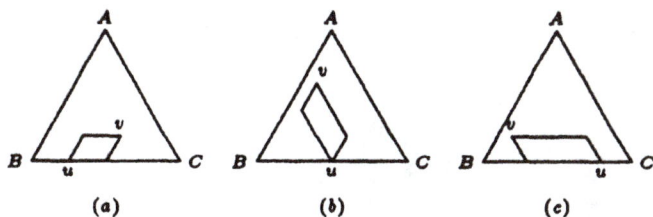

Figure 6.2.4.

parallelogram at which the angles of the parallelogram are acute (see Figure 6.2.4).

It is evident that this correspondence defines a bijection from X to Y. Thus, by (BP),

$$|X| = |Y|. \tag{2}$$

Since

(i) there are $n + 2$ nodes u on BC,

(ii) there are $1 + 2 + \cdots + (n+1) = \frac{1}{2}(n+1)(n+2)$ nodes v *not* on BC, and

(iii) u and v are *not* on a common line segment,

it follows, by (CP), that

$$
\begin{aligned}
|Y| &= (n+2) \cdot \frac{1}{2}(n+1)(n+2) - (n+2)(n+1) \\
&= \frac{1}{2}(n+1)(n+2)(n+2-2) \\
&= \frac{1}{2}n(n+1)(n+2) \\
&= 3\binom{n+2}{3}.
\end{aligned} \tag{3}
$$

Combining (1), (2) and (3), we arrive at the following recurrence relation

$$a_n = a_{n-1} + 3\binom{n+2}{3} \tag{6.2.3}$$

for $n \geq 2$.

To solve the recurrence relation (6.2.3), we apply the backward substitution to obtain the following:

$$a_n = a_{n-1} + 3\binom{n+2}{3}$$
$$= a_{n-2} + 3\binom{n+1}{3} + 3\binom{n+2}{3}$$
$$\vdots$$
$$= a_1 + 3\binom{4}{3} + \cdots + 3\binom{n+1}{3} + 3\binom{n+2}{3}$$
$$= 3\left\{\binom{3}{3} + \binom{4}{3} + \cdots + \binom{n+1}{3} + \binom{n+2}{3}\right\}$$
$$= 3\binom{n+3}{4} \qquad \text{(by identity (2.5.1)).}$$

Thus, $a_n = 3\binom{n+3}{4}$ is the required solution. ∎

Note. The recurrence relation (6.2.3) is not a special case of the recurrence relation (6.2.2) since the term $3\binom{n+2}{3}$ in (6.2.3) depends on "n", and is thus not a constant.

6.3. Linear Homogeneous Recurrence Relations

In Examples 6.2.1 and 6.2.2, we solved the recurrence relations (6.2.1) and (6.2.3) using the method of backward substitution. Of course, not every recurrence relation can be solved in this way. In this and the next section, we shall introduce a general method that enables us to solve a class of recurrence relations, called *linear* recurrence relations. For the first step towards this end, we consider a sub-class of linear recurrence relations, called linear *homogeneous* recurrence relations.

Let (a_n) be a given sequence of numbers. A recurrence relation of the form:

$$c_0 a_n + c_1 a_{n-1} + \cdots + c_r a_{n-r} = 0 \qquad (6.3.1)$$

where the c_i's are constants with $c_0, c_r \neq 0$, and $1 \leq r \leq n$, is called an *rth order linear homogeneous* recurrence relation for the sequence (a_n).

For instance, the recurrence relations

$$a_n = a_{n-1} + a_{n-2}$$

and
$$a_n - 2a_{n-1} + 3a_{n-2} - 5a_{n-3} = 0$$

are, respectively, linear homogeneous recurrence relations of 2nd and 3rd order.

Replacing the terms "a_i" by "x^i", $i = n, n-1, ..., n-r$, in (6.3.1), we obtain the following equation in "x":

$$c_0 x^n + c_1 x^{n-1} + c_2 x^{n-2} + \cdots + c_r x^{n-r} = 0$$

or
$$c_0 x^r + c_1 x^{r-1} + c_2 x^{r-2} + \cdots + c_{r-1} x + c_r = 0 \qquad (6.3.2)$$

The equation (6.3.2) is called the *characteristic equation* of (6.3.1). Any root of the equation (6.3.2) is called a *characteristic root* of the recurrence relation (6.3.1).

The notion of characteristic roots of a linear homogeneous recurrence relation plays a key role in the solution of the recurrence relation, which is shown in the following two results.

(I)   If $\alpha_1, \alpha_2, ..., \alpha_r$ are the *distinct* characteristic roots of the recurrence relation (6.3.1), then

$$a_n = A_1(\alpha_1)^n + A_2(\alpha_2)^n + \cdots + A_r(\alpha_r)^n,$$

where the A_i's are constants, is the general solution of (6.3.1)

(II) $\alpha_1, \alpha_2, ..., \alpha_k$ $(1 \le k \le r)$ are the *distinct* characteristic roots of (6.3.1) such that α_i is of multiplicity m_i, $i = 1, 2, ..., k$, then the general solution of (6.3.1) is given by

$$
\begin{aligned}
a_n = {} & (A_{11} + A_{12}n + \cdots A_{1m_1}n^{m_1-1})(\alpha_1)^n \\
& + (A_{21} + A_{22}n + \cdots A_{2m_2}n^{m_2-1})(\alpha_2)^n \\
& + \quad \cdots \\
& + (A_{k1} + A_{k2}n + \cdots A_{km_k}n^{m_k-1})(\alpha_k)^n,
\end{aligned}
$$

where the A_{ij}'s are constants.

Result (I) is a clearly a special case of result (II). The proofs of these results can be found in many standard books in combinatorics (see, for instance, Roberts [12], pp. 210-213). Here, we shall only give a number of examples to illustrate the use of these results.

We first solve the recurrence relation obtained in the problem of paving a rectangle that is discussed in Section 1.

Example 6.3.1.   Solve the recurrence relation

$$a_n = a_{n-1} + a_{n-2} \tag{6.1.1}$$

given that $a_0 = 1$ and $a_1 = 1$.

Notes.   (1)   Since the recurrence relation (6.1.1) is of 2nd order, we need two initial conditions to solve it.

(2)   The original initial conditions for the paving problem are "$a_1 = 1$ and $a_2 = 2$". We replace "$a_2 = 2$" by "$a_0 = 1$" here simply for the ease of computation that could be seen later. Such a replacement does not affect the solution since $a_0 = 1$, $a_1 = 1$ and $a_2 = 2$ satisfy the recurrence relation (6.1.1).

Solution.   The recurrence relation (6.1.1) may be written as

$$a_n - a_{n-1} - a_{n-2} = 0.$$

Its characteristic equation is

$$x^2 - x - 1 = 0,$$

and its characteristic roots are

$$\alpha_1 = \frac{1 + \sqrt{5}}{2} \quad \text{and} \quad \alpha_2 = \frac{1 - \sqrt{5}}{2}.$$

Thus, by result (I), the general solution of (6.1.1) is given by

$$a_n = A \left(\frac{1 + \sqrt{5}}{2} \right)^n + B \left(\frac{1 - \sqrt{5}}{2} \right)^n, \tag{1}$$

where A and B are constants to be determined.

The initial conditions $a_0 = a_1 = 1$ imply that

$$\begin{cases} A + B = 1 \\ A\left(\frac{1+\sqrt{5}}{2}\right) + B\left(\frac{1-\sqrt{5}}{2}\right) = 1, \end{cases}$$

i.e.,

$$\begin{cases} A + B = 1 \\ (A + B) + \sqrt{5}(A - B) = 2. \end{cases} \tag{2}$$

Solving the system (2) for A and B gives

$$\begin{cases} A = \frac{1+\sqrt{5}}{2\sqrt{5}} \\ B = -\frac{1-\sqrt{5}}{2\sqrt{5}}. \end{cases} \tag{3}$$

(Determining A and B using the initial conditions $a_1 = 1$ and $a_2 = 2$ is more tedious than the above. This is the advantage of using $a_0 = a_1 = 1$.)

By substituting (3) into (1), we obtain the desired solution of (6.1.1):

$$a_n = \left(\frac{1+\sqrt{5}}{2\sqrt{5}}\right)\left(\frac{1+\sqrt{5}}{2}\right)^n - \left(\frac{1-\sqrt{5}}{2\sqrt{5}}\right)\left(\frac{1-\sqrt{5}}{2}\right)^n;$$

i.e.,

$$a_n = \frac{1}{\sqrt{5}}\left[\left(\frac{1+\sqrt{5}}{2}\right)^{n+1} - \left(\frac{1-\sqrt{5}}{2}\right)^{n+1}\right]. \tag{6.3.3}$$

for all $n \geq 0$. ∎

From the recurrence relation (6.1.1) and the initial conditions $a_0 = a_1 = 1$, we obtain the first few terms of the sequence (a_n) as shown below:

$$1, 1, 2, 3, 5, 8, 13, 21, 34, 55, 89, 144, \ldots$$

These numbers were named *Fibonacci numbers* by the French mathematician Edouard Locus (1842-1891), as they arose from a famous problem – the rabbit problem (see Problem 6.51) that was contained in the book "Liber Abaci" (1202) written by one of the great mathematical innovators of the Middle Ages, Leonardo Fibonacci (1175–1230) of Pisa. The beautiful formula (6.3.3) for the nth Fibonacci numbers is called the *Binet* formula after the French mathematician Jacques-Phillipe-Marie Binet (1786-1856). This formula was also derived independently by de Moivre (1667-1754) and D. Bernoulli (1700-1782). Locus had done a great deal of work on Fibonacci numbers, and the following variation of numbers:

$$2, \ 1, \ 3, \ 4, \ 7, \ 11, \ 18, \ 29, \ 47, \ 76, \ 123, \ 199, \ \ldots$$

bears his name.

In 1963, the American mathematician Verner E. Hoggatt, Jr. and his associates set up an organization, called the *Fibonacci Association* at the University of Santa Clara, in California, U.S.A.. Since then, the Association has been organizing a series of Fibonacci conferences, including the First International Conference on Fibonacci Numbers and Their Applications held in Patras, Greece. The Association has even been publishing an international mathematical journal, called the *Fibonacci Quarterly* for the promotion of all kinds of research related to Fibonacci numbers.

Fibonacci numbers and their related results can now be found in many branches of mathematics such as Geometry, Number Theory, Combinatorics, Linear Algebra, Numerical Analysis, Probability and Statistics, and in other disciplines outside of mathematics like Architectural Designs, Biology, Chemistry, Physics, Engineering, and so on. For those who wish to find out more about these numbers, the following books: Vorobyov [Vo], Hoggart [Hg], Vajda [Va], and the article by Honsberger (see [Hn], p.102-138) are recommended.

Example 6.3.2.   Solve the recurrence relation

$$a_n - 7a_{n-1} + 15a_{n-2} - 9a_{n-3} = 0, \qquad (6.3.4)$$

given that $a_0 = 1, a_1 = 2$ and $a_2 = 3$.

Solution.   The characteristic equation of (6.3.4) is

$$x^3 - 7x^2 + 15x - 9 = (x - 3)^2(x - 1) = 0$$

and thus the characteristic roots of (6.3.4) are

$$\alpha_1 = 3 \quad \text{(of multiplicity 2)}$$
$$\text{and} \quad \alpha_2 = 1.$$

By result (II), the general solution of (6.3.4) is given by

$$a_n = (A + Bn)(3)^n + C(1)^n;$$
$$\text{i.e.,} \quad a_n = (A + Bn)3^n + C, \tag{1}$$

where A, B and C are constants to be determined.
The initial conditions

$$a_0 = 1, \ a_1 = 2, \ \text{and} \ a_2 = 3$$

imply that

$$\begin{cases} A & +C & = 1 \\ 3A & + 3B & +C & = 2 \\ 9A & +18B & +C & = 3. \end{cases} \tag{2}$$

Solving the system (2) yields

$$A = 1, \quad B = -\frac{1}{3} \quad \text{and} \quad C = 0. \tag{3}$$

It follows from (1) and (3) that the required solution of (6.3.4) is given by

$$a_n = (1 - \frac{n}{3})3^n$$
$$\text{or} \quad a_n = (3 - n)3^{n-1} \quad \text{for } n \geq 0. \quad \blacksquare$$

In solving a polynomial equation, it is possible to obtain complex roots. In this case, it is sometimes convenient to express such roots in trigonometric form. We also note that if $\alpha = a + bi$ is a complex roots of a *real* polynomial equation $P(x) = 0$ (i.e., all the coefficients of $P(x)$ are real), then its conjugate $\bar{\alpha} = a - bi$ is also a root of $P(x) = 0$; i.e., complex roots of $P(x) = 0$ always occur in conjugate pairs. An example of this type is given below.

Example 6.3.3. Solve the recurrence relation

$$a_n = 2(a_{n-1} - a_{n-2}) \tag{6.3.5}$$

given that $a_0 = 1$ and $a_1 = 0$.

Solution.   The characteristic equation of (6.3.5) is

$$x^2 - 2x + 2 = 0$$

and its roots are

$$\alpha = 1 + i \quad \text{and} \quad \bar{\alpha} = 1 - i.$$

Expressing α and $\bar{\alpha}$ in trigonometric form, we have

$$\alpha = \sqrt{2}(\cos\frac{\pi}{4} + i\sin\frac{\pi}{4})$$
$$\text{and} \quad \bar{\alpha} = \sqrt{2}(\cos\frac{\pi}{4} - i\sin\frac{\pi}{4}).$$

Thus the general solution of (6.3.5) is given by

$$a_n = A(\alpha)^n + B(\bar{\alpha})^n$$
$$= (\sqrt{2})^n \left\{ A(\cos\frac{n\pi}{4} + i\sin\frac{n\pi}{4}) + B(\cos\frac{n\pi}{4} - i\sin\frac{n\pi}{4}) \right\}$$
$$= (\sqrt{2})^n (C\cos\frac{n\pi}{4} + D\sin\frac{n\pi}{4}),$$

where $C = A + B$ and $D = i(A - B)$ are constants to be determined.

The initial conditions $a_0 = 1$ and $a_1 = 0$ imply that

$$\begin{cases} C = 1 \\ \sqrt{2}(\frac{\sqrt{2}}{2}C + \frac{\sqrt{2}}{2}D) = 0; \end{cases}$$

i.e.
$$C = 1 \quad \text{and} \quad D = -1.$$

Thus the required solution of (6.3.5) is

$$a_n = (\sqrt{2})^n (\cos\frac{n\pi}{4} - \sin\frac{n\pi}{4})$$

for $n \geq 0$. ∎

6.4. General Linear Recurrence Relations

Let (a_n) be a given sequence of numbers. A recurrence relation of the form

$$c_0 a_n + c_1 a_{n-1} + \cdots + c_r a_{n-r} = f(n) \tag{6.4.1}$$

where the c_i's are constants with $c_0, c_r \neq 0$, $1 \leq r \leq n$, and f is a function of n, is called an *rth order linear recurrence relation* for the sequence (a_n).

Thus a linear homogeneous recurrence relation is a linear recurrence relation of the form (6.4.1) in which $f(n) = 0$ for all n. While the recurrence relations

$$a_n - 2a_{n-1} = 1 \tag{6.2.1}$$

$$a_n - a_{n-1} = 3\binom{n+2}{3} \tag{6.2.3}$$

are examples of linear recurrence relations of first order, the recurrence relation

$$a_n + 7a_{n-1} + 12a_{n-2} = 2^n$$

is a 2nd order linear recurrence relation.

How can we solve a linear recurrence relation of the form (6.4.1)? A way to do so is given below:

Step 1°. Find the general solution $a_n^{(h)}$ of the linear homogeneous recurrence relation obtained from (6.4.1)

$$c_0 a_n + c_1 a_{n-1} + \cdots + c_r a_{n-r} = 0.$$

Step 2°. Find a particular solution $a_n^{(p)}$ of (6.4.1).

Step 3°. The general solution of (6.4.1) is given by

$$a_n = a_n^{(h)} + a_n^{(p)}. \tag{6.4.2}$$

Remarks. **(1)** Those who are familiar with the theory of differential equations may note the analogy between the above method of solving general linear recurrence relations and a corresponding method of solving linear differential equations.

(2) The method of finding $a_n^{(h)}$ in Step $1°$ has been discussed in the preceding section.

(3) There is no general way of finding $a_n^{(p)}$ in Step $2°$. However, $a_n^{(p)}$ could be found by inspection if the function 'f' in (6.4.1) is relatively simple. For instance, if $f(n)$ is a polynomial in n or an exponential function of n, then $a_n^{(p)}$ could be chosen as a function of similar type. We shall further elaborate this point through the following examples.

Example 6.4.1. Solve the recurrence relation

$$a_n - 3a_{n-1} = 2 - 2n^2 \qquad (6.4.3)$$

given that $a_0 = 3$.

Solution. First of all, we find $a_n^{(h)}$. The characteristic equation of

$$a_n - 3a_{n-1} = 0$$

is $x - 3 = 0$, and its root is $\alpha = 3$. Thus

$$a_n^{(h)} = A \cdot 3^n, \qquad (1)$$

where A is a constant.

Next, we find $a_n^{(p)}$. Since $f(n) = 2 - 2n^2$ is a polynomial in n of degree 2, we let

$$a_n^{(p)} = Bn^2 + Cn + D \qquad (2)$$

where B, C and D are constants.

Since $a_n^{(p)}$ satisfies (6.4.3), we have

$$(Bn^2 + Cn + D) - 3\{B(n-1)^2 + C(n-1) + D\} = 2 - 2n^2.$$

Equating the coefficients of n^2, n and the constant terms, respectively, on both sides, we obtain:

$$\begin{cases} B - 3B = -2 \\ C + 6B - 3C = 0 \\ D - 3B + 3C - 3D = 2. \end{cases} \qquad (3)$$

Solving the system (3) yields

$$B = 1, \ C = 3 \text{ and } D = 2. \tag{4}$$

It follows from (2) and (4) that

$$a_n^{(p)} = n^2 + 3n + 2.$$

By (6.4.2), the general solution of (6.4.3) is given by

$$\begin{aligned} a_n &= a_n^{(h)} + a_n^{(p)} \\ &= A \cdot 3^n + n^2 + 3n + 2. \end{aligned} \tag{5}$$

Putting $a_0 = 3$ (initial condition) in (5) gives

$$3 = A + 2, \quad \text{i.e.,} \quad A = 1.$$

Hence the required solution of (6.4.3) is

$$a_n = 3^n + n^2 + 3n + 2, \quad n \geq 0. \quad \blacksquare$$

Example 6.4.2. Solve the recurrence relation

$$a_n - 3a_{n-1} + 2a_{n-2} = 2^n \tag{6.4.4}$$

given that $a_0 = 3$ and $a_1 = 8$.

Solution. The characteristic equation of $a_n - 3a_{n-1} + 2a_{n-2} = 0$ is $x^2 - 3x + 2 = 0$, and its roots are 1 and 2. Thus

$$a_n^{(h)} = A(1)^n + B(2)^n = A + B2^n. \tag{1}$$

Corresponding to $f(n) = 2^n$, we may choose

$$a_n^{(p)} = C2^n.$$

However, as the term 2^n has appeared in (1), we need to multiply it by 'n', and set

$$a_n^{(p)} = Cn2^n. \tag{2}$$

(For a more general way to choose such particular solutions, the reader is referred to Table 6.4.1.)

Since $a_n^{(p)}$ satisfies (6.4.4), we have:

$$Cn2^n - 3C(n-1)2^{n-1} + 2C(n-2)2^{n-2} = 2^n,$$

which implies that $C = 2$.

Thus, by (2),

$$a_n^{(p)} = n2^{n+1}$$

and so the general solution of (6.4.4) is

$$\begin{aligned} a_n &= a_n^{(h)} + a_n^{(p)} \\ &= A + B2^n + n2^{n+1}. \end{aligned} \tag{3}$$

It follows from (3) and the initial conditions $a_0 = 3$ and $a_1 = 8$ that

$$\begin{cases} A + B = 3 \\ A + 2B + 4 = 8. \end{cases} \tag{4}$$

Solving the system (4) gives

$$A = 2 \quad \text{and} \quad B = 1.$$

Thus the required solution of (6.4.4) is

$$a_n = 2 + 2^n + n2^{n+1} \quad \text{for } n \geq 0. \quad \blacksquare$$

To end this section, we give in Table 6.4.1 more precise forms of $a_n^{(p)}$ for some special functions $f(n)$ in different situations.

In addition, we would like to point out that if $f(n)$ is a sum of an exponential function $f_1(n)$ and a polynomial $f_2(n)$, then $a_n^{(p)}$ can be chosen as the sum of the two particular solutions corresponding to $f_1(n)$ and $f_2(n)$.

6.5. Two Applications

In this section, we shall apply what we have learnt in the preceding two sections to solve two counting problems: one on the number of colourings of a certain map and the other on the evaluation of determinants of certain matrices.

$f(n)$	$a_n^{(p)}$
Exponential function	
(i) $\quad Ak^n$	Bk^n
k is not a characteristic root	
(ii) $\quad Ak^n$	$Bn^m k^n$
k is a characteristic root of multiplicity m	
Polynomial	
(i) $\quad \sum_{i=0}^{t} p_i n^i$	$\sum_{i=0}^{t} q_i n^i$
l is not a characteristic root	
(ii) $\quad \sum_{i=0}^{t} p_i n^i$	$n^m \sum_{i=0}^{t} q_i n^i$
l is a characteristic root of multiplicity m	
Special combined function	
(i) $\quad An^t k^n$	$\left(\sum_{i=0}^{t} q_i n^i\right) k^n$
k is not a characteristic root	
(ii) $\quad An^t k^n$	$n^m \left(\sum_{i=0}^{t} q_i n^i\right) k^n$
k is a characteristic root of multiplicity m	

Table 6.4.1

Example 6.5.1. The n sectors, $n \geq 1$, of the circle of Figure 6.5.1 are to be coloured by k distinct colours, where $k \geq 3$, in such a way that each sector is coloured by one colour and any two adjacent sectors must be coloured by different colours. Let a_n denote the number of ways this can be done.

(i) Evaluate a_1, a_2 and a_3.

(ii) Find a recurrence relation for (a_n), $n \geq 4$, and solve the recurrence relation.

Solution. (i) Evidently, we have

$$a_1 = k,$$

and

$$a_2 = k(k - 1).$$

As shown in Figure 6.5.2, we have

$$a_3 = k(k - 1)(k - 2).$$

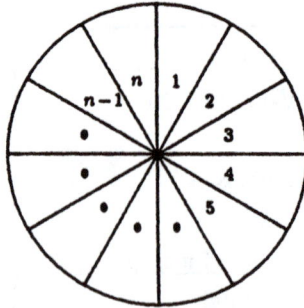

Figure 6.5.1.

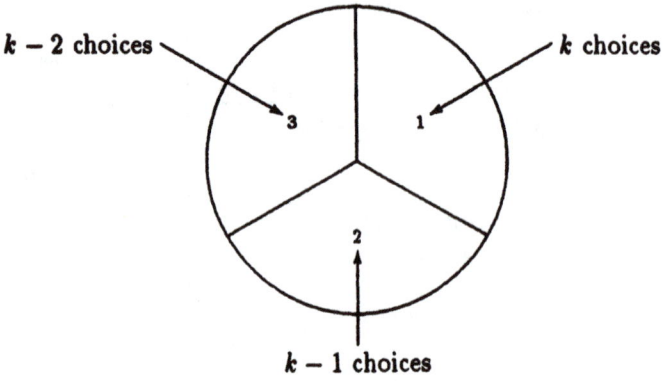

$k-2$ choices

k choices

$k-1$ choices

Figure 6.5.2.

(ii)   It is no longer true that $a_4 = k(k-1)(k-2)(k-3)$. For $n \geq 3$, we shall obtain a recurrence relation for (a_n) in an indirect way. Imagine that the circle of Figure 6.5.1 is cut along the boundary separating sectors 1 and n as shown in Figure 6.5.3.

It is much easier now to count the number of ways to colour the n sectors of Figure 6.5.3 subject to the given conditions. The number of ways this can be done is clearly

$$k(k-1)(k-1)\cdots(k-1) = k(k-1)^{n-1}.$$

$$\uparrow \quad \uparrow \quad \uparrow \qquad \uparrow$$

number of choices of sectors: 1   2   3 n

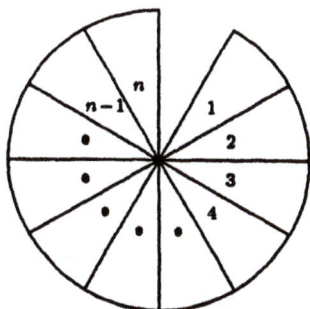

Figure 6.5.3.

These $k(k-1)^{n-1}$ ways of colourings can be divided into two groups:

  (1) those colourings in which sectors 1 and n receive different colours;

  (2) those colourings in which sectors 1 and n receive same colours.

  Observe that the colourings in group (1) are precisely the colourings of the n sectors of Figure 6.5.1. On the other hand, there is a bijection between the colourings in group (2) and the colourings of the $(n-1)$ sectors of Figure 6.5.4.

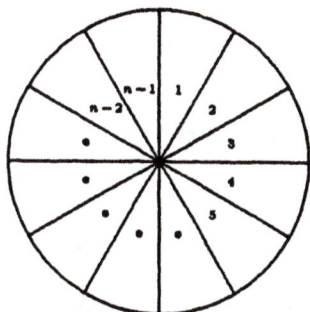

Figure 6.5.4

Thus, by (AP) and (BP), we have:

$$a_n + a_{n-1} = k(k-1)^{n-1} \tag{6.5.1}$$

where $n = 3, 4, \ldots$.

  Finally, we solve the recurrence relation (6.5.1). The characteristic root of $a_n + a_{n-1} = 0$ is $\alpha = -1$, and so

$$a_n^{(h)} = A(-1)^n,$$

where A is a constant.

Since $f(n) = k(k-1)^{n-1}$, let

$$a_n^{(p)} = B(k-1)^{n-1}.$$

As $a_n^{(p)}$ satisfies (6.5.1), we have:

$$B(k-1)^{n-1} + B(k-1)^{n-2} = k(k-1)^{n-1};$$

i.e., $$Bk(k-1)^{n-2} = k(k-1)^{n-1}.$$

Thus $B = k-1$ and so $a_n^{(p)} = (k-1)^n$. Hence the general solution of (6.5.1) is

$$a_n = a_n^{(h)} + a_n^{(p)}$$
$$= A(-1)^n + (k-1)^n.$$

Since $a_3 = k(k-1)(k-2)$, it follows that

$$k(k-1)(k-2) = -A + (k-1)^3,$$

and so

$$A = (k-1)^3 - k(k-1)(k-2)$$
$$= (k-1)(k^2 - 2k + 1 - k^2 + 2k)$$
$$= k-1.$$

Consequently, the required solution is

$$a_n = (-1)^n(k-1) + (k-1)^n$$

for all $n \geq 3$ and $k \geq 3$. ∎

Example 6.5.2. The $n \times n$ determinant a_n is defined for $n \geq 1$ by

$$a_n = \begin{vmatrix} p & p-q & 0 & 0 & \cdots & 0 & 0 \\ q & p & p-q & 0 & \cdots & 0 & 0 \\ 0 & q & p & p-q & \cdots & 0 & 0 \\ 0 & 0 & q & p & \cdots & 0 & 0 \\ \vdots & \vdots & \vdots & \vdots & \ddots & \vdots & \vdots \\ 0 & 0 & 0 & 0 & \cdots & p & p-q \\ 0 & 0 & 0 & 0 & \cdots & q & p \end{vmatrix}$$

where p and q are distinct nonzero constants. Find a recurrence relation for (a_n), and solve the recurrence relation.

Note. In the following solution, we assume that the reader is familiar with the cofactor expansion of a determinant.

Solution. By applying the cofactor expansion of a_n along the first row, it follows that

$$a_n = p \underbrace{\begin{vmatrix} p & p-q & 0 & \cdots & 0 & 0 \\ q & p & p-q & \cdots & 0 & 0 \\ 0 & q & p & \cdots & 0 & 0 \\ \vdots & \vdots & \vdots & \ddots & \vdots & \vdots \\ 0 & 0 & 0 & \cdots & p & p-q \\ 0 & 0 & 0 & \cdots & q & p \end{vmatrix}}_{n-1} \Bigg\} n-1$$

$$- (p-q) \underbrace{\begin{vmatrix} q & p-q & 0 & \cdots & 0 & 0 \\ 0 & p & p-q & \cdots & 0 & 0 \\ 0 & q & p & \cdots & 0 & 0 \\ \vdots & \vdots & \vdots & \ddots & \vdots & \vdots \\ 0 & 0 & 0 & \cdots & p & p-q \\ 0 & 0 & 0 & \cdots & q & p \end{vmatrix}}_{n-1} \Bigg\} n-1$$

Now by applying the cofactor expansion of the second determinant along the first column, we have

$$a_n = pa_{n-1} - (p-q)qa_{n-2}, \tag{6.5.2}$$

which is the desired recurrence relation.

The characteristic equation of (6.5.2) is

$$x^2 - px + (p-q)q = 0$$

and its roots are $p-q$ and q.

Case 1. $p - q \neq q$.

In this case, as the roots are distinct, the general solution is

$$a_n = A(p-q)^n + Bq^n \tag{1}$$

To find A and B, we first evaluate a_1 and a_2. Clearly,

$$a_1 = p$$

and

$$a_2 = \begin{vmatrix} p & p-q \\ q & p \end{vmatrix} = p^2 - q(p-q) = p^2 + q^2 - pq.$$

We define a_0 as the number such that a_0, a_1 and a_2 satisfy the recurrence relation (6.5.2). Thus

$$a_2 = pa_1 - (p-q)qa_0,$$

and so

$$p^2 + q^2 - pq = p^2 - (p-q)qa_0,$$

which implies that

$$a_0 = 1.$$

Letting $a_0 = 1$ and $a_1 = p$ in (1) gives

$$\begin{cases} A + B = 1 \\ A(p-q) + Bq = p. \end{cases} \tag{2}$$

Solving the system (2) yields

$$A = \frac{p-q}{p-2q} \quad \text{and} \quad B = \frac{-q}{p-2q}.$$

Note that $p - 2q \neq 0$ in this case. Hence the desired solution is

$$a_n = \frac{(p-q)^{n+1} - q^{n+1}}{p-2q}.$$

Case 2. $p - q = q$.

In this case, q is a root of multiplicity 2, and the general solution is

$$a_n = (A + Bn)q^n. \tag{3}$$

Since $a_0 = 1$ and $a_1 = p$, it follows that

$$\begin{cases} A = 1 \\ (A + B)q = p = 2q; \end{cases}$$

i.e.,

$$A = B = 1.$$

Thus

$$a_n = (1 + n)q^n$$

is the required solution of (6.5.2) in this case.

We conclude that

$$a_n = \begin{cases} \dfrac{(p-q)^{n+1} - q^{n+1}}{p-2q} & \text{if } p \neq 2q, \\[2mm] (1 + n)q^n & \text{if } p = 2q. \quad \blacksquare \end{cases}$$

6.6. A System of Linear Recurrence Relations

In the preceding three sections, we learned how to solve a *single* linear recurrence relation for a given sequence (a_n). In this section, we shall proceed one step further to consider systems of linear recurrence relations for two given sequences (a_n) and (b_n), that are of the form:

$$\begin{cases} a_n = pa_{n-1} + qb_{n-1} \\ b_n = rb_{n-1} + sa_{n-1}, \end{cases} \tag{6.6.1}$$

where p, q, r and s are arbitrary constants.

Recall that the method of *substitution* is an easy and standard method of solving "systems of equations". This method can similarly be used to solve systems of recurrence relations of the form (6.6.1).

Example 6.6.1. Solve the system of recurrence relations

$$\begin{cases} a_n + 2a_{n-1} - 4b_{n-1} = 0 & (1) \\ b_n + 5a_{n-1} - 7b_{n-1} = 0 & (2) \end{cases}$$

given that $a_1 = 4$ and $b_1 = 1$.

Solution. From (1),

$$b_{n-1} = \frac{1}{4}(a_n + 2a_{n-1}) \tag{3}$$

Substituting into (2) gives

$$\frac{1}{4}(a_{n+1} + 2a_n) + 5a_{n-1} - 7\{\frac{1}{4}(a_n + 2a_{n-1})\} = 0$$

or $$a_{n+1} - 5a_n + 6a_{n-1} = 0. \tag{4}$$

The characteristic equation of (4) is

$$x^2 - 5x + 6 = 0$$

and its roots are 2 and 3.
Thus the general solution of (4) is

$$a_n = A2^n + B3^n \tag{5}$$

where A and B are constants.

Substituting into (3) gives

$$b_n = \frac{1}{4}(a_{n+1} + 2a_n)$$
$$= \frac{1}{4}(A2^{n+1} + B3^{n+1} + 2A2^n + 2B3^n)$$
$$= \frac{1}{4}(4A2^n + 5B3^n). \tag{6}$$

As $a_1 = 4$ and $b_1 = 1$, we have

$$\begin{cases} 2A + 3B = 4 \\ 2A + \frac{15}{4}B = 1. \end{cases} \tag{7}$$

Solving (7) gives

$$A = 8 \quad \text{and} \quad B = -4.$$

Hence

$$\begin{cases} a_n = 2^{n+3} - 4 \cdot 3^n \\ b_n = 2^{n+3} - 5 \cdot 3^n \end{cases}$$

for $n \geq 1$, are the required solutions. ∎

We shall now see how a system of linear recurrence relations can be set up to solve an IMO problem.

Example 6.6.2.   **(IMO, 1979/6)** Let A and E be opposite vertices of a regular octagon. A frog starts jumping at vertex A. From any vertex of the octagon except E, it may jump to either of the two adjacent vertices. When it reaches vertex E, the frog stops and stays there. Let a_n be the number of distinct paths of exactly n jumps ending at E. Prove that

$$a_{2n-1} = 0$$

and $a_{2n} = \dfrac{1}{\sqrt{2}}\{(2 + \sqrt{2})^{n-1} - (2 - \sqrt{2})^{n-1}\}, \quad n = 1, 2, 3, \dots .$

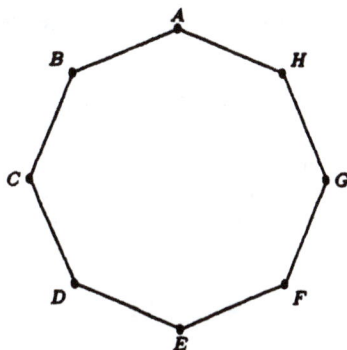

Figure 6.6.1.

Solution. The given regular octagon is shown in Figure 6.6.1.

Since the number of edges in any path joining A and E is even, it is impossible to reach E from A in an odd number of jumps. Thus $a_{2n-1} = 0$, for all $n \geq 1$.

It is obvious that $a_2 = 0$. Also, as $ABCDE$ and $AHGFE$ are the only 2 different paths of 4 jumps from A to E, we have $a_4 = 2$.

To find a recurrence relation for a_{2n}, we introduce a new supplementary sequence (b_n) as follows: For each $n \geq 1$, let b_n be the number of paths of exactly n jumps from C (or G) to E.

Starting at A, there are 4 ways for the frog to move in the first 2 jumps, namely,

$$A \to B \to A, \quad A \to H \to A$$
$$A \to B \to C, \quad A \to H \to G.$$

Thus, by definitions of (a_n) and (b_n),

$$a_{2n} = 2a_{2n-2} + 2b_{2n-2}. \qquad (1)$$

On the other hand, starting at C, there are 3 ways for the frog to move in the next 2 jumps if it does not stop at E, namely,

$$C \to B \to C, \quad C \to D \to C, \quad C \to B \to A.$$

Thus,

$$b_{2n} = 2b_{2n-2} + a_{2n-2}. \qquad (2)$$

We shall now solve the system of linear recurrence relations (1) and (2). From (1),

$$b_{2(n-1)} = \frac{1}{2}a_{2n} - a_{2(n-1)}. \tag{3}$$

Substituting (3) into (2) gives

$$\frac{1}{2}a_{2(n+1)} - a_{2n} = a_{2n} - 2a_{2(n-1)} + a_{2(n-1)}$$

or

$$a_{2(n+1)} - 4a_{2n} + 2a_{2(n-1)} = 0. \tag{4}$$

Let $d_n = a_{2n}$. Then (4) may be written as

$$d_{n+1} - 4d_n + 2d_{n-1} = 0. \tag{5}$$

The characteristic equation of (5) is

$$x^2 - 4x + 2 = 0,$$

and its roots are $2 \pm \sqrt{2}$. Thus the general solution of (4) is

$$a_{2n} = d_n = A(2 + \sqrt{2})^n + B(2 - \sqrt{2})^n, \tag{6}$$

for $n \geq 1$, where A and B are constants.

To find A and B, we use the initial conditions $d_1 = a_2 = 0$ and $d_2 = a_4 = 2$. We define d_0 to be the number such that d_0, d_1 and d_2 satisfy (5). Thus

$$d_2 - 4d_1 + 2d_0 = 0,$$

and so

$$d_0 = \frac{1}{2}(4d_1 - d_2) = -1.$$

From (6) and the initial conditions that $d_0 = -1$ and $d_1 = 0$, it follows that

$$\begin{cases} A + B = -1 \\ A(2 + \sqrt{2}) + B(2 - \sqrt{2}) = 0, \end{cases} \tag{7}$$

Solving (7) gives

$$A = \frac{1}{\sqrt{2}}\left(\frac{1}{2 + \sqrt{2}}\right) \quad \text{and} \quad B = -\frac{1}{\sqrt{2}}\left(\frac{1}{2 - \sqrt{2}}\right).$$

Thus, by (6), the required solution is

$$a_{2n} = \frac{1}{\sqrt{2}}\left\{(2 + \sqrt{2})^{n-1} - (2 - \sqrt{2})^{n-1}\right\}, \quad \text{for } n \geq 1. \quad \blacksquare$$

6.7. The Method of Generating Functions

In Chapter 5, we introduced the concept of a generating function for a given sequence and witnessed that, as a mathematical tool, generating functions are very powerful in solving combinatorial problems. In this section, we shall discuss how generating functions can be used also to help solve certain recurrence relations. We note that the method of generating functions could incorporate the initial conditions to find both $a_n^{(h)}$ and $a_n^{(p)}$ simultaneously when it is used to solve linear recurrence relations.

Example 6.7.1. Solve the recurrence relation

$$a_n - 2a_{n-1} = 2^n \tag{6.7.1}$$

given that $a_0 = 1$.

Solution. Let $A(x)$ be the generating function for the sequence (a_n). Then

$$A(x) = a_0 + a_1 x + a_2 x^2 + a_3 x^3 + \cdots + a_n x^n + \cdots$$

$$-2x A(x) = -2a_0 x - 2a_1 x^2 - 2a_2 x^3 - \cdots - 2a_{n-1} x^n - \cdots .$$

By taking their sum, we have

$$(1 - 2x) A(x) = a_0 + (a_1 - 2a_0)x + (a_2 - 2a_1)x^2 + \cdots$$
$$+ (a_n - 2a_{n-1})x^n + \cdots .$$

Since $a_0 = 1$ and the sequence (a_n) satisfies (6.7.1), it follows that

$$(1 - 2x) A(x) = 1 + 2x + 2^2 x^2 + \cdots + 2^n x^n + \cdots$$

$$= \frac{1}{1 - 2x} .$$

Thus

$$A(x) = \left(\frac{1}{1 - 2x} \right)^2 = \sum_{r=0}^{\infty} (r + 1)(2x)^r$$

and hence

$$a_n = (n + 1)2^n,$$

for $n \geq 0$. ∎

As shown in the above solution, in applying the method of generating functions to solve a recurrence relation for a sequence (a_n), we first form the generating function $A(x)$ for the sequence (a_n). By using the given recurrence relation and initial conditions, we obtain $A(x)$ through some algebraic manipulations. Finally, the solution of recurrence relation is obtained by taking $a_n = g(n)$ where $g(n)$ is the coefficient of x^n in the expansion of $A(x)$.

Example 6.7.2.　Solve, by the method of generating function, the recurrence relation

$$a_n - 5a_{n-1} + 6a_{n-2} = 5^n, \qquad (6.7.2)$$

given that $a_0 = 0$ and $a_1 = 1$.

Solution.　Let $A(x)$ be the generating function for the sequence (a_n). Then

$$A(x) = a_0 + a_1 x + a_2 x^2 + a_3 x^3 + a_4 x^4 + \cdots$$
$$-5x A(x) = -5a_0 x - 5a_1 x^2 - 5a_2 x^3 - 5a_3 x^4 - \cdots$$
$$6x^2 A(x) = 6a_0 x^2 + 6a_1 x^3 + 6a_2 x^4 + \cdots$$

and so

$$A(x)(1 - 5x + 6x^2) = x + \sum_{i=2}^{\infty} (a_i - 5a_{i-1} + 6a_{i-2}) x^i$$

$$= x + \sum_{i=2}^{\infty} 5^i x^i$$

$$= x + \frac{(5x)^2}{1 - 5x}$$

$$= \frac{25x^2 + x - 5x^2}{1 - 5x}$$

$$= \frac{20x^2 + x}{1 - 5x}.$$

Thus,

$$A(x) = \frac{20x^2 + x}{(1 - 5x)(1 - 2x)(1 - 3x)} = \frac{B}{1 - 5x} + \frac{C}{1 - 2x} + \frac{D}{1 - 3x}. \qquad (1)$$

It follows from (1) that

$$20x^2 + x = B(1 - 2x)(1 - 3x) + C(1 - 5x)(1 - 3x) + D(1 - 5x)(1 - 2x). \quad (2)$$

Putting $x = 0$ in (2) gives

$$B + C + D = 0. \qquad (3)$$

Putting $x = \frac{1}{2}$ in (2) gives

$$5 + \frac{1}{2} = C(1 - \frac{5}{2})(1 - \frac{3}{2}) = (-\frac{3}{2})(-\frac{1}{2})C,$$

or

$$C = \frac{22}{3}.$$

Putting $x = \frac{1}{3}$ in (2) gives

$$\frac{20}{9} + \frac{1}{3} = D(1 - \frac{5}{3})(1 - \frac{2}{3}) = D(-\frac{2}{3})(\frac{1}{3}) = \frac{-2}{9}D$$

or

$$D = -\frac{23}{2}.$$

Thus, by (3), we have

$$B = -C - D = \frac{25}{6}.$$

Hence,

$$A(x) = \frac{25}{6}\left(\frac{1}{1 - 5x}\right) + \frac{22}{3}\left(\frac{1}{1 - 2x}\right) - \frac{23}{2}\left(\frac{1}{1 - 3x}\right)$$

$$= \frac{25}{6}\sum_{i=0}^{\infty}(5x)^i + \frac{22}{3}\sum_{i=0}^{\infty}(2x)^i - \frac{23}{2}\sum_{i=0}^{\infty}(3x)^i$$

and so the required solution is

$$a_n = \frac{25}{6} \cdot 5^n + \frac{22}{3} \cdot 2^n - \frac{23}{2} \cdot 3^n,$$

for $n \geq 1$. ∎

Finally, we use the method of generating functions to solve a system of linear recurrence relations.

Example 6.7.3. Solve the system of recurrence relations

$$\begin{cases} a_n + 2a_{n-1} + 4b_{n-1} = 0 \\ b_n - 4a_{n-1} - 6b_{n-1} = 0, \end{cases} \tag{6.7.3}$$

given that $a_0 = 1$ and $b_0 = 0$.

Solution.   Let $A(x)$ be the generating function for (a_n) and $B(x)$ the generating function for (b_n). Then

$$
\begin{aligned}
A(x) &= 1 & +a_1x & \quad +a_2x^2 & \quad +a_3x^3 + \cdots \\
B(x) &= & b_1x & \quad +b_2x^2 & \quad +b_3x^3 + \cdots \\
2xA(x) &= & 2x & \quad +2a_1x^2 & \quad +2a_2x^3 + \cdots \\
4xB(x) &= & & \quad 4b_1x^2 & \quad +4b_2x^3 + \cdots
\end{aligned}
$$

and so

$$
(1 + 2x)A(x) + 4xB(x) = 1 + (a_1 + 2)x + (a_2 + 2a_1 + 4b_1)x^2
$$
$$
+ (a_3 + 2a_2 + 4b_2)x^3 + \cdots
$$
$$
= 1,
$$

by the first recurrence relation of (6.7.3).

Also,

$$
\begin{aligned}
-4xA(x) &= & -4x & \quad -4a_1x^2 & \quad -4a_2x^3 & \quad -4a_3x^4 & \quad -\cdots \\
-6xB(x) &= & & \quad -6b_1x^2 & \quad -6b_2x^3 & \quad -6b_3x^4 & \quad -\cdots ,
\end{aligned}
$$

and so

$$
B(x) - 4xA(x) - 6xB(x) = (b_1 - 4)x + (b_2 - 4a_1 - 6b_1)x^2
$$
$$
+ (b_3 - 4a_2 - 6b_2)x^3 + \cdots ,
$$

i.e.,

$$
(1 - 6x)B(x) - 4xA(x) = 0,
$$

by the second recurrence relation of (6.7.3). Thus we have

$$
\begin{cases} (1 + 2x)A(x) + 4xB(x) = 1 \\ -4xA(x) + (1 - 6x)B(x) = 0 \end{cases} \tag{1}
$$

Solving the system (1) for $A(x)$ and $B(x)$ gives

$$
A(x) = \frac{1 - 6x}{(1 - 2x)^2} \quad \text{and} \quad B(x) = \frac{4x}{(1 - 2x)^2}.
$$

Now,

$$
A(x) = (1 - 6x) \sum_{r=0}^{\infty} (r + 1)(2x)^r
$$

and

$$
B(x) = 4x \sum_{r=0}^{\infty} (r + 1)(2x)^r.
$$

Hence, by determining the coefficients of x^n in $A(x)$ and $B(x)$ respectively, we obtain the desired solutions:

$$
a_n = (n + 1)2^n - 6n2^{n-1} = 2^n(1 - 2n)
$$

and

$$
b_n = 4n \cdot 2^{n-1} = n2^{n+1},
$$

for all $n \geq 1$. ∎

6.8. A Nonlinear Recurrence Relation and Catalan Numbers

We begin with a famous combinatorial problem of dissecting a polygon by means of nonintersecting diagonals into triangles, that was studied by Euler and others about 200 years ago. A way of solving the problem leads to an important class of nonlinear recurrence relations. These nonlinear recurrence relations can be solved by the method of generating functions.

Example 6.8.1. A *triangulation* of an n-gon P_n, $n \geq 3$, is a subdivision of P_n into triangles by means of nonintersecting diagonals of P_n. Let $a_0 = 1$ and for $n \geq 1$, let a_n be the number of different triangulations of an $(n+2)$-gon. Show that for $n \geq 1$,

$$a_n = a_0 a_{n-1} + a_1 a_{n-2} + a_2 a_{n-3} + \cdots + a_{n-2} a_1 + a_{n-1} a_0, \qquad (6.8.1)$$

and solve the recurrence relation.

Solution. It is obvious that $a_1 = 1$. For $n = 2, 3$, the respective triangulations of P_4 and P_5 are shown in Figure 6.8.1, which show that

$$a_2 = 2 \quad \text{and} \quad a_3 = 5.$$

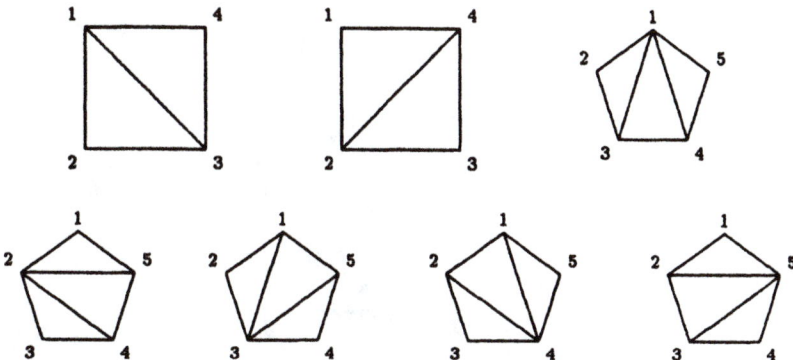

Figure 6.8.1.

To establish the recurrence relation (6.8.1), we form the $(n+2)$-gon P_{n+2} of Figure 6.8.2 and fix a triangulation of this P_{n+2}, where $n \geq 2$. (Note that the recurrence relation (6.8.1) holds trivially when $n = 1$.) Choose an arbitrary side, say $[1, n + 2]$, which joins vertices 1 and $n + 2$ of P_{n+2}. Clearly, $[1, n+2]$ belongs to a unique triangle of this triangulation. Denote the 3rd vertex of this triangle by r ($r = 2, 3, \ldots, n+1$), and the triangle by $\Delta(1, n + 2, r)$ (see Figure 6.8.2). Observe that $\Delta(1, n + 2, r)$ divides P_{n+2} into 2 smaller polygons:

$$\text{the } r\text{-gon (1)} \quad \text{and} \quad \text{the } (n + 3 - r)\text{-gon (2)}$$

of Figure 6.8.2. By definition, the r-gon (1) can be triangulated in a_{r-2} ways while the $(n+3-r)$-gon (2) in a_{n+1-r} ways independently. Thus, by (MP), the number of different triangulations of P_{n+2} in which $\Delta(1, n+2, r)$ occurs is

$$a_{r-2}a_{n+1-r}.$$

As the value of r ranges from 2 to $n + 1$, it follows by (AP) that

$$a_n = \sum_{r=2}^{n+1} a_{r-2}a_{n+1-r},$$

i.e.,

$$a_n = \sum_{k=0}^{n-1} a_k a_{n-1-k}, \tag{6.8.1}$$

for all $n \geq 1$.

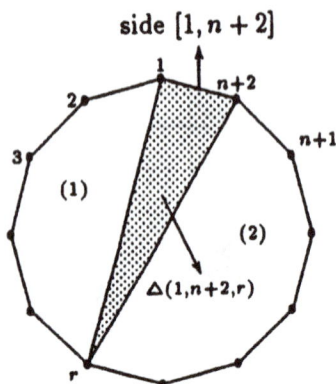

Figure 6.8.2.

We shall now solve (6.8.1) by the method of generating functions. Let $A(x) = \sum_{n=0}^{\infty} a_n x^n$ be the generating function for (a_n). Then

$$A(x) - a_0 = \sum_{n=1}^{\infty} a_n x^n = \sum_{n=1}^{\infty} \left(\sum_{k=0}^{n-1} a_k a_{n-1-k} \right) x^n$$

$$= (a_0 a_0)x + (a_0 a_1 + a_1 a_0)x^2 + (a_0 a_2 + a_1 a_1 + a_2 a_0)x^3 + \cdots$$

$$= (a_0 + a_1 x + a_2 x^2 + a_3 x^3 + \cdots)(a_0 x + a_1 x^2 + a_2 x^3 + \cdots)$$

$$= x(A(x))^2.$$

Thus, as $a_0 = 1$,

$$x(A(x))^2 - A(x) + 1 = 0.$$

Solving for $A(x)$ yields

$$A(x) = \frac{1 \pm \sqrt{1 - 4x}}{2x}$$

$$= \frac{1}{2x} \{1 \pm (1 - 4x)^{\frac{1}{2}}\}. \tag{1}$$

The coefficient of x^n $(n \geq 1)$ in $(1 - 4x)^{\frac{1}{2}}$ is

$$\binom{\frac{1}{2}}{n}(-4)^n = \frac{\frac{1}{2}(\frac{1}{2} - 1)(\frac{1}{2} - 2) \cdots (\frac{1}{2} - n + 1)}{n!}(-4)^n$$

$$= (-4)^n (\frac{1}{2})^n (-1)^{n-1} \frac{1 \cdot 1 \cdot 3 \cdot 5 \cdots (2n - 3)}{n!}$$

$$= -2^n \frac{(2n - 2)!}{n! 2 \cdot 4 \cdot 6 \cdots (2n - 2)}$$

$$= -2^n \frac{(2n - 2)!}{n! 2^{n-1} \cdot (n - 1)!}$$

$$= -\frac{2}{n} \frac{(2n - 2)!}{(n - 1)!(n - 1)!}$$

$$= -\frac{2}{n} \binom{2(n - 1)}{n - 1}.$$

Since $a_n \geq 1$, it follows from (1) that

$$A(x) = \frac{1}{2x} \{1 - (1 - 4x)^{\frac{1}{2}}\}$$

$$= \frac{1}{2x} \sum_{n=1}^{\infty} \frac{2}{n} \binom{2(n - 1)}{n - 1} x^n.$$

Hence, for $n \geq 1$,

$$a_n = \frac{1}{2} \cdot \frac{2}{n+1} \binom{2n}{n} = \frac{1}{n+1} \binom{2n}{n}. \quad \blacksquare$$

Recall that the numbers $\frac{1}{n+1} \binom{2n}{n}$, called the *Catalan* numbers, was introduced in Example 2.6.4 as the number of increasing mappings $\alpha : N_n \rightarrow N_{n-1}$ with the property that $\alpha(a) < a$ for each a in N_n. The above problem of dissecting an n-gon was first studied by Johann Andreas von Seguer (1704-1777) and then independently by L. Euler (1707-1783). Some other examples which give rise to these numbers are shown in Table 6.8.1. For more examples, references and generalizations of these interesting numbers, the reader may refer to Cohen [4], Breckenridge et.al. [B], Gardner [Ga], Gould [Go], Guy [Gu], Hilton and Pedersen [HP] and Chu [C].

6.9. Oscillating Permutations and an Exponential Generating Function

In this final section, we shall introduce another interesting problem studied by the French combinatorist D. André (1840-1917) in 1879 (see André [A1, A2] and also Honsberger [Hn], 69-75) on a special kind of permutations. The notion of generating functions has just been used in Sections 7 and 8 to help solve certain recurrence relations. We shall see here how this problem gives rise to a system of nonlinear recurrence relations and how the notion of exponential generating functions can be used to solve the recurrence relations.

Let S be a set of n natural numbers. A permutation $e_1 e_2 \cdots e_n$ of S is said to be *oscillating* if the following condition is satisfied:

$$e_1 < e_2 > e_3 < e_4 > e_5 < \cdots$$

where

$$\begin{cases} e_{n-1} > e_n & \text{if } n \text{ is odd} \\ e_{n-1} < e_n & \text{if } n \text{ is even.} \end{cases}$$

The *length* of a permutation $e_1 e_2 \cdots e_n$ of n numbers is defined to be n. Table 6.9.1 shows all oscillating permutations of length n of N_n $(= \{1, 2, ..., n\})$, for each $n = 1, 2, 3, 4, 5$.

The numbers of increasing mappings $\alpha : \{1,2,3\} \to \{0,1,2\}$

such that $\alpha(a) \leq a$

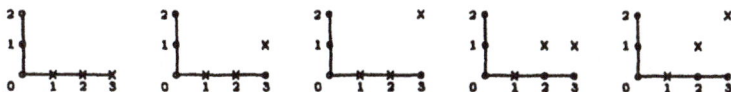

The number of ways of putting brackets in $x_1 x_2 x_3 x_4$

$$(((x_1 x_2)x_3)x_4) \; ((x_1(x_2 x_3))x_4) \; ((x_1 x_2)(x_3 x_4)) \; (x_2((x_2 x_3)x_4)) \; (x_1(x_2(x_3 x_4)))$$

The number of sequences with 3 1's and 3 (-1)'s

such that each partial sum is nonnegative

$$(1,1,1,-1,-1,-1), \; (1,1,-1,1,-1,-1), \; (1,1,-1,-1,1,-1),$$
$$(1,-1,1,1,-1,-1), \; (1,-1,1,-1,1,-1)$$

The number of rooted binary trees with 3 nodes

The number of ways to pair off 6 points on a circle

by nonintersecting chords

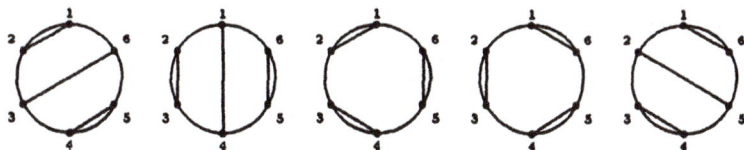

Table 6.8.1.

Length	Oscillating Permutations	No. of such permutations
1	1	1
2	12	1
3	132,231	2
4	1324,1423,2314,2413,3412	5
5	13254,14253,14352,15243,	16
	15342,23154,24153,24351,	
	25143,25341,34152,34251,	
	35142,35241,45132,45231	

Table 6.9.1

The problem that André considered is:

"What is the number of oscillating permutations of N_n for each $n \geq 1$?"

Before presenting André's solution, we have the following simple but useful observation.

Observation. Let $S = \{s_1, s_2, ..., s_n\}$ be any set of n distinct natural numbers. The number of oscillating permutations of S is the same as the number of oscillating permutations of N_n.

This observation simply says that as far as the number of oscillating permutations of S is concerned, only the size $|S|$ of S matters and the magnitudes of numbers in S are not important. The observation can easily be verified by establishing a bijection between the oscillating permutations of S and those of N_n. For instance, if $S = \{3, 5, 6, 9\}$, then from the correspondence:

$$3 \leftrightarrow 1, \; 5 \leftrightarrow 2, \; 6 \leftrightarrow 3, \; 9 \leftrightarrow 4,$$

one can establish the following bijection:

$$3659 \leftrightarrow 1324$$
$$3956 \leftrightarrow 1423$$
$$5639 \leftrightarrow 2314$$
$$5936 \leftrightarrow 2413$$
$$6935 \leftrightarrow 3412.$$

For convenience, given an oscillating permutation $e_1 e_2 \cdots e_n$, we underline e_i if e_i is smaller than its adjacent number (or numbers). Thus, we have

$$1\underline{3}2\underline{4}$$
$$\underline{3}5\underline{1}4\underline{2}$$
$$\underline{2}4\underline{1}6\underline{3}5$$
$$\underline{2}7\underline{1}5\underline{4}6\underline{3} \; ; .$$

Clearly, with this convention, an oscillating permutation $e_1 e_2 \cdots e_n$ ends up with an underlined e_n iff n is odd.

According to the parity of n, André introduced the following two sequences (a_n) and (b_n): For $n \geq 0$,

$$a_n = \begin{cases} \text{the no. of oscillating permutations of } N_n & \text{if } n \text{ is odd,} \\ 0 & \text{if } n \text{ is even,} \end{cases}$$

$$b_n = \begin{cases} 0 & \text{if } n \text{ is odd,} \\ 1 & \text{if } n = 0, \\ \text{the no. of oscillating permutations of } N_n & \text{if } n \geq 2 \text{ is even.} \end{cases}$$

It follows readily that for each $n \geq 1$, $a_n + b_n$ counts the number of oscillating permutations of N_n.

Claim 1. For odd n,

$$a_n = \sum_{k=0}^{n-1} \binom{n-1}{k} a_k a_{n-1-k}. \qquad (6.9.1)$$

Proof. Let $\underline{e_1} e_2 \underline{e_3} \cdots e_{n-1} \underline{e_n}$ (n odd) be an oscillating permutation of N_n and let $e_{k+1} = n$. Clearly, $e_{k+1} (= n)$ splits the permutation into 2 oscillating permutations of odd length k and $n - 1 - k$ respectively, where $k = 1, 3, 5, \ldots, n - 2$:

$$\underbrace{(\underline{e_1} e_2 \underline{e_3} \cdots e_{k-1} \underline{e_k})}_{\substack{\text{odd} \\ \text{(left)}}} e_{k+1} \underbrace{(\underline{e_{k+2}} \cdots e_{n-1} \underline{e_n})}_{\substack{\text{odd} \\ \text{(right)}}}$$

Since there are

(i) $\binom{n-1}{k}$ ways of choosing k numbers from N_{n-1} (to be arranged on the left),

  (ii) a_k ways to form an oscillating permutation of odd length k on the left (see observation),   and

  (iii) a_{n-1-k} ways to form oscillating permutations of odd length $n-1-k$ on the right,

and since the value of k ranges from $1, 3, 5, \ldots$ to $n-2$, we have

$$a_n = \binom{n-1}{1} a_1 a_{n-2} + \binom{n-1}{3} a_3 a_{n-4} + \cdots + \binom{n-1}{n-2} a_{n-2} a_1.$$

As $a_n = 0$ if n is even, it follows that

$$a_n = \sum_{k=0}^{n-1} \binom{n-1}{k} a_k a_{n-1-k},$$

as required. ∎

  Claim 2. For even n,

$$b_n = \sum_{k=0}^{n-1} \binom{n-1}{k} a_k b_{n-1-k} \tag{6.9.2}$$

  Proof. Let $\underline{e_1 e_2 \cdots e_k} e_{k+1} e_{k+2} \cdots e_{n-1} e_n$ (n even) be an oscillating permutation of $\mathbf{N}_n$ where $e_{k+1} = n$. Again, $e_{k+1}(= n)$ splits the permutation into an oscillating permutation of odd length k on the left and an oscillating permutation of even length $n - 1 - k$ on the right, where $k = 1, 3, 5, \ldots, n-1$:

$$\underbrace{(\underline{e_1} \underline{e_2} \underline{e_3} \cdots e_{k-1} \underline{e_k})}_{\substack{\text{odd} \\ \text{(left)}}} e_{k+1} \underbrace{(\underline{e_{k+2}} e_{k+3} \cdots \underline{e_{n-1}} e_n)}_{\substack{\text{even} \\ \text{(right)}}}$$

Since there are

  (i) $\binom{n-1}{k}$ ways of choosing k numbers from $\mathbf{N}_{n-1}$,

  (ii) a_k ways to form an oscillating permutation of odd length k on the left,   and

  (iii) b_{n-1-k} ways to form oscillating permutations of even length $n-1-k$ on the right, it follows similarly that

$$b_n = \sum_{k=0}^{n-1} \binom{n-1}{k} a_k b_{n-1-k},$$

as desired. ∎

We are now ready to use the notion of exponential generating function to solve the recurrence relations (6.9.1) and (6.9.2). First, let

$$A(x) = \sum_{k=0}^{\infty} a_k \frac{x^k}{k!}$$

be the exponential generating function for the sequence (a_n).

Claim 3. $1 + A(x)^2 = A'(x)$.

Proof. Indeed,

$$1 + A(x)^2$$
$$= 1 + (a_0 + a_1 \frac{x}{1!} + a_2 \frac{x^2}{2!} + a_3 \frac{x^3}{3!} + \cdots)^2$$
$$= 1 + a_0 a_0 + (a_0 a_1 + a_1 a_0)x + \left(\frac{a_0 a_2}{2!} + \frac{a_1 a_1}{1!1!} + \frac{a_2 a_0}{2!} \right) x^2$$
$$+ \left(\frac{a_0 a_3}{3!} + \frac{a_1 a_2}{1!2!} + \frac{a_2 a_1}{2!1!} + \frac{a_3 a_0}{3!} \right) x^3 + \cdots,$$

and the coefficient of $\frac{x^{n-1}}{(n-1)!}$ $(n \geq 2)$ in this expansion is

$$(n-1)! \left(\frac{a_0 a_{n-1}}{(n-1)!} + \frac{a_1 a_{n-2}}{1!(n-2)!} + \cdots + \frac{a_{n-1} a_0}{(n-1)!} \right)$$
$$= \sum_{k=0}^{n-1} \frac{(n-1)!}{k!(n-1-k)!} a_k a_{n-1-k}$$
$$= \sum_{k=0}^{n-1} \binom{n-1}{k} a_k a_{n-1-k}$$
$$= a_n,$$

by (6.9.1) and that $a_n = 0$ if n is even.
On the other hand,

$$A'(x) = a_1 + a_2 \frac{x}{1!} + a_3 \frac{x^2}{2!} + a_4 \frac{x^3}{3!} + \cdots$$

and the coefficient of $\frac{x^{n-1}}{(n-1)!}$ ($n \geq 2$) in this expansion is a_n. Further, the constant term in $1 + A(x)^2$ is $1 + a_0 a_0 = 1$, which is the same as $a_1 = 1$, the constant term in $A'(x)$. We thus conclude that

$$1 + A(x)^2 = A'(x).$$

Let $B(x) = \sum_{k=0}^{\infty} b_k \frac{x^k}{k!}$ be the exponential generating function for the sequence (b_n).

Claim 4. $A(x)B(x) = B'(x)$.

Proof. Indeed,

$$A(x)B(x)$$

$$= (a_0 + a_1 \frac{x}{1!} + a_2 \frac{x^2}{2!} + a_3 \frac{x^3}{3!} + \cdots)(b_0 + b_1 \frac{x}{1!} + b_2 \frac{x^2}{2!} + b_3 \frac{x^3}{3!} + \cdots)$$

$$= a_0 b_0 + (\frac{a_0 b_1}{1!} + \frac{a_1 b_0}{1!})x + (\frac{a_0 b_2}{2!} + \frac{a_1 b_1}{1!1!} + \frac{a_2 b_0}{2!})x^2 + \cdots$$

and the coefficient of $\frac{x^{n-1}}{(n-1)!}$ ($n \geq 2$) in this expansion is

$$(n-1)! \left(\frac{a_0 b_{n-1}}{(n-1)!} + \frac{a_1 b_{n-2}}{1!(n-2)!} + \cdots + \frac{a_{n-1} b_0}{(n-1)!} \right)$$

$$= \sum_{k=0}^{n-1} \binom{n-1}{k} a_k b_{n-1-k}$$

$$= b_n,$$

by (6.9.2) and the definition that $a_{k-1} = b_k = 0$ if k is odd. On the other hand,

$$B'(x) = b_1 + b_2 \frac{x}{1!} + b_3 \frac{x^2}{2!} + \cdots$$

and the coefficient of $\frac{x^{n-1}}{(n-1)!}$ ($n \geq 2$) in this expansion is b_n.

Further, the constant terms in $A(x)B(x)$ and $B'(x)$ are, respectively, $a_0 b_0 = 0$ and $b_1 = 0$, which are equal. We thus conclude that

$$A(x)B(x) = B'(x). \quad \blacksquare$$

Our final task is to determine the generating functions $A(x)$ and $B(x)$ from Claim 3 and Claim 4.

By Claim 3, we have

$$\int \frac{A'(x)}{1 + A(x)^2} dx = \int dx$$

and so $\tan^{-1} A(x) = x + C$.

When $x = 0$, $C = \tan^{-1} A(0) = \tan^{-1}(a_0) = \tan^{-1} 0 = 0$. Thus

$$\tan^{-1} A(x) = x$$

and
$$A(x) = \tan x \qquad (1)$$

By Claim 4 and (1), we have

$$\frac{B'(x)}{B(x)} = A(x) = \tan x$$

and so

$$\int \frac{B'(x)}{B(x)} dx = \int \tan x \, dx$$

or

$$\ln B(x) = \ln(\sec x) + C.$$

When $x = 0$,

$$C = \ln B(0) - \ln(\sec 0)$$
$$= \ln \frac{B(0)}{\sec 0} = \ln \frac{b_0}{1}$$
$$= \ln 1 = 0.$$

Thus $\ln B(x) = \ln(\sec x)$ and so

$$B(x) = \sec x. \qquad (2)$$

Consequently, the desired number of oscillating permutations of N_n is $a_n + b_n$, which is the coefficient of $\frac{x^n}{n!}$ in $\tan x + \sec x$.

The first 11 terms of the series expansion of $\tan x$ and $\sec x$ are given below:

$$\tan x = \frac{x^1}{1!} + 2 \cdot \frac{x^3}{3!} + 16 \cdot \frac{x^5}{5!} + 272 \cdot \frac{x^7}{7!} + 7936 \cdot \frac{x^9}{9!} + \cdots$$
$$\sec x = 1 + \frac{x^2}{2!} + 5 \cdot \frac{x^4}{4!} + 61 \cdot \frac{x^6}{6!} + 1385 \cdot \frac{x^8}{8!} + 50521 \cdot \frac{x^{10}}{10!} + \cdots$$

and the first 11 terms of $a_n + b_n$ are

$$1, \ 1, \ 1, \ 2, \ 5, \ 16, \ 61, \ 272, \ 1385, \ 7936, \ 50521.$$

Exercise 6

1. Solve

$$a_n = 3a_{n-1} - 2a_{n-2},$$

   given that $a_0 = 2$ and $a_1 = 3$.

2. Solve

$$a_n - 6a_{n-1} + 9a_{n-2} = 0,$$

   given that $a_0 = 2$ and $a_1 = 3$.

3. Solve

$$a_n = \frac{1}{2}(a_{n-1} + a_{n-2}),$$

   given that $a_0 = 0$ and $a_1 = 1$.

4. Solve

$$a_n - 4a_{n-1} + 4a_{n-2} = 0,$$

   given that $a_0 = -\frac{1}{4}$ and $a_1 = 1$.

5. Solve

$$2a_n = a_{n-1} + 2a_{n-2} - a_{n-3},$$

   given that $a_0 = 0$, $a_1 = 1$ and $a_2 = 2$.

6. Solve

$$a_n - 6a_{n-1} + 11a_{n-2} - 6a_{n-3} = 0,$$

   given that $a_0 = \frac{1}{3}$, $a_1 = 1$ and $a_2 = 2$.

7. Solve

$$a_n = -a_{n-1} + 16a_{n-2} - 20a_{n-3},$$

   given that $a_0 = 0$, $a_1 = 1$ and $a_2 = -1$.

8. Find the general solution of the recurrence relation

$$a_n + a_{n-1} - 3a_{n-2} - 5a_{n-3} - 2a_{n-4} = 0.$$

9. Solve

$$a_n = \frac{1}{2}a_{n-1} - 3,$$

   given that $a_0 = 2(3 + \sqrt{3})$.

10. Solve
$$a_n - 3a_{n-1} = 3 \cdot 2^n - 4n,$$
given that $a_1 = 2$.

11. Solve
$$a_n - a_{n-1} = 4n - 1,$$
given that $a_0 = 1$.

12. Solve
$$a_n = pa_{n-1} + q,$$
given that $a_0 = r$, where p, q and r are constants.

13. Let (a_n) be a sequence of numbers such that
    (i) $a_0 = 1$, $a_1 = \frac{3}{5}$ and
    (ii) the sequence $(a_n - \frac{1}{10}a_{n-1})$ is a geometric progression with common ratio $\frac{1}{2}$.

    Find a general formula for a_n, $n \geq 0$.

14. Solve
$$a_n^4 a_{n-1} = 10^{10},$$
given that $a_0 = 1$ and $a_n > 0$ for all n.

15. A sequence (a_n) of positive numbers satisfies
$$a_n = 2\sqrt{a_{n-1}}$$
with the initial condition $a_0 = 25$. Show that $\lim_{n \to \infty} a_n = 4$.

16. A sequence (a_n) of numbers satisfies
$$\left(\frac{a_n}{a_{n-1}}\right)^2 = \frac{a_{n-1}}{a_{n-2}}$$
with the initial conditions $a_0 = \frac{1}{4}$ and $a_1 = 1$. Solve the recurrence relation.

17. Solve
$$a_n + 3a_{n-1} = 4n^2 - 2n + 2^n,$$
given that $a_0 = 1$.

18. Solve
$$a_n - 2a_{n-1} + 2a_{n-2} = 0,$$
given that $a_0 = 1$ and $a_1 = 2$.

19. Solve
$$a_n - 4a_{n-1} + 4a_{n-2} = 2^n,$$
given that $a_0 = 0$ and $a_1 = 3$.

20. Solve
$$a_n - a_{n-1} - 2a_{n-2} = 4n,$$
given that $a_0 = -4$ and $a_1 = -5$.

21. Solve
$$a_n + a_{n-1} - 2a_{n-2} = 2^{n-2},$$
given that $a_0 = a_1 = 0$.

22. Solve
$$a_n - 3a_{n-1} + 2a_{n-2} = 2^n,$$
given that $a_0 = 0$ and $a_1 = 5$.

23. Solve
$$a_n + 5a_{n-1} + 6a_{n-2} = 3n^2,$$
given that $a_0 = 0$ and $a_1 = 1$.

24. Let (a_n) be a sequence of numbers satisfying the recurrence relation
$$pa_n + qa_{n-1} + ra_{n-2} = 0$$
with the initial conditions $a_0 = s$ and $a_1 = t$, where p, q, r, s, t are constants such that $p + q + r = 0$, $p \neq 0$ and $s \neq t$. Solve the recurrence relation.

25. Let (a_n) be a sequence of numbers satisfying the recurrence relation
$$a_n = \frac{pa_{n-1} + q}{ra_{n-1} + s}$$
where p, q, r and s are constants with $r \neq 0$.

(i) Show that
$$ra_n + s = p + s + \frac{qr - ps}{ra_{n-1} + s}. \qquad (1)$$

(ii) By the substitution $ra_n + s = \frac{b_{n+1}}{b_n}$, show that (1) can be reduced to the second order linear homogeneous recurrence relation for (b_n):

$$b_{n+1} - (p+s)b_n + (ps - qr)b_{n-1} = 0.$$

26. Solve

$$a_n = \frac{3a_{n-1}}{2a_{n-1} + 1},$$

given that $a_o = \frac{1}{4}$.

27. Solve

$$a_n = \frac{3a_{n-1} + 1}{a_{n-1} + 3},$$

given that $a_o = 5$.

28. A sequence (a_n) of numbers satisfies the condition

$$(2 - a_n)a_{n+1} = 1, \qquad n \geq 1.$$

Find $\lim_{n \to \infty} a_n$.

29. For $n \in \mathbf{N}$, recall that D_n is the number of derangements of the set $\mathbf{N}_n$. Prove by a combinatorial argument that

$$D_n = (n-1)(D_{n-1} + D_{n-2}).$$

30. For $n \in \mathbf{N}$, let a_n denote the number of ternary sequences of length n in which no two 0's are adjacent. Find a recurrence relation for (a_n) and solve the recurrence relation.

31. Let $C_0, C_1, C_2, \ldots$ be the sequence of circles in the Cartesian plane defined as follows:

(1) C_0 is the circle $x^2 + y^2 = 1$,

(2) for $n = 0, 1, 2, \ldots$, the circle C_{n+1} lies in the upper half-plane and is tangent to C_n as well as to both branches of the hyperbola $x^2 - y^2 = 1$.

Let a_n be the radius of C_n.

(i) Show that $a_n = 6a_{n-1} - a_{n-2}$, $n \geq 2$.

(ii) Deduce from (i) that a_n is an integer and

$$a_n = \frac{1}{2}[(3 + 2\sqrt{2})^n + (3 - 2\sqrt{2})^n].$$

(Proposed by B. A. Reznick, see *Amer. Math. Monthly*, **96** (1989), 262.)

32. The $n \times n$ determinant a_n is defined by

$$
a_n = \begin{vmatrix}
p+q & pq & 0 & 0 & \cdots & 0 & 0 \\
1 & p+q & pq & 0 & \cdots & 0 & 0 \\
0 & 1 & p+q & pq & \cdots & 0 & 0 \\
0 & 0 & 1 & p+q & \cdots & 0 & 0 \\
\vdots & \vdots & \vdots & \vdots & \ddots & \vdots & \vdots \\
0 & 0 & 0 & 0 & \cdots & p+q & pq \\
0 & 0 & 0 & 0 & \cdots & 1 & p+q
\end{vmatrix}
$$

where p and q are nonzero constants. Find a recurrence relation for (a_n), and solve the recurrence relation.

33. Consider the following $n \times n$ determinant:

$$
a_n = \begin{vmatrix}
pq+1 & q & 0 & 0 & \cdots & 0 \\
p & pq+1 & q & 0 & \cdots & 0 \\
0 & p & pq+1 & q & \cdots & 0 \\
0 & 0 & p & pq+1 & \cdots & 0 \\
\vdots & \vdots & \vdots & \vdots & \ddots & \vdots \\
0 & 0 & 0 & 0 & \cdots & q \\
0 & 0 & 0 & 0 & \cdots & pq+1
\end{vmatrix}
$$

where p and q are nonzero constants. Find a recurrence relation for (a_n), and solve the recurrence relation.

34. Given $n \in \mathbf{N}$, find the number of n-digit positive integers which can be formed from $1, 2, 3, 4$ such that 1 and 2 are not adjacent.

35. A $2 \times n$ rectangle $(n \in \mathbf{N})$ is to be paved with 1×2 identical blocks and 2×2 identical blocks. Let a_n denote the number of ways that can be done. Find a recurrence relation for (a_n), and solve the recurrence relation.

36. For $n \in \mathbf{N}$, let a_n denote the number of ways to pave a $3 \times n$ rectangle $ABCD$ with 1×2 identical dominoes. Clearly, $a_n = 0$ if n is odd. Show that

$$
a_{2r} = \frac{1}{2\sqrt{3}} \left\{ (\sqrt{3}+1)(2+\sqrt{3})^r + (\sqrt{3}-1)(2-\sqrt{3})^r \right\},
$$

where $r \in \mathbf{N}$. (Proposed by I. Tomescu, see *Amer. Math. Monthly*, **81** (1974), 522-523.)

37. Solve the system of recurrence relations:

$$\begin{cases} a_{n+1} = a_n - b_n \\ b_{n+1} = a_n + 3b_n, \end{cases}$$

given that $a_0 = -1$ and $b_0 = 5$.

38. Solve the system of recurrence relations:

$$\begin{cases} a_n + a_{n-1} + 2b_{n-1} = 0 \\ b_n - 2a_{n-1} - 3b_{n-1} = 0, \end{cases}$$

given that $a_0 = 1$ and $b_0 = 0$.

39. Solve the system of recurrence relations:

$$\begin{cases} 10a_n = 9a_{n-1} - 2b_{n-1} \\ 5b_n = -a_{n-1} + 3b_{n-1}, \end{cases}$$

given that $a_0 = 4$ and $b_0 = 3$.

40. Solve the system of recurrence relations:

$$\begin{cases} 3a_n - 2a_{n-1} - b_{n-1} = 0 \\ 3b_n - a_{n-1} - 2b_{n-1} = 0, \end{cases}$$

given that $a_0 = 2$ and $b_0 = -1$.

41. Let (a_n) and (b_n) be two sequences of positive numbers satisfying the recurrence relations:

$$\begin{cases} a_n^2 = a_{n-1}b_n \\ b_n^2 = a_n b_{n-1} \end{cases}$$

with the initial conditions $a_0 = \frac{1}{8}$ and $b_0 = 64$. Show that

$$\lim_{n \to \infty} a_n = \lim_{n \to \infty} b_n,$$

and find the common limit.

42. For $n \in \mathbf{N}^*$, let a_n, b_n, c_n and d_n denote the numbers of binary sequences of length n satisfying the respective conditions:

	Number of 0's	Number of 1's
a_n	even	even
b_n	even	odd
c_n	odd	even
d_n	odd	odd

(i) Show that

$$a_n = b_{n-1} + c_{n-1},$$
$$b_n = a_{n-1} + d_{n-1} = c_n,$$
$$d_n = b_{n-1} + c_{n-1}.$$

(ii) Let $A(x)$, $B(x)$, $C(x)$ and $D(x)$ be, respectively, the generating functions of the sequences (a_n), (b_n), (c_n) and (d_n). Show that

$$A(x) = \frac{1 - 2x^2}{1 - 4x^2},$$
$$B(x) = C(x) = \frac{x}{1 - 4x^2},$$
$$D(x) = \frac{2x^2}{1 - 4x^2}.$$

(iii) Deduce from (ii) that

$$a_n = (-2)^{n-2} + 2^{n-2} \quad (n \geq 1),$$
$$b_n = c_n = -(-2)^{n-2} + 2^{n-2} \quad (n \geq 0),$$
$$d_n = (-2)^{n-2} + 2^{n-2} \quad (n \geq 1).$$

43. Three given sequences (a_n), (b_n) and (c_n) satisfy the following recurrence relations:

$$a_{n+1} = \frac{1}{2}(b_n + c_n - a_n),$$
$$b_{n+1} = \frac{1}{2}(c_n + a_n - b_n),$$

and

$$c_{n+1} = \frac{1}{2}(a_n + b_n - c_n),$$

with the initial conditions $a_0 = p$, $b_0 = q$ and $c_0 = r$, where p, q, r are positive constants.

(i) Show that $a_n = \frac{1}{3}(p+q+r)(\frac{1}{2})^n + (-1)^n \frac{1}{3}(2p-q-r)$ for all $n \geq 0$.

(ii) Deduce that if $a_n > 0$, $b_n > 0$ and $c_n > 0$ for all $n \geq 0$, then $p = q = r$.

44. For $n \in \mathbf{N}$, let F_n denote the nth Fibonacci number. Thus

$$F_1 = 1, \quad F_2 = 1, \quad F_3 = 2, \quad F_4 = 3, \quad F_5 = 5, \quad F_6 = 8, \quad \ldots$$

and by Example 6.3.1,

$$F_{n+2} = F_n + F_{n+1}$$

and

$$F_n = \frac{1}{\sqrt{5}}\left\{(\frac{1+\sqrt{5}}{2})^n - (\frac{1-\sqrt{5}}{2})^n\right\}.$$

Show that

(i) $\sum_{r=1}^{n} F_r = F_{n+2} - 1$;

(ii) $\sum_{r=1}^{n} F_{2r} = F_{2n+1} - 1$;

(iii) $\sum_{r=1}^{n} F_{2r-1} = F_{2n}$;

(iv) $\sum_{r=1}^{n} (-1)^{r+1} F_r = (-1)^{n+1} F_{n-1} + 1.$

45. Show that for $m, n \in \mathbf{N}$ with $n \geq 2$,

(i) $F_{m+n} = F_m F_{n-1} + F_{m+1} F_n$;

(ii) $\begin{pmatrix} 1 & 1 \\ 1 & 0 \end{pmatrix}^n = \begin{pmatrix} F_{n+1} & F_n \\ F_n & F_{n-1} \end{pmatrix}$;

(iii) $F_{n+1} F_{n-1} - F_n^2 = (-1)^n$;

(iv) $F_{n+1}^2 = 4F_n F_{n-1} + F_{n-2}^2$, $\quad n \geq 3$;

(v) $(F_n, F_{n+1}) = 1$, where (a, b) denotes the HCF of a and b.

Remark. In general, $(F_m, F_n) = F_{(m,n)}$. Also, $F_m | F_n$ iff $m | n$.

46. Show that for $n \geq 2$

(i) $F_n^2 + F_{n-1}^2 = F_{2n-1}$;

(ii) $F_{n+1}^2 - F_{n-1}^2 = F_{2n}$;

(iii) $F_{n+1}^3 + F_n^3 - F_{n-1}^3 = F_{3n}.$

47. Show that

(i) $\sum_{r=1}^{n} F_r^2 = F_n F_{n+1}$,

(ii) $\displaystyle\sum_{r=1}^{2n-1} F_r F_{r+1} = F_{2n}^2$,

(iii) $\displaystyle\sum_{r=1}^{2n} F_r F_{r+1} = F_{2n+1}^2 - 1.$

48. Show that for $n \in \mathbf{N}^*$,

$$F_{n+1} = \sum_{r=0}^{\lfloor \frac{n}{2} \rfloor} \binom{n-r}{r}.$$

49. Show that for $m, n \in \mathbf{N}$,

$$\sum_{r=0}^{n} \binom{n}{r} F_{m+r} = F_{m+2n}.$$

50. Show that

$$\lim_{n \to \infty} \frac{F_n}{F_{n+1}} = \frac{\sqrt{5}-1}{2} \approx 0.618.$$

Note. The constant $\frac{\sqrt{5}-1}{2}$ is called the *golden number.*

51. Beginning with a pair of baby rabbits, and assuming that each pair gives birth to a new pair each month starting from the 2nd month of its life, find the number a_n of pairs of rabbits at the end of the nth month. (Fibonacci, Liber Abaci, 1202.)

52. Show that for $n \in \mathbf{N}^*$,

$$F_{n+1} = \begin{vmatrix} 1 & -1 & 0 & 0 & \cdots & 0 & 0 \\ 1 & 1 & -1 & 0 & \cdots & 0 & 0 \\ 0 & 1 & 1 & -1 & \cdots & 0 & 0 \\ \vdots & \vdots & \vdots & \vdots & \ddots & \vdots & \vdots \\ 0 & 0 & 0 & 0 & \cdots & 1 & -1 \\ 0 & 0 & 0 & 0 & \cdots & 1 & 1 \end{vmatrix}.$$

53. A man wishes to climb an n-step staircase. Let a_n denote the number of ways that this can be done if in each step he can cover either one step or two steps. Find a recurrence relation for (a_n).

54. Given $n \in \mathbf{N}$, find the number of binary sequences of length n in which no two 0's are adjacent.

55. For $n \in \mathbf{N}$ with $n \geq 2$, let a_n denote the number of ways to express n as a sum of positive integers greater than 1, taking order into account. Find a recurrence relation for (a_n) and determine the value of a_n.

56. Find the number of subsets of $\{1, 2, \ldots, n\}$, where $n \in \mathbf{N}$, that contain no consecutive integers. Express your answer in terms of a Fibonacci number.

57. Prove that
$$\sum_{j=0}^{n} \frac{\binom{n}{2j-n-1}}{5^j} = \frac{1}{2}(0.4)^n F_n.$$

(Proposed by S. Rabinowitz, see *Crux Mathematicorum*, **10** (1984), 269.)

58. Call an ordered pair (S, T) of subsets of $\{1, 2, \ldots, n\}$ *admissible* if $s > |T|$ for each $s \in S$, and $t > |S|$ for each $t \in T$. How many admissible ordered pairs of subsets of $\{1, 2, \ldots, 10\}$ are there? Prove your answer. (Putnam, 1990)

59. For each $n \in \mathbf{N}$, let a_n denote the number of natural numbers N satisfying the following conditions: the sum of the digits of N is n and each digit of N is taken from $\{1, 3, 4\}$. Show that a_{2n} is a perfect square for each $n = 1, 2, \ldots$. (Chinese Math. Competition, 1991)

60. Find a recurrence relation for a_n, the number of ways to place parentheses to indicate the order of multiplication of the n numbers $x_1 x_2 x_3 \ldots x_n$, where $n \in \mathbf{N}$.

61. For $n \in \mathbf{N}$, let b_n denote the number of sequences of $2n$ terms:
$$z_1, z_2, \ldots, z_{2n},$$

where each z_i is either 1 or -1 such that

(1) $\sum_{i=1}^{2n} z_i = 0$ and

(2) $\sum_{i=1}^{k} z_i \geq 0$ for each $k = 1, 2, \ldots, 2n - 1$.

(i) Find b_n for $n = 1, 2, 3$.

(ii) Establish a bijection between the set of all sequences of $2n$ terms as defined above and the set of all parenthesized expressions of the $n + 1$ numbers $x_1 x_2 \ldots x_n x_{n+1}$.

62. For $n \in \mathbf{N}$, let a_n denote the number of ways to pair off $2n$ distinct points on the circumference of a circle by n nonintersecting chords. Find a recurrence relation for (a_n).

63. Let $p(x_1, x_2, \ldots, x_n)$ be a polynomial in n variables with constant term 0, and let $\#(p)$ denote the number of distinct terms in p after terms with like exponents have been collected. Thus for example $\#((x_1+x_2)^5) = 6$. Find a formula for $\#(q_n)$ where

$$q_n = x_1(x_1 + x_2)(x_1 + x_2 + x_3) \cdots (x_1 + \cdots + x_n).$$

(Proposed by J. O. Shallit, see *Amer. Math. Monthly*, **93** (1986), 217-218.)

64. Find the total number of ways of arranging in a row the $2n$ integers $a_1, a_2, \ldots, a_n, b_1, b_2, \ldots, b_n$ with the restriction that for each i, a_i precede b_i, a_i precede a_{i+1} and b_i precede b_{i+1}. (Proposed by E. Just, see *Amer. Math. Monthly*, **76** (1969), 419-420.)

65. Mr. Chen and Mr. Lim are the two candidates taking part in an election. Assume that Mr. Chen receives m votes and Mr. Lim receives n votes, where $m, n \in \mathbf{N}$ with $m > n$. Find the number of ways that the ballots can be arranged in such a way that when they are counted, one at a time, the number of votes for Mr. Chen is always more than that for Mr. Lim.

66. For $n \in \mathbf{N}$, let a_n denote the number of mappings $f : \mathbf{N}_n \to \mathbf{N}_n$ such that if $j \in f(\mathbf{N}_n)$, then $i \in f(\mathbf{N}_n)$ for all i with $1 \le i \le j$.

   (i) Find the values of a_1, a_2 and a_3 by listing all such mappings f.

   (ii) Show that

$$a_n = \sum_{k=1}^{n} \binom{n}{k} a_{n-k}.$$

   (iii) Let $A(x)$ be the exponential generating function for (a_n), where $a_0 = 1$. Show that

$$A(x) = \frac{1}{2 - e^x}.$$

   (iv) Deduce that

$$a_n = \sum_{r=0}^{\infty} \frac{r^n}{2^{r+1}}.$$

67. Define S_0 to be 1. For $n \geq 1$, let S_n be the number of $n \times n$ matrices whose elements are nonnegative integers with the property that $a_{ij} = a_{ji}$ $(i, j = 1, 2, \ldots, n)$ and where $\sum_{i=1}^{n} a_{ij} = 1$, $(j = 1, 2, \ldots, n)$. Prove

    (a) $S_{n+1} = S_n + nS_{n-1}$,

    (b) $\displaystyle\sum_{n=0}^{\infty} S_n \frac{x^n}{n!} = e^{x + \frac{x^2}{2}}$.

    (Putnam, 1967)

68. A sequence (a_n) of numbers satisfies the following conditions:

    (1) $a_1 = \frac{1}{2}$ and

    (2) $a_1 + a_2 + \cdots + a_n = n^2 a_n$, $n \geq 1$.

    Determine the value of a_n.

69. What is the sum of the greatest odd divisors of the integers $1, 2, 3, \ldots, 2^n$, where $n \in \mathbb{N}$? (West German Olympiad, 1982)

    (*Hint*: Let a_n be the sum of the greatest odd divisors of $1, 2, 3, \ldots, 2^n$. Show that $a_n = a_{n-1} + 4^{n-1}$.)

70. Let d_n be the determinant of the $n \times n$ matrix in which the element in the ith row and the jth column is the absolute value of the difference of i and j. Show that

$$d_n = (-1)^{n-1}(n-1)2^{n-2}.$$

    (Putnam, 1969)

71. A sequence (a_n) of natural numbers is defined by $a_1 = 1$, $a_2 = 3$ and

$$a_n = (n+1)a_{n-1} - na_{n-2} \qquad (n \geq 2).$$

    Find all values of n such that $11 | a_n$.

72. A sequence (a_n) of positive numbers is defined by

$$a_n = \frac{1}{16}\left(1 + 4a_{n-1} + \sqrt{1 + 24a_{n-1}}\right)$$

    with $a_0 = 1$. Find a general formula for a_n.

73. A sequence (a_n) of numbers is defined by

$$2a_n = 3a_{n-1} + \sqrt{5a_{n-1}^2 + 4} \quad (n \geq 1)$$

    with $a_0 = 0$. Show that for all $m \geq 1$, $1992 \nmid a_{2m+1}$.

74. Solve the recurrence relation

$$na_n = (n-2)a_{n-1} + (n+1),$$

given that $a_0 = 0$.

75. Solve the recurrence relation

$$n(n-1)a_n - (n-2)^2 a_{n-2} = 0,$$

given that $a_0 = 0$ and $a_1 = 1$.

76. A sequence (a_n) of numbers satisfies the recurrence relation

$$(a_n - a_{n-1})f(a_{n-1}) + g(a_{n-1}) = 0$$

with the initial condition $a_0 = 2$, where

$$f(x) = 3(x-1)^2 \quad \text{and} \quad g(x) = (x-1)^3.$$

Solve the recurrence relation.

77. A sequence (a_n) of numbers satisfies the recurrence relation

$$n(n-1)a_n = (n-1)(n-2)a_{n-1} - (n-3)a_{n-2}$$

with the initial conditions $a_0 = 1$ and $a_1 = 2$.
Find the value of

$$\sum_{k=0}^{1992} \frac{a_k}{a_{k+1}}.$$

78. Let $a(n)$ be the number of representations of the positive integer n as the sums of 1's and 2's taking order into account. For example, since

$$4 = 1+1+2 = 1+2+1 = 2+1+1$$
$$= 2+2 = 1+1+1+1,$$

then $a(4) = 5$. Let $b(n)$ be the number of representations of n as the sum of integers greater than 1, again taking order into account and counting the summand n. For example, since $6 = 4+2 = 2+4 = 3+3 = 2+2+2$, we have $b(6) = 5$. Show that for each n, $a(n) = b(n+2)$. (Putnam, 1957)

79. Show that the sum of the first n terms in the binomial expansion of $(2-1)^{-n}$ is $\frac{1}{2}$, where $n \in \mathbf{N}$. (Putnam, 1967)

80. Prove that there exists a unique function f from the set $\mathbf{R}^+$ of positive real numbers to $\mathbf{R}^+$ such that

$$f(f(x)) = 6x - f(x)$$

and $f(x) > 0$ for all $x > 0$. (Putnam, 1988)

81. Let $T_0 = 2$, $T_1 = 3$, $T_2 = 6$, and for $n \geq 3$,

$$T_n = (n+4)T_{n-1} - 4nT_{n-2} + (4n-8)T_{n-3}.$$

The first few terms are

$$2, 3, 6, 14, 40, 152, 784, 5168, 40576.$$

Find, with proof, a formula for T_n of the form $T_n = A_n + B_n$, where (A_n) and (B_n) are well-known sequences. (Putnam, 1990)

82. Let $\{a_n\}$ and $\{b_n\}$ denote two sequences of integers defined as follows:

$$a_0 = 1, \quad a_1 = 1, \quad a_n = a_{n-1} + 2a_{n-2} \quad (n \geq 2),$$
$$b_0 = 1, \quad b_1 = 7, \quad b_n = 2b_{n-1} + 3b_{n-2} \quad (n \geq 2).$$

Thus, the first few terms of the sequences are:

$$a : 1, 1, 3, 5, 11, 21, \ldots$$
$$b : 1, 7, 17, 55, 161, 487, \ldots$$

Prove that, except for the "1", there is no term which occurs in both sequences. (USA MO, 1973)

83. The sequence $\{x_n\}$ is defined as follows: $x_1 = 2$, $x_2 = 3$, and

$$x_{2m+1} = x_{2m} + x_{2m-1}, \quad m \geq 1$$
$$x_{2m} = x_{2m-1} + 2x_{2m-2}, \quad m \geq 2.$$

Determine x_n (as a function of n). (Austrian MO, 1983)

84. Determine the number of all sequences $(x_1, x_2, \ldots, x_n)$, with $x_i \in \{a, b, c\}$ for $i = 1, 2, \ldots, n$ that satisfy $x_1 = x_n = a$ and $x_i \neq x_{i+1}$ for $i = 1, 2, \ldots, n-1$. (18th Austrian MO)

85. The sequence x_1, x_2, ... is defined by the equalities $x_1 = x_2 = 1$ and

$$x_{n+2} = 14x_{n+1} - x_n - 4, \quad n \geq 1.$$

Prove that each number of the given sequence is a perfect square. (Bulgarian MO, 1987)

86. How many words with n digits can be formed from the alphabet $\{0, 1, 2, 3, 4\}$, if adjacent digits must differ by exactly one? (West Germany, 1987)

87. The sequence (a_n) of integers is defined by

$$-\frac{1}{2} < a_{n+1} - \frac{a_n^2}{a_{n-1}} \leq \frac{1}{2}$$

with $a_1 = 2$ and $a_2 = 7$. Show that a_n is odd for all values of $n \geq 2$. (British MO, 1988)

88. In the network illustrated by the figure below, where there are n adjacent squares, what is the number of paths (not necessarily shortest) from A to B which do not pass through any intersection twice?

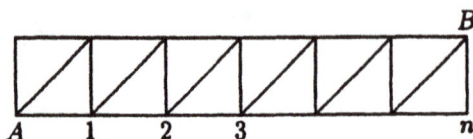

(Proposed by P. Andrews and E. T. H. Wang, see *CRUX Mathematicorum*, **14** (1988), 62-64.)

89. Let $a_1 = 1$ and $a_{n+1} = a_n + \lfloor \sqrt{a_n} \rfloor$ for $n \in \mathbb{N}$. Show that a_n is a square iff $n = 2^k + k - 2$ for some $k \in \mathbb{N}$. (Proposed by T. C. Brown, see *Amer. Math. Monthly*, **85** (1978), 52-53.)

90. Determine all pairs (h, s) of positive integers with the following property: If one draws h horizontal lines and another s lines which satisfy

   (i) they are not horizontal,

   (ii) no two of them are parallel,

   (iii) no three of the $h + s$ lines are concurrent,

   then the number of regions formed by these $h + s$ lines is 1992. (APMO, 1992)

91. Show that
$$S(r,n) = \sum_{k=n-1}^{r-1} \binom{r-1}{k} S(k, n-1),$$

where $r \geq n \geq 2$.

92. Let $B_0 = 1$ and for $r \in \mathbf{N}$, let $B_r = \sum_{n=1}^{r} S(r,n)$ denote the rth Bell number (see Section 1.7). Show that

$$B_r = \sum_{k=0}^{r-1} \binom{r-1}{k} B_k,$$

where $r \geq 1$.

93. Two sequences $P(m,n)$ and $Q(m,n)$ are defined as follows (m, n are integers). $P(m,0) = 1$ for $m \geq 0$, $P(0,n) = 0$ for $n \geq 1$, $P(m,n) = 0$ for $m, n < 0$. $P(m,n) = \sum_{j=0}^{n} P(m-1,j)$ for $m \geq 1$. $Q(m,n) = P(m-1,n) + P(m-1,n-1) + P(m-1,n-2)$ for $m \geq 1$. Express $Q(m,n)$ in terms of m and n for $m \geq 1$. (Proposed by L. Kuipers, see *Amer. Math. Monthly*, **76** (1969), 97-98.)

94. For $n, k \in \mathbf{N}$, let $S_k(n) = \sum_{j=1}^{n} j^k$ (see Problem 2.85). Show that

(i) $S_k(n) = n^{k+1} - \sum_{r=0}^{k-1} \binom{k}{r} S_{r+1}(n-1)$ for $n \geq 2$,

(ii) $(k+1)S_k(n) = (n+1)^{k+1} - (n+1)^k - \sum_{r=0}^{k-2} \binom{k}{r} S_{r+1}(n).$

References.

[A1] D. André, Developpments de sec x et tan x, *C.R. Acad. Sci., Paris*, **88** (1879), 965-967.

[A2] D. André, Memoire sur le permutations alterees, *J. of Mathematics*, **7** (1881), 167-184.

[B] W. Breckenridge, H. Gastineau-Hills, A. Nelson, P. Bos, G. Calvert, K. Wehrhahn, Lattice paths and Catalan numbers, *Bulletin of Institute of Combinatorics and Its Applications*, **1** (1991), 41-55.

[C] W. Chu, A new combinatorial interpretation for generalized Catalan numbers, *Discrete Math.* **65** (1987), 91-94.

[Ga] M. Gardner, Catalan numbers: an integer sequence that materializes in unexpected places, *Scientific Amer.* **234** (no.6) June 1976, 120-125.

[Go] H.W. Gould, Bell and Catalan numbers, Research bibliography of two special number sequences, Department of Mathematics, West Virginia University, Morgantown, WV26506. (The 1979 edition sells for US$3.00 and contains over 500 references pertaining to Catalan numbers.)

[Gu] R.K. Guy, A medley of Malayan mathematical memories and mantissae, *Math. Medley, Singapore Mathematical Society,* **12(1)** (1984), 9-17.

[HP] P. Hilton and J. Pedersen, Catalan numbers, their generalization, and their uses, *Mathematical Intelligencer,* **13(2)** (1991), 64-75.

[Hg] V.E. Hoggatt, Jr., *Fibonacci and Lucas Numbers*, Houghton Mifflin Company, 1969.

[Hn] R. Honsberger, *Mathematical Gems III*, Mathematical Association of America, 1985.

[Va] S. Vajda, *Fibonacci & Lucas Numbers, and the Golden Section. Theory and Applications.* Ellis Horwood Series: Mathematics and Its Applications. Ellis Horwood Ltd., Chichester, Halsted Press, New York, 1989.

[Vo] N.N. Vorobyov, *The Fibonacci Numbers*, Boston: D.C. Heath and Company, 1963.

Bibliography

[1] I. Anderson, *A First Course in Combinatorial Mathematics*, Oxford University Press, 1974.

[2] C. Berge, *Principles of Combinatorics*, Academic Press, 1971.

[3] R.A. Brualdi, *Introductory Combinatorics*, North Holland, 1977.

[4] D.I.A. Cohen, *Basic Techniques of Combinatorial Theory*, John Wiley & Sons, 1978.

[5] L. Comtet, *Advanced Combinatorics*, D. Reidel, 1974.

[6] R.L. Graham, D.E. Knuth and O. Patashnik, *Concrete Mathematics*, Addison-Wesley, 1989.

[7] D.E. Knuth, *The Art of Computer Programming, Vol. 1: Fundamental Algorithms*, Addison-Wesley, 1968 (2nd ed. 1973).

[8] C.L. Liu, *Introduction to Combinatorial Mathematics*, McGraw-Hill, 1968.

[9] L. Lovász, *Combinatorial Problems and Exercises*, North-Holland, 1979.

[10] J. Riordan, *An Introduction to Combinatorial Analysis*, Wiley, 1958.

[11] J. Riordan, *Combinatorial Identities*, Wiley, 1968.

[12] F.S. Roberts, *Applied Combinatorics*, Prentice-Hall, 1984.

[13] I. Tomescu, *Introduction to Combinatorics*, Collet's, 1975.

[14] I. Tomescu, *Problems in Combinatorics and Graph Theory*, John Wiley & Sons, 1985.

[15] M. Townsend, *Discrete Mathematics: Applied Combinatorics and Graph Theory*, Benjamin, 1987.

[16] A. Tucker, *Applied Combinatorics*, 2nd ed., Wiley, 1984.

Answers to Exercises

Exercise 1

1.(i) 45   **1.(ii)** 235   **2.(i)** 12!   **2.(ii)** 8!5!

2.(iii) $7! \cdot \binom{8}{5} \cdot 5!$ **2.(iv)** $8! \cdot 120$

3.(i) $(m + n)!$ **3.(ii)** $n! P_m^{n+1}$

3.(iii) $(m + 1)! n!$ **3.(iv)** $(m + n - 1)! \times 2$

4.(i) P_5^{10} **4.(ii)** $P_3^6 \cdot P_2^4$ **5.** $(2P_5^{24})(20!)$

6. 1232   **7.** $(n + 1)! - 1$ **8.** $1 - \frac{1}{(n+1)!}$ **10.** 1271

11.(i) 8   **11.(ii)** 16   **11.(iii)** 108

15.(i) $\binom{5}{3}\binom{10}{6}$ **15.(ii)** $\binom{5}{3}\binom{10}{6} \cdot 9!$ **16.** $7!\binom{8}{3}$

17. $\binom{6}{3} \cdot 5! = 2400$ **18.** $\binom{13}{7} \cdot (10!)^2$ **19.** $7! \times 10$

20.(i) $\binom{3}{1}\binom{12}{6} + \binom{3}{2}\binom{12}{5} + \binom{3}{3}\binom{12}{4}$ or $\binom{15}{7} - \binom{12}{7}$ by (CP)

20.(ii) $7!\{\binom{15}{7} - \binom{12}{7}\}$ **21.** $\binom{m+1}{n}$ **22.** $\binom{p}{2}\binom{q}{2}$

23. $\binom{10}{4}\binom{15}{1}\binom{10}{2} + \binom{10}{3}\binom{4}{1}\binom{15}{2}\binom{10}{1} + \binom{10}{2}\binom{4}{2}\binom{15}{3}$ **24.** $\frac{25}{132}$

25.(i) $\binom{5}{2}\binom{8}{3}$ **25.(ii)** $\binom{5}{2}\binom{7}{3}$

25.(iii) $\binom{5}{2}\binom{4}{1}\binom{4}{2}$ **25.(iv)** $\binom{13}{5} - \binom{5}{2}\binom{7}{3}$

26.(i) $\binom{n}{k}$ **26.(ii)** $\binom{n}{2k} \cdot 2^{2k}$

26.(iii) $\binom{2n}{2k} - \binom{n}{2k} \cdot 2^{2k}$ **26.(iv)** $\binom{n}{2}\binom{n-2}{2k-4} \cdot 2^{2k-4}$

28.(i) 675   **28.(ii)** 115   **29.(i)** 96   **29.(ii)** 445

30. 11754   **31.** 2844   **32.** 179900

33.(i) 13   **33.(ii)** 40   **33.(iii)** 256   **34.** $\frac{n}{3}\binom{n-4}{2}$

35.(i) 10!   **35.**(ii) $5!P_5^6$ **35.**(iii) 6!5!   **35.**(iv) $8! \times 2$

38. $r = 5$ **43.** $\frac{(kn)!}{n!(k!)^n}$ **44.** 57   **45.** 770

46. 560   **47.**(i) 72nd position   **47.**(ii) 51342

48. 1156th, 1375th   **49.** 141 and 161

50. $\binom{6}{2}$, $\binom{5}{2}$ **51.**(i) 4^{10} **51.**(ii) $4 \cdot 3^9$

52. $(r_1 + 1)(r_2 + 1) \cdots (r_n + 1)$

55. $\binom{r+n-3}{r-1} + \binom{r+n-2}{r}$ **56.** $\binom{12}{4} \cdot 6!$

57. $3 \cdot \binom{11}{5} \cdot 6!$ **58.**(i) $\binom{14}{5}$ **58.**(ii) $\binom{11}{5} + 3\binom{10}{4} + 3\binom{9}{3} + \binom{8}{2}$

59.(i) 6^{10} **59.**(ii) $\frac{(10)!}{3!3!}$ **59.**(iii) $\binom{15}{5}$ **59.**(iv) $\binom{9}{4}$

60. $\binom{r-n(k-1)-1}{n-1}$ **61.** $2 \cdot \frac{9!}{3!}$ **62.** $42 \cdot 9!$ **63.** $11! \cdot 825$

64. $\frac{r!}{n!}\binom{r-1}{n-1}$ **65.**(i) $\binom{50}{5}$ **65.**(ii) $\binom{50}{5} - \binom{44}{5}$

66.(i) $\binom{33}{3}$ **66.**(ii) $\binom{31}{3} - \binom{25}{3}$ **66.**(iii) $\binom{36}{3}$

67. $\binom{1996}{4}$ **68.** $\binom{16}{2} + \binom{11}{2} + \binom{6}{2}$ **69.** $\sum\limits_{i=0}^{k} \binom{r(k-i)+n-2}{n-2}$

70. 36   **71.** $\binom{6}{2}\binom{10}{3} + \binom{10}{2}\binom{6}{3}$ **72.** $2n\binom{p+n-1}{p}$

73. $\binom{r+n-1}{r}$ **74.** $\binom{r-1}{n-1}$ **75.** $\binom{18}{9} - 1$

76.(i) $2^9 - 1$ **76.**(ii) 381   **78.** $r = n + 2m$

79.(i) $\binom{p}{2}$ **79.**(ii) $\binom{p}{4}$ **79.**(iii) $\binom{n}{2} + 2\binom{n}{4}$

79.(iv) $\binom{n}{6}$ **80.** $\binom{n+1}{2} \cdot n!$ **81.**(a)(i) m^n **81.**(a)(ii) P_n^m

81.(b) $\binom{m}{n}$ **81.**(c) $m!S(n, m)$

88. If $n = p_1^{\alpha_1} p_2^{\alpha_2} \cdots p_k^{\alpha_k}$ is the prime factorization of n, then the required number is $(2\alpha_1 + 1)(2\alpha_2 + 1) \cdots (2\alpha_k + 1)$.

89.(i) $3\binom{664}{3} + (664)^3$ **89.**(ii) $\binom{498}{3} + (498)^3 + 3 \cdot 498 \cdot \binom{498}{2}$

90. $\frac{6}{26^{10}}$ **91.** $\binom{n-(m-1)(r-1)}{r}$ **93.** 448

94. 106   **95.** 25   **96.** 141   **97.** 560

98.(i) 300   **98.**(ii) 600   **99.** 634   **100.** 840

101. 23 **102.** $\lfloor \frac{n^2}{4} \rfloor$ **103.** $(n, m) = (2, 3), (3, 6), (4, 10)$

105. $\frac{1}{5}\binom{1990}{31}$ **109.** $n \equiv 0, 1 \pmod{4}$ **112.** 315

114. $(c-1)\binom{m-2+c}{c}$ **115.** 4

Exercise 2

1. 2^{n-1} **2.** $\binom{2n}{n}$

3.(i) $\sum_{i=0}^{r} \binom{n}{i}$ **3.(ii)** 2^n **3.(iii)** $\sum_{i=r-m}^{r} \binom{n}{i}$

4. 968 **5.** 504 **6.** $2\binom{9}{3} + 5\binom{9}{4} + \binom{9}{2}\binom{7}{2} = 1554$

7. $\binom{100}{6} + 97 \cdot 98 \cdot \binom{100}{2} + 97 \cdot \binom{100}{3}$ **8.** $\binom{1000}{3}\binom{997}{2} + \binom{1000}{4}\binom{996}{1}$

9.(i) 21 **9.(ii)** 45 **11.** $\binom{m+n+1}{n}$

12. $H(n, r) = \frac{r(n+1)}{r+1}$ **13.** $\Delta(n) = \binom{n+3}{3}$

14. $\binom{2n+1}{n}$, $\binom{2n+1}{n+r} - \binom{n}{r-1}$ **23.** $m!\binom{m+n+1}{n}$

53.(i) $\binom{m}{p} \cdot p! \cdot S(n, p)$ **53.(ii)** $\sum_{k=p}^{m} \binom{m-p}{k-p} S(n, k) \cdot k!$

57. 35 **58.** 981 **59.** 816 **60.** 704

61. 166 **72.** $n + 1$ **75.** 2^{n-1}

80. Write $n = 2^k \cdot r$, where $r \geq 1$ is odd. Then the gcd is 2^{k+1}.

82. $\frac{n}{2^{n-1}} \binom{n-1}{\lfloor \frac{n-1}{2} \rfloor}$ **86.** $2^{n+2} - 2$ **89.** $2^{n+1} - 2 - 2n$

91.(i) $9\left(\frac{11^{10}-1}{10}\right) = 23343682140$

91.(ii) $S_n = \begin{cases} bm & \text{if } a+b = 1 \\ b\frac{(a+b)^m - 1}{a+b-1} & \text{if } a+b \neq 1 \end{cases}$

95. $\frac{1}{n+1}\binom{2n}{n}$ **97.** $2^{\ell}\binom{m-n}{\ell}$

Exercise 4

1. 39 **2(b)** 229

3. $E(0) = 27, E(1) = 53, E(2) = 32, E(3) = 8, E(4) = 0$. # of primes = 30

4. 2301   **5.** 73001   **6.(i)** 9883   **6.(ii)** 8921

8. 485   **9.** $\sum_{r=0}^{n}(-1)^r\binom{n}{r}\{(n-r)!\}^2$ **10.** 36

11. $27720 - 2044 + 92 - 6 = 25762$ **12.(i)** 1314   **12.(ii)** 174

13. $\binom{12}{4} - 3\binom{8}{3} - 4\binom{7}{2} - 4\binom{7}{3} + 3\binom{7}{2} + 3\binom{7}{3}$ **14.** 28

15. $\binom{21}{2} - \binom{11}{2} - 2\binom{5}{2}$ **16.** $\binom{16}{3} - 3\binom{11}{3} - \binom{8}{3} + 3\binom{6}{3} + 3$

19. $\sum_{r=0}^{n}(-1)^r 2^r \binom{n}{r}(2n-r)!$ **20.(i)** $\frac{q!}{2}$

20.(ii) $\frac{1}{2}\lfloor\frac{p}{2}\rfloor^q\left(\sum_{i=0}^{q}(-1)^i\binom{q}{i}2^i(2q-i)!\right)$

20.(iii) $\frac{1}{2}\sum_{j=0}^{q}\frac{1}{2^j}\lfloor\frac{p}{2}\rfloor^{q-j}\left(\sum_{i=j}^{q}(-1)^{i-j}\binom{i}{j}\binom{q}{i}2^i(2q-i)!\right)$

20.(iv) $\frac{1}{2}\sum_{j=0}^{q}\frac{1}{2^j}\lfloor\frac{p-2}{2}\rfloor^{q-j}\left(\sum_{i=j}^{q}(-1)^{i-j}\binom{i}{j}\binom{q}{i}2^i(2q-i)!\right)$

21.(a) $\binom{r-1}{n-1}$ **22.(a)** $\binom{n-m}{r-m} = \binom{n-m}{n-r}$ **23.(a)** $n+1$

24.(i) $\lambda^4 - 4\lambda^3 + 5\lambda^2 - 2\lambda$ **24.(ii)** $\lambda^4 - 5\lambda^3 + 8\lambda^2 - 4\lambda$

24.(iii) $(\lambda - 1)^5 - (\lambda - 1)$

25. $(-1)^m \frac{q!n!}{m!}\sum_{j=m}^{q}(-1)^j \frac{(q-j)^{n-kj}}{(k!)^j(n-kj)!(j-m)!(q-j)!}$

28.(i) $C_n = \sum_{i=0}^{n-1}(-1)^i\binom{n-1}{i}(n-i)!$

29. $D_m \cdot D_{n-m}$ **30.(i)** $(m!)^2$ **30.(ii)** $m \cdot (m!)^2$

30.(iii) $m! \cdot \{\sum_{i=0}^{r}(-1)^i\binom{r}{i} \cdot (m+r-i)!\}$

39.(i) $\varphi(100) = 40, \varphi(300) = 80$ **45.** No   **53.** 85657

54. $\frac{(17 \cdot 20^{16} - 15 \cdot 20^4)}{20^{28}}$ **55.** $\frac{(22 \cdot 26^{21} - 36 \cdot 26^7)}{26^{35}}$

57. $m^{1989} - m^{663} - m^{153} - m^{117} + m^{51} + m^{39} + m^9 - m^3$

60. $(-1)^{p+q}$ **63.** 217

Exercise 5

1. $\binom{13}{2}$ **2.** $\binom{12}{3} - 4\binom{6}{3}$, $\binom{17}{3} - 4\binom{11}{3} + 6\binom{5}{3}$

4. $(x + x^2)(1 - x)^{-4}$ **5.** $\frac{2x}{(1-2x)^3(1-x)}$

8. $\binom{12}{2} - 3\binom{7}{2} + 3 = 6$ **9.** $\binom{43}{6} - \binom{35}{6}$

10. $\binom{2n+2}{2} - 3\binom{n+1}{2}$ **11.** 68

12.(i) $x^3(1-x)^{-5}$ **12.(ii)** $x^4(1-x)^{-5}$

13. $x^{10}(1-x^7)(1-x^9)(1-x^{11})(1-x)^{-3}$,

$\qquad a_{28} = \binom{20}{2} - \binom{13}{2} - \binom{11}{2} - \binom{9}{2} + \binom{4}{2} + 1$

14. $\binom{99}{3} - 4\binom{64}{3} + 6\binom{29}{3}$ **15.** $\binom{15}{6} - \binom{11}{6}$

16.(i) $x^2(1 + x + x^2 + x^3)(1-x)^{-6}$

16.(ii) $\{(1-x)(1-x^2)(1-x^3)(1-x^5)(1-x^8)\}^{-1}$

16.(iii) $(1+x^5)(1+x^{10})(1+x^{15})$

16.(iv) $\prod_{k=0}^{\infty}(1 + x^{2k+1})$ **16.(v)** $\prod_{k=1}^{\infty}(1 + x^{2k})$

16.(vi) $x^5(1-x^6)^5(1-x)^{-6}$ **17.** $\binom{4n+2}{2} - 3\binom{n+1}{2}$

18. $\binom{3n+m-1}{m-1} - m\binom{2n+m-2}{m-1} + \binom{m}{2}\binom{n+m-3}{m-1}$

19. $\frac{780}{6^5} \approx 0.1003$ **20.** $\{1 - (x + x^2 + \cdots + x^6)\}^{-1}$

21.(i) $x^{k+1}(1-x)^{-2k-1}$ **21.(ii)** $x^{mk}(1-x)^{-2k-1}$

22. $\prod_{i=1}^{4}(1-x^i)^{-1}$ **23.** $x^7(1-x)^{-5}$

24. $x^{t(m-1)+1}(1-x)^{-m-1}$

25. $x^6(1-x^7)(1-x^{10})(1-x)^{-5}$, $a_{20} = \binom{18}{4} - \binom{11}{4} - \binom{8}{4}$

27.(ii) $B(x)^2$ **29.** $S_n = 1$ **31.** $\frac{1}{2}(3^n + 1)$

32. $\frac{1}{4}\{4^n - 3^n + (-1)^n\}$, $n \geq 1$ **33.(i)** $\frac{1}{2}(6^n + 2^n)$ **33.(ii)** $\frac{1}{2}(6^n - 2^n)$

34. $\frac{1}{32}\{5^r - 2 + (-3)^r - 3^r + 2(-1)^r - (-5)^r\}$

38.(i) $4^{18} - 4 \cdot 3^{18} + 6 \cdot 2^{18} - 4$ **38.(ii)** $4^8(4^{10} - 4 \cdot 3^{10} + 6 \cdot 2^{10} - 4)$

38.(iii) $(4^{10} - 4 \cdot 3^{10} + 6 \cdot 2^{10} - 4) \cdot (4^8 - 4 \cdot 3^8 + 6 \cdot 2^8 - 4)$

39. $\begin{cases} 4^{r-1} & \text{if } r \geq 1 \\ 0 & \text{if } r = 0 \end{cases}$ **40.** $(e^x - 1)^n$

41. $A_n(x) = \frac{(e^x - 1)^n}{n!}$ **43.(a)** $n(n+1)\cdots(n+r-1)$

44.(i). $(1-x)^{-4}$ **44.(ii)** $x^4(1-x)^{-4}$

44.(iii) $x^4 \prod_{i=1}^{4}(1 - x^i)^{-1}$ **44.(iv)** $\prod_{i=1}^{4}(1 - x^i)^{-1}$

46. $x^n \prod_{i=1}^{n}(1 - x^i)^{-1}$ **47.** $\prod_{i=1}^{n}(1 - x^i)^{-1}$

49.(i) $(1 + x)(1 + x^2)(1 + x^4) \cdots = \frac{1}{1-x}$

49.(iii) Every natural number can be expressed uniquely as a sum of some distinct powers of 2.

53. $p(5, 1) = 1$, $p(5, 2) = 2$, $p(5, 3) = 2$, $p(8, 3) = 5$

54.(i) $p(5, 3) = 2$, $p(7, 2) = 3$, $p(8, 3) = 5$

62.(a)(i) $8 = 6 + 1 + 1 = 5 + 2 + 1 = 4 + 3 + 1 = 4 + 2 + 2 = 3 + 3 + 2$

62.(a)(ii) $(7, 7, 2)$, $(7, 6, 3)$, $(7, 5, 4)$, $(6, 6, 4)$, $(6, 5, 5)$

62.(a)(iii) Yes, all equal to 5.

62.(b)(ii) $x^3 \{(1 - x)(1 - x^2)(1 - x^3)\}^{-1}$

63.(i) $15 = 8 + 1 + 1 + 1 + 1 + 1 + 1 + 1 = 6 + 3 + 3 + 1 + 1 + 1$

$\qquad = 5 + 4 + 3 + 2 + 1 = 4 + 4 + 4 + 3$

63.(ii) $15 = 15 = 11 + 3 + 1 = 9 + 5 + 1 = 7 + 5 + 3$

65. $\frac{x^{m^2}}{\prod_{k=1}^{m}(1-x^{2k})}$ **66.(i)** $A(x) = \{\prod_{k=1}^{\infty}(1 - x^k)\}^{-1}$

Exercise 6

1. $a_n = 1 + 2^n$ **2.** $a_n = (2 - n)3^n$

3. $a_n = \frac{2}{3}\{1 - (-\frac{1}{2})^n\}$ **4.** $a_n = (3n - 1)2^{n-2}$

5. $a_n = \frac{5}{2} + \frac{1}{6}(-1)^n - \frac{8}{3}(\frac{1}{2})^n$ **6.** $a_n = -\frac{1}{2} + 2^n - \frac{1}{6} \cdot 3^n$

7. $a_n = \frac{1}{7}(n + 1)2^n - \frac{1}{49}(2^{n+1} + (-1)^n 5^{n+1})$

8. $a_n = (A + Bn + Cn^2)(-1)^n + D \cdot 2^n$

9. $a_n = (\frac{1}{2})^{n-1}(\sqrt{3} + 6) - 6$

10. $a_n = 3^{n+1} - 6 \cdot 2^n + 2n + 3$ **11.** $a_n = 2n^2 + n + 1$

12. $a_n = \begin{cases} rp^n + \frac{(1-p^n)q}{1-p} & \text{if } p \neq 1 \\ r + qn & \text{if } p = 1 \end{cases}$ **13.** $a_n = \frac{1}{4}(5(\frac{1}{2})^n - (\frac{1}{10})^n)$

14. $a_n = 10^{2\{1+(-1)^{n+1}2^{-2n}\}}$ **16.** $a_n = 2^{2(1-2^{1-n})}$

17. $a_n = \frac{3}{5}(-3)^n + n^2 + n + \frac{1}{5} \cdot 2^{n+1}$

18. $a_n = (\sqrt{2})^n(\cos\frac{n\pi}{4} + \sin\frac{n\pi}{4})$ **19.** $a_n = (n + \frac{1}{2}n^2)2^n$

20. $a_n = 2^n - 2n - 5$ **21.** $a_n = \begin{cases} \frac{1}{3}(2^{n-1} - 1) & \text{if } n \text{ is odd} \\ \frac{1}{3}(2^n - 1) & \text{if } n \text{ is even} \end{cases}$

22. $a_n = -1 + 2^n + n2^{n+1}$

23. $a_n = -\frac{14}{9}(-2)^n + \frac{37}{32}(-3)^n + \frac{1}{4}n^2 + \frac{17}{24}n + \frac{115}{288}$

24. $a_n = \begin{cases} s + \frac{p(t-s)}{p-r}\{1 - (\frac{r}{p})^n\} & \text{if } p \neq r \\ s + (t - s)n & \text{if } p = r \end{cases}$ **26.** $a_n = \frac{3^{n-1}}{1+3^{n-1}}$

27. $a_n = \frac{3 \cdot 2^{n-1}+1}{3 \cdot 2^{n-1}-1}$ **28.** 1

30. $a_n = 2a_{n-1} + 2a_{n-2}$, $a_n = \frac{3+2\sqrt{3}}{6}(1 + \sqrt{3})^n + \frac{3-2\sqrt{3}}{6}(1 - \sqrt{3})^n$

32. $a_n = (p+q)a_{n-1} - pqa_{n-2}$, $a_n = \begin{cases} \frac{1}{p-q}(p^{n+1} - q^{n+1}) & \text{if } p \neq q \\ (1+n)p^n & \text{if } p = q \end{cases}$

33. $a_n = (pq + 1)a_{n-1} - pqa_{n-2}$, $a_n = \begin{cases} \frac{1-(pq)^{n+1}}{1-pq} & \text{if } pq \neq 1 \\ 1 + n & \text{if } pq = 1 \end{cases}$

34. $\frac{\sqrt{17}+5}{2\sqrt{17}}\left(\frac{3+\sqrt{17}}{2}\right)^n + \frac{\sqrt{17}-5}{2\sqrt{17}}\left(\frac{3-\sqrt{17}}{2}\right)^n$

35. $a_n = a_{n-1} + 2a_{n-2}$ with $a_1 = 1$ and $a_2 = 3$, $a_n = \frac{1}{3}(2^{n+1} + (-1)^n)$

37. $a_n = -(1 + 2n)2^n$, $b_n = (5 + 2n)2^n$

38. $a_n = 1 - 2n$, $b_n = 2n$

39. $a_n = 2(1 + (\frac{1}{2})^n)$, $b_n = -1 + (\frac{1}{2})^{n-2}$

40. $a_n = \frac{1}{2}\{1 + (\frac{1}{3})^{n-1}\}$, $b_n = \frac{1}{2}\{1 - (\frac{1}{3})^{n-1}\}$

41. $2^{\frac{3}{2}}$ **51.** $a_n = F_n$ **53.** $a_n = a_{n-1} + a_{n-2}$

54. F_{n+2} **55.** $a_n = a_{n-1} + a_{n-2}$, $a_n = F_{n-1}$

56. F_{n+2} **58.** $F_{22} = 17711$

60. $a_n = a_1a_{n-1} + a_2a_{n-2} + \cdots + a_{n-1}a_1$

61.(i) $b_1 = 1$, $b_2 = 2$, $b_3 = 5$

62. $a_n = a_0 a_{n-1} + a_1 a_{n-2} + \cdots + a_{n-1} a_0$ for $n \geq 1$, where $a_0 = 1$

63. $\frac{1}{2n+1}\binom{2n+1}{n}$ **64.** $\frac{1}{n+1}\binom{2n}{n}$ **65.** $\frac{m-n}{m+n}\binom{m+n}{m}$

66.(i) $a_1 = 1, a_2 = 3, a_3 = 13$ **68.** $a_n = \frac{1}{n(n+1)}$

69. $\frac{1}{3}(4^n + 2)$ **71.** $n = 4, 8$, or $n \geq 10$

72. $a_n = \frac{1}{24}\{(3 + 2^{1-n})^2 - 1\}$

74. $a_0 = 0, a_1 = 2$, $a_n = \frac{1}{6}(2n+5)$, $n \geq 2$

75. $\begin{cases} a_{2n} = 0 \\ a_{2n+1} = \frac{1}{2^{2n}(2n+1)}\binom{2n}{n} \end{cases}$ **76.** $a_n = 1 + (\frac{2}{3})^n$ for all $n \geq 0$

77. $1991 \cdot 998 + \frac{9}{2}$ **80.** $f(x) = 2x$ **81.** $T_n = n! + 2^n$

84. $\frac{2}{3}\{2^{n-2} + (-1)^{n+1}\}$

86. The required number is $\begin{cases} 5 & \text{if } n = 1 \\ 14 \cdot 3^{\frac{n-3}{2}} & \text{if } n \text{ is odd and } n > 1 \\ 8 \cdot 3^{\frac{n-2}{2}} & \text{if } n \text{ is even} \end{cases}$

88. $a_0 = 1, a_1 = 3, a_2 = 9$ and $a_{n+1} = 3a_n + a_{n-1} + a_{n-2}$, $n \geq 2$

90. $(995, 1), (176, 10), (80, 21)$ **93.** $Q(m, n) = \binom{m+n-1}{m-1} - \binom{m+n-4}{m-1}$

Index

Printed in the USA
CPSIA information can be obtained
at www.ICGtesting.com
JSHW012310290924
70674JS00006B/17

9 789810 211394